OP
CJ
7⁵⁰

THE DYNAMIC NATURAL GAS INDUSTRY

THE DYNAMIC NATURAL GAS INDUSTRY

THE DESCRIPTION OF
AN AMERICAN INDUSTRY
FROM THE HISTORICAL,
TECHNICAL, LEGAL, FINANCIAL,
AND ECONOMIC STANDPOINTS

by Alfred M. Leeston
John A. Crichton
and John C. Jacobs

UNIVERSITY OF OKLAHOMA PRESS · NORMAN

LIBRARY OF CONGRESS CATALOG CARD NUMBER: 62–16486

Copyright 1963 by the University of Oklahoma Press,
Publishing Division of the University.
Composed and printed at Norman, Oklahoma, U.S.A.,
by the University of Oklahoma Press. First edition.

To the memory of E. L. DeGolyer (1886–1956),

GEOLOGIST, OIL AND GAS EXPERT, ENTREPRENEUR,

AND FRIEND OF LETTERS,

and to N. C. McGowen,

NATURAL GAS TRANSMISSION COMPANY PIONEER,

and to L. T. Potter,

NATURAL GAS ENGINEER

AND EXECUTIVE AND CIVIC LEADER,

and to all those men who built the natural gas industry,
a brilliant testimony to the courage and spirit of
American Enterprise

PREFACE

ONE of the brightest spots on the United States industrial scene is the natural gas industry. Its growth—impressive since the 1920's and spectacular since 1940—has been encouraged by such favorable conditions as the availability of large supplies of natural gas, the technical achievements which have made possible the construction and operation of pipe lines to carry gas over long distances at high pressures, the financial developments which provided large-magnitude loans over long periods of time, the distribution of gas under conditions which emphasize consumer preference for natural gas as a heating fuel, the dependability of service delivered at low cost, and the time and talent given to the industry by the myriad of people who work with gas every day.

This book has been written from the historical, technical, and business points of view and is an attempt to describe the gas industry as it is, rather than as it ought to be. There is no intention to denigrate any section of the industry, any competitive fuel, any area in which natural gas is produced or used throughout the world, or any opinion regarding the industry. Nevertheless, it is the authors' basic economic position that the most important factor in the growth of the natural gas industry is the freedom of the markets in which this industry operates. Though gas markets are subject to the control of many governmental agencies, they are essentially free in that they are competitive and in the sense that there is freedom of access so that they are not subject to the stultification which results from extensive integration. The possibilities of industrial growth in a free market which provides challenge and promises reward are practically unlimited.

While the character of this work as a whole required the closest

vii

possible collaboration among the three authors at all stages of its production, the high degree of specialization within the gas industry made individual responsibility for certain chapters necessary from the outset. Thus Alfred M. Leeston prepared chapters 1, 5, 6, 7, 8, and 11; John A. Crichton, chapter 2; and John C. Jacobs, chapters 3, 4, 12, 13, and 15. In the case of chapters 9, 10, and 14, joint responsibility was shared by Mr. Leeston and Mr. Crichton.

The authors wish to thank those persons who have helped in the preparation of this book, the friends and teachers who have influenced us since our school days and those who have taught us about the natural gas industry. We express special gratitude to our wives who have exhibited manifold tolerance towards this work over the more than five years of its preparation.

In particular, we want to thank Mrs. E. DeGolyer, president, and Mr. Everett L. DeGolyer, Jr., secretary of the DeGolyer Foundation; Mr. L. T. Potter, president of the Lone Star Gas Company and past president of the American Gas Association; Francis Kernan, president of White, Weld and Company; Chester S. Stackpole, managing director of the American Gas Association; and Henry E. Littlehales, secretary of the general management section of the American Gas Association.

ALFRED M. LEESTON, JOHN A. CRICHTON, *and* JOHN C. JACOBS

Dallas and Gay Hill, Texas
October 1, 1962

As of the date of Mr. Leeston's last work on this volume, indicated by the date of the preface, two months before that author's death, his contributions to the book were no longer subject to revision or updating. The reader may find that some data, particularly those of a statistical character, have been superseded in recent months. In editions subsequent to this one, these statistical data will be revised. We wish meanwhile to acknowledge with thanks the helpful comments from the staff of the American Gas Association. Our feeling of personal loss in the passing of our gifted colleague and friend, Mr. Leeston, will be understood by all who knew him and respected his work.

JOHN A. CRICHTON *and* JOHN C. JACOBS

CONTENTS

/ Local Control by Franchise / Control by State Commissions / The Rate-Making Formula / Limitations on State Control / Federal Control « *The Natural Gas Act, Pipe-Line Certificates, Gas for Industrial Uses, Pipe-Line Rates, Processing Operations, Company-produced Gas* » Federal Control of Independent Producers « *Jurisdiction Over Field Sales, Initial Prices, Price Increases* » Federal Control Under Other Statutes

PLATES

TABLES

FIGURES

xvii

THE DYNAMIC NATURAL GAS INDUSTRY

I

AN INDUSTRY IS BORN

by Alfred M. Leeston

NATURAL GAS was first discovered and put to use long ago in the Orient. The Chinese, who were first in the invention and application of many useful things later adopted by Western civilization, were among the first to use natural gas for fuel. They burned gas from wells drilled to depths of two thousand feet in search of salt. The gas was transported from these wells to the place of consumption in bamboo pipes.

In Japan gas wells were known as early as 615 B.C.[1] The Japanese word for natural gas is *Kaza-Kusodzu,* the first two syllables meaning wind or air, and evidently identical, entymologically, with the Western word *gas,* which is the invention (1609) of the Belgian chemist Von Helmont. He perhaps obtained the word from some colloquial expression in use since ancient times, one clearly identical in its turn with the German word *geist* and the English word *ghost* (spirit, the Latin *spiritus,* breath or breeze).[2]

In the West there was, before and during the time of Julius Caesar, a famous *fontaine ardente* or burning fountain near Grenoble, France. At an early date the city of Genoa, Italy, was lighted by gas brought from the wells of Aminiamo in Parma.

[1] C. Engler and H. v. Höfer, *Das Erdöl seine Physik, Chemie, Geologie, Technologie und sein Wirtschaffsbetriel,* IV, 234.

[2] Joseph D. Weeks, *Mineral Resources of the United States* (for 1888), 512. According to Martin C. Glaeser, *Public Utilities in American Capitalism,* 29, n. 4, natural gas was first discovered by Thomas Shirley in England in 1659. The first book on the gas industry, T. S. Peckston's *The Theory and Practice of Gas Lighting,* was published in London in 1819. The first written reference to gas is Constantine Prophyrogenitus, *De Administrando Imperio* (edited by Gy. Moravcsik, Budapest, 1949), 285, where the Byzantine Emperor in A.D. 949 describes the location of condensate wells which supplied naphtha for the manufacture of Greek fire.

More romantic than the early Chinese pipe lines of bamboo sticks is the history of natural gas in Russia. There the magic blue flame even inspired a religious cult. On the oil-rich Apsheron Peninsula at Surakhany near Baku in the Caspian Sea, fire columns that were visible for many miles sprang from a naphtha deposit. This was reported by Massudi in 967. He also told of an island three days' voyage from Baku, a region which then belonged to Persia, where a crater released fire columns as high as mountain summits amid terrible thundering. These awe-inspiring miracles of nature, inexplicable in those times, inspired Zoroaster to his cult of fire-worship, and a temple devoted to this religion was built at Surakhany. The gases responsible for these fires were mostly from Miocene sandstones. Now Surakhany is more important for the production of oil than gas, and Russia's principal gas resources occur in other areas.

It was not until many centuries after its use by the Chinese people that natural gas became a primary source of energy. This happened in the United States, where the natural gas industry was born in the village of Fredonia in western New York. There, in 1821, a well one and one-half inches in diameter and twenty-seven feet deep was completed near the Main Street bridge across Canada-way Creek. This was probably the first well sunk in search of natural gas.[3] It produced gas sufficient for thirty burners. The light from one of these burners was regarded as equal to that of two good candles. Commented a historian in 1886, "Gas of 2-candle power could hardly answer the demand of today." When General Lafayette passed through Fredonia at two o'clock on the morning of June 4, 1825, the hotel (the old Taylor House) was brilliantly illuminated by burning gas from this well. A great throng had gathered to greet him. Refreshments were served even at this untimely hour by the light of natural gas. Being familiar with Greek mythology, the illustrious guest remarked that he had "better get away from a place where gas came from a mysterious underground source as it was evidently too near to Hades."[4]

Of great significance was the 1825 decision of the Fredonians to put in a small gasometer (gas holder) and to replace the wooden pipes with lead ones. This improved the conditions so much that the Fredonia *Censor* of December, 1825, could record: "We witnessed last

[3] Earlier, in 1815, a gas well was discovered at Charleston, West Virginia.
[4] Louis Stotz and Alexander Jamison, *History of the Gas Industry,* 70.

evening the burning of 66 beautiful gas-lights, and 150 lights could be supplied by this gasometer. There is now sufficient gas to supply another one as large."

The use of natural gas in Fredonia attracted much attention. The fact became widely known both in this country and abroad, and excited the liveliest interest and professional—or professorial—curiosity among scientists. But the presence of the enormous volume of gas since discovered throughout the country was so little suspected that the Fredonia gas supply was pronounced "unparalleled on the face of the globe." The great German naturalist and explorer, Alexander von Humboldt, is said to have declared it the eighth wonder of the world.[5]

Although a company was formed in 1858 to carry out the improvements made in Fredonia, it was not until 1865 that the first American natural gas corporation, the Fredonia Gas Light and Water Works Company, was organized. This transaction was entirely eclipsed, however, by the completion of the nation's first commercial oil well, Colonel Drake's well, drilled to a depth of seventy feet at Oil Creek, Pennsylvania, on Saturday afternoon, August 27, 1859, and the feverish search for "black gold" that followed and became an epidemic. With the oil, huge quantities of gas were discovered for which there was no known use. Thus, the history of the miraculous fuel was one of appalling waste for many decades; for, while small fractions of natural gas were utilized here and there, enormous volumes of it were simply blown into the air.

There were farsighted men like the eminent geologist Edward Orton, state geologist of Ohio and a leading natural gas expert in his time, and the well-trained staff of the United States Geological Survey, who recognized very early the excellent properties of natural gas and deplored its prodigal waste. The industrialist Andrew Carnegie also realized the inherent qualities of natural gas and the competition it meant for coal. In 1884 he said that one natural gas company had 335 miles of pipe lines within the city of Pittsburgh and was supplying a quantity of natural gas that would displace 10,000 tons of coal a day.

A booklet written and published by Lemuel Bannister in New York in 1886 points out quite accurately the many advantages of natural

[5] Von Humboldt visited this country in 1854. The Humboldt Bay and Humboldt County in California are named for him.

gas. He quotes the favorable opinions of a number of experts who, like Orton, were highly regarded scientists at the time. Bannister was also well aware of the technical shortcomings that then, and for forty more years, prevented the safe transmission of natural gas over long distances. One of them was the inability to manufacture absolutely tight joints for the pipe. (S. R. Dresser did not invent his couplings until around 1890.) Bannister recommended severe tests for "pipe systems for gas" to avoid leakages, which were taken for granted at the time. He advocated a number of other technical improvements, and his keen vision was remarkable and defied emphatically the prevalent opinion that gas was largely a nuisance.

It was not until the 1920's that oil producers generally realized that natural gas was the motive force that lifts, or helps lift, the oil to the surface and that gas increases the fluidity of oil. The recognition of these two intrinsic features of natural gas marked the beginning of the appreciation of natural gas by the oil industry.

The first "gasser" or "roarer" on record was a gas well struck in 1841 by William Tompkins a short distance up the Kanawha River in West Virginia, where, in 1775, George Washington had observed a "burning spring" mentioned by Thomas Jefferson in his *Notes on Virginia*. In 1872 the ancestor of modern steel pipe lines was born. A two-inch, wrought-iron pipe brought waste gas from nearby oil wells to Titusville, Pennsylvania, a distance of five and one-half miles. It delivered four million cubic feet of gas a day to 250 domestic and industrial consumers.

The first industrial use of natural gas in the United States was in 1868, only nine years after the drilling of the Drake well, when an oil-well supply firm, Jarecki Manufacturing Company, began to use gas in its plant at Erie, Pennsylvania. In 1874 the firm of Rogers and Burchfield at Leechburg, Pennsylvania, for the first time made iron and steel with natural gas by using it as a boiler fuel and for puddling and heating furnaces.

It is ironic that the great coal city of Pittsburgh was one of the earliest and most important consumers of natural gas, later to be coal's strongest competitor. In 1885 the Pittsburgh district of western Pennsylvania was the leading natural gas area in production and consumption. It was another twist of fate that a man who became a pioneer in the electrical industry, George Westinghouse, also of Pitts-

6

burgh, founded there in 1884 the Philadelphia Company because he discovered gas on his property. In 1883, the Chartier Valley Gas Company was established by manufacturers to bring natural gas to their glass and steel plants in Pittsburgh. The gas was piped in from Murrysville in Westmoreland County, Pennsylvania.

Pennsylvania was not the only old oil state where early use and early exhaustion of natural gas made history. Other states belonging geologically to the Appalachian Oil Province found large volumes of natural gas in their search for oil. Ohio was among them. There, gas was discovered in 1860 around East Liverpool, known for its manufacture of pottery. One of the ceramic plants, that of Homer Laughlin, used gas in 1873. Earlier uses of the fuel in that state are reported from the city of Findlay—now the home of the Ohio Oil Company.

The early concentration of natural gas production in the Appalachian region—Pennsylvania, New York, Ohio, West Virginia, Kentucky, and Tennessee—meant that the natural gas industry also had an early beginning in these states. Industrial centers such as Buffalo, Cleveland, Youngstown, Cincinnati, and Toledo were supplied with natural gas from the producing fields in these states. In 1900, Pennsylvania was the leading gas-producing state, surrendering this supremacy to West Virginia in 1909. Then, in 1923, came Oklahoma, followed by Texas. Ohio's relative importance was short-lived because of unbelievable wastage, despite repeated warnings by farsighted citizens.

The first high-pressure, long-distance pipe line was constructed outside of the eastern gas-producing fields, from Indiana to Illinois, by the Indiana Natural Gas and Oil Company. Two parallel eight-inch lines of wrought-iron pipe with screwed couplings were laid a distance of 120 miles from gas fields near Greenstown, Indiana, to Chicago. A notable feature was the 525 pounds per square inch maximum working pressure, unusual for that period. This enterprise marked the beginning of long-distance, high-pressure transmission in the United States. But this venture was short-lived as it soon ran out of natural gas supply. Thus, the eastern states retained their predominant position in producing and supplying natural gas. For example, Cincinnati received natural gas in 1909 through a 183-mile, twenty-inch pipe line from fields in West Virginia, which were also the source for a 120-mile line to the other big Ohio metropolis, Cleve-

7

land. To the Buffalo-Pittsburgh-Toledo area, the supply of a cheap and superior fuel such as natural gas meant a spur to industrial and economic development in a densely populated region with excellent transportation and marketing facilities.

The Mid-Continent area—Kansas—also was the scene of early pipe-line construction (1904), but there it did not have those immediate beneficial results characteristic of the eastern region of the country. The area was sparsely settled, and the big cities like Kansas City and St. Louis were chiefly trading centers with vast agricultural hinterlands. The pipe lines suffered from insufficient gas supplies, and their performance was anything but encouraging.[6]

Although marketed production had reached one trillion cubic feet in 1923, development of the natural gas industry was slow. Gas reserves were enormous. The Texas Panhandle Field at Amarillo, the Monroe Field at the city of Monroe, Louisiana, and the huge reserves in the Gulf Coast were crying out for markets. Some remarkable expansion started in the Southwest in 1925 when the Magnolia Gas Company, subsidiary of Magnolia Petroleum Company at Dallas, Texas, completed a 217-mile line from the fields of northeastern Texas and northern Louisiana to Beaumont. This first long-distance, all-welded pipe line consisting of fourteen, sixteen, and eighteen-inch telescoped pipe, acetylene welded, was followed in quick succession by one of 220 miles from southwestern Texas fields to Houston and one of 217 miles from northeastern Texas to Houston and Port Arthur. In 1938 the total capacity of gas lines in the coastal territory of Texas, including these terminating at coast points but originating elsewhere, was estimated at 400,000,000 cubic feet a day, of which

[6] J. D. Creveling, "A Brief History of the Natural Gas Industry," *Natural Gas,* Vol. XVI, No. 5 (May, 1935), 5–8; Stoltz and Jamison, *History of the Gas Industry.*

The most elaborate survey on the history of the natural gas industry is found in the special issue published jointly by the *Oil and Gas Journal* and the *Oil City Derrick,* August 27, 1934, and entitled "The Diamond Jubilee of the Petroleum Industry." Not only the story itself is interesting, but also the advertisements which spotlight individual companies and tell of their share in the development of the natural gas industry. In this special issue, the history of natural gas is divided into five distinct eras: 1859–74, 1874–89, 1889–1904, 1904–19, 1919–34.

A chronology of the natural gas industry was compiled by Luis Hilt for the *American Gas Journal,* May, 1950. A much more complete chronological outline may be found in "Diary of an Industry," *American Gas Journal,* Vol. CLXXXVI, No. 11 (October, 1959), 21. This is the publication's one-hundredth anniversary issue.

250,000,000 cubic feet were being utilized daily—100,000,000 cubic feet by industrial consumers of southern Texas.

The development of these gas pipe-line systems revolutionized the fuel situation in this area with virtually all the major industries changing over from fuel oil to natural gas. Both the industrial user and the residential consumer rejoiced in obtaining natural gas from the producer who sold it for a pittance. In 1926 the twenty-two-inch line from the Monroe fields to Baton Rouge—location of Standard Oil (New Jersey) Company's giant refinery—was laid over a distance of 170 miles. The pipe line owned by Interstate Natural Gas Company[7] was extended to New Orleans in the following year for a total length of 260 miles. Then came the line from Texas to Colorado in 1927, a distance of 340 miles, which was heralded as an engineering achievement.[8] New areas were continually brought within the range of distribution, but all this was only a prelude. The real turn of events was the completion of the 1,000-mile, twenty-four-inch welded steel pipe line of the Natural Gas Pipeline Company of America, a subsidiary of the Peoples Gas Light and Coke Company of Chicago, in 1931. It brought natural gas from the Texas Panhandle to a great industrial center and ushered in the age of long-distance transmission of natural gas as we know it today.

The year 1931 was a "banner year" in interstate movement of gas in other respects too. It saw the completion of several important pipe lines: Southern Fuel Company's twenty-six-inch line from Kettleman Hills to Los Angeles,[9] Panhandle Eastern Pipeline Company's line

[7] This company belonged to the Standard Oil (New Jersey) interests; but in June, 1953, Olin Industries, Incorporated, acquired 89.2 per cent of the stock. See John Moody, *Public Utilities Manual* (for 1959), 253. This was one of the many casualties of the death sentence clause of the Public Utility Holding Company Act of 1935.

[8] This was in June, 1927, when Denver and Pueblo, Colorado, changed from using coal as the principal fuel to using natural gas. The gas was transported through about 200 miles of the Canadian River Gas Company line from Amarillo, Texas, in the Panhandle Field to Clayton Junction, New Mexico. There the Canadian River line connected with Colorado Interstate Gas Company's 254-mile line of twenty- and twenty-two-inch pipe. See Hilt, "Chronology of the Natural Gas Industry," *American Gas Journal*, Vol. CLXXII, No. 5 (May, 1950), 29–30.

[9] San Francisco and Oakland, California, received gas from this large field and from Buttonwillow through a 250-mile pipe line in August, 1929. The line was built for Pacific Gas and Electric Company. See Charles M. Coleman, *P.G.& E. of California: The Centennial Story of Pacific Gas and Electric Company, 1852–1952.*

from Amarillo to Indiana, Atlantic Seaboard Corporation's line from Kentucky to Washington, Northern Natural Gas Company's line from Amarillo to Omaha and Minneapolis, and others.

This vast expansion undertaken despite the Depression was the immediate result of revolutionary technological and technical innovations in pipe making and pipelaying.[10] One of the most startling changes was the development of electrical welding that made possible the use of high-carbon steel in pipe making and the manufacturing of larger pipe than could be produced by the seamless process.[11] With the perfection of pipe making, protection of pipe to combat corrosion was also improved. No less startling was the progress in pipelaying. Machine methods replaced work formerly done by "mules and men." Pipe-line construction moved from a rather primitive stage to the application of very efficient techniques.[12]

In 1936 the Federal Trade Commission submitted to Congress a report indicating that there were monopolistic practices in the industry which should be corrected by legislation.[13] Largely on the basis of

[10] See E. B. Swanson, *The Natural Gas Invasion—An Example of the Sudden Expansion of Transport in Mineral Economics,* A.I.M.E. Series (1932), 98–110. This is probably the most searching essay on the rapid growth of the natural gas industry between 1925 and 1930. The textbooks by Clement, Glaeser, and Troxel also deal with historic developments of the natural gas industry.

[11] "America's Expanding Pipeline System," *U.S. Steel News,* Vol. XXI, No. 1 (July, 1956), 3. This is an informative article about pipe for oil, gas, and coal. While National Tube Division of U. S. Steel pioneered in larger, longer seamless pipe, A. O. Smith, Republic Steel, National Tube, and Youngstown Sheet and Tube Company were among the prominent developers of electric-welded pipe. See B. C. V. Luty, "Development of Pipe Manufacture," *Oil and Gas Journal,* Vol. XXIX, No. 3 (June 6, 1930), 85. The first manufacture of seamless pipe took place in Germany where Mannesmann Brothers patented and produced seamless tubes for bicycles.

[12] Swanson, *The Natural Gas Invasion,* 105–107.

[13] The Federal Trade Commission report is known as the "Temporary National Economic Committee Report on Natural Gas and Natural Gas Pipelines," Monograph No. 36. See pages 7–32 and 88–89. On page 32 of this report, the Federal Trade Commission describes the problem in the industry as follows:

> . . . A few large holding companies controlling the greater part of the business soon found it to their mutual advantage to recognize territorial rights, and to allocate territory to the end that each should monopolize the business in certain areas and stay out of the territory occupied or claimed by another. Without the competition of any rival line, such an organization to be completely successful need only take steps to preserve its rate structure before public service commissions and the courts. . . .
>
> There was always danger, however, that an independent group attracted by the large profits to be made, would obtain gas reserves in one of the large producing fields where natural gas could be obtained cheaply and would then extend a line into the

the Federal Trade Commission study, Congress passed the Natural Gas Act in 1938 without a dissenting vote in either house. Since that time the interstate phases of the natural gas industry have operated under the jurisdiction of the Federal Power Commission.

Great changes in the gas industry came about during the era of World War II. Ample gas supply in the southwestern United States, steadily improving construction techniques, readily available financing, and dependable service were fully assured. The industry has expanded rapidly, principally through the substitution of natural gas for artificial gas in population centers of the northeastern United States, and through the introduction of natural gas to the West Coast.[14] Today all parts of the United States are served, or will be served, by natural gas pipe-line systems. In 1944, a 1,265-mile system (Tennessee Gas Transmission Company) from Texas to West Virginia was finished. In 1947, a 1,200-mile system (El Paso Natural Gas Company) from Texas to California was placed in operation. In 1947, the Texas Eastern Transmission Corporation system commenced operating between Texas and New York, and it was joined by the Transcontinental Gas Pipe Line Company system in 1949. More recently lines between Louisiana and West Virginia (Gulf Interstate Gas Pipe Line Company), Louisiana-Chicago-Detroit (American Louisiana Gas Pipe Line Company), Texas-Florida (Coastal Transmission Company-Houston, Texas Oil and Gas Company), and Tex-

territory of one of the large holding companies. This constituted a real threat of competition, through the offering of cheap gas to break down the rate structure maintained by the holding company dominating the particular territory. Such independent groups were called "raiders." Wherever such a group attempted to do business, the natural course of the large holding company was either to destroy it or to buy it out.

Such activities were clearly against the interests of the independent gas well owners, prospective markets, and consumers in general. Two examples of such a "raid" was [*sic*] Panhandle Eastern's and American Fuel and Power Company's efforts to build a line into Detroit. . . . Both companies were forced into bankruptcy. . . .

However, the Federal Trade Commission also recognized the contributions of the gas industry in the following words:

It may be taken for granted, in view of the many thousands of pipe lines built at costs of hundreds of millions of dollars, of the billions of cubic feet of gas moved thereby from source locations where otherwise *gross waste* of this high form fuel would have been intensified to areas where its delivery meant *increased convenience and economy in living and manufacturing* to many millions of people, that the industry has performed a useful service to the public.

See page 272 for a discussion of the history of the Natural Gas Act.
[14] American Gas Association Rate Committee, *Gas Rate Fundamentals*, 10–30.

as-California (Transwestern Pipeline Company) have been constructed or authorized. The interstate transmission picture is completed with gas importation authorized from Canada and from Mexico.

The tremendous growth of the natural gas industry and the high favor in which gas is held by the American public can be seen by comparing two articles on natural gas in *Fortune* magazine. In 1931, *Fortune* said: "The success (or failure) of the pipeline depends not upon what it can deliver but upon what it can sell."[15] In 1949 *Fortune* wrote: "Today the mere thought of *not* getting some natural gas . . . is horrifying to every gas utility from Maine to Florida."[16] These two statements made eighteen years apart are the history of the natural gas industry in a nutshell, as gas was transformed from a waste product to a vital necessity and became both child and father of an industry.

[15] "Gas Balloon," *Fortune,* Vol. IV, No. 2 (August, 1931), 109. This article tells the story of two pioneers in the gas industry, Odie Richard Seagraves and William Lewis Moody, III. Mr. Seagraves' Houston company became part of the nucleus for United Gas Corporation of Shreveport, an integrated pipe-line system.

[16] "Natural Gas—Whoosh!" *Fortune,* Vol. XL, No. 6 (December, 1949), 199. Maine still has no natural gas.

The cost of drilling is high, and so the stakes are large when men gamble on finding oil. In 1945 it cost about $9.00 a foot to drill a well (including materials and services in addition to those provided by the contractor). In 1958 it cost $13.25 a foot. The wholesale price index of major drilling equipment rose from 100 in 1947 to 158 in 1958. For drilling off the Gulf Coast in the tidelands, the drilling barges must be equipped for stormy weather and all the other hazards of a treacherous sea and must carry special drilling apparatus. Fully equipped, these barges cost up to five million dollars each. The average offshore wildcat costs about one million dollars. At one time, drilling to a depth of fifteen thousand feet was sensational; today a depth of twenty thousand feet is not an isolated case. Only by improvement and economies in drilling, by more efficient discovery and development of oil reservoirs, and by improved refining methods has the oil industry been able to keep product prices down to a reasonable level. Since the oil industry is by far the greatest producer of natural gas, this cost-price relationship is of vital importance for the natural gas industry also. When wildcat wells drilled with an outlay of considerable amounts of money result in gas instead of oil, a good price for this fuel is imperative to cover the time and money that has been expended. Prospecting is an enterprise attractive to men only when the rewards for success are commensurate with the risk. Unless the reward expressed in terms of a good price is likely to be reaped, the producer lacks the incentive to take the large financial risk.

CONDENSATE RESERVOIR — A PROLIFIC SOURCE

Some of the most prolific sources of gas are the *gas-condensate reservoirs,* reservoirs in which the hydrocarbons are originally in a single gaseous phase at reservoir pressure and temperature and where, upon reduction in pressure, condensation of some of the hydrocarbons results. The liquid produced in this way is called *condensate.* These reservoirs produce gas accompanied by considerable quantities of this light oil or condensate. When, in the late 1920's, some fields in the Gulf Coast discovered at considerable depths produced a straw-colored or water-white liquid resembling gasoline, it was thought that this was liquid from the reservoir. Later it was recognized that the liquid was in a gaseous state as long as it was in the reservoir at the original temperature and pressure and that this gas became a liquid only after it

17

underwent a reduction in pressure during its rise to the earth's surface.

The condensation of a gas to form a liquid by reduction in pressure is a phenomenon directly opposite to usual behavior. Normally, when a substance is near the dew point (the temperature at which vapor starts to condense), an increase in pressure results in condensation and a reduction in pressure causes evaporation. The apparent anomaly of condensation by pressure reduction was suggested by Kuenen, a German scientist, as early as 1892, but was ignored by the oil industry until 1932. This phenomenon in which a reduction in the pressure of the gas forms a liquid is called *retrograde condensation*.

A condensate reservoir is considered a gas reservoir, and a producing well from such a reservoir is classified as a gas well by most states, even though considerable quantities of light oil, or condensate, are recovered. In addition to the condensate liquid, gas from this type of reservoir also contains the lighter hydrocarbons found in casinghead gas. All of these extractable constituents, which exist in the gaseous phase in the reservoir, fall in the broader classification of *natural gas liquids*. As of December 31, 1960, it was estimated that there were 6.8 billion barrels of recoverable natural gas liquids in the United States. This is a valuable addition to our fuel and petrochemicals supply. In addition, deeper drilling means finding increasing amounts of natural hydrocarbons in the gaseous phase, and with greater depths the proportion of natural gas discovered will be greater. Further, as more wells are drilled to greater depths, higher reservoir pressures will be encountered. If only oil is present within these pools, it is likely to be charged with natural gas to a greater degree per unit volume than the oil obtained in shallower reservoirs. If only gas is present, it will also be under higher pressure and the porous strata, per unit volume, will contain more gas. For instance, a unit volume of pay zone under normal conditions at ten thousand feet contains almost twice the amount of gas in a similar unit volume of pay zone at a depth of five thousand feet.

Reserves of natural gas will increase with more deep drilling. But deep drilling is expensive, and the cost of finding additional reserves will increase. This cost should be partially offset by the larger gas volumes per unit of pore space at depths and by the presence of natural gas liquids in the gas.

The producer of gas-condensate wells faces two problems: he must

recover the maximum amount of condensate and other liquid hydrocarbons and must sell the natural gas for a fair price. One answer to
these problems is found in the *cycling* process. By this ingenious
method, gas is produced from gas condensate wells and stripped of
its condensate and natural gas liquids. It is then compressed and reinjected through other wells into the reservoir from which it came,
where it is available for sale to pipe-line companies at some future
time. The pressure is maintained in the reservoir and prevents irre-
coverable loss through the falling out of natural gas liquids.

Cycling is an achievement of modern technology which serves important economic ends. It permits the producer to sell the liquids and
not waste the gas, enabling him to conserve the gas until an attractive
market is available. Reserves of natural gas are thus stored for the
industry and are available when needed. It provides the petrochemical
industry with a constant, ample supply of raw materials for countless
semi-finished and finished products (synthetic rubber, plastics, etc.).
For technical and economic reasons, it cannot be used in all gas condensate fields. In some cases the amount of liquid loss in the reservoir
is too small to justify the installation of plants.

THE SOUTHWEST — PRINCIPAL SOURCE OF SUPPLY

The nation's principal natural gas source of supply is the Southwest.
The major gas-producing states during 1960 were Texas, Louisiana,
Oklahoma, New Mexico, and Kansas. The net production of these five
states during that year amounted to 87 per cent of the total United
States net production of 13.1 trillion cubic feet. Texas alone produced
almost 45 per cent of the nation's gas during 1959. The production
of such a large percentage of the nation's gas requirements has had a
great economic impact on this area. It is bountifully supplied with
readily usable energy and has an inexpensive fuel for industrial,
commercial, and domestic use. It offers a raw material to attract
chemical and petrochemical plants. Other important gas-producing
states are California, Wyoming, West Virginia, Mississippi, Pennsylvania, and Colorado.

In the early stages of the natural gas industry's development in this
country, the eastern states were the principal producers. In geological
terms, this was the *Appalachian Oil Province,* embracing Pennsylvania, New York, Ohio, West Virginia, Kentucky, and Tennessee.

19

These states supplied the major part of the gas produced until as late as 1923, when Oklahoma displaced West Virginia as the leading state in natural gas production.

The largest proved natural gas reserves are located in those states having the largest current production. (See Table 1.) As of December 31, 1960, the American Gas Association estimated that of the 264 trillion cubic feet of natural gas reserves in the United States, Texas contained 120 trillion cubic feet or 45 per cent, Louisiana contained 63 trillion or 34 per cent, Kansas, 20 trillion or 8 per cent, Oklahoma, 17 trillion or 6 per cent; and New Mexico, 16 trillion or 6 per cent. Thus, five states contained 99 per cent of the total gas reserves in the United States.

There is certainly no area in the world with proved quantities of natural gas comparable to those in Texas. Moreover, most of these Texas reserves are accessible, transportable, and salable—decisive criteria for the efficient utilization of natural resources. Precious mineral resources in many countries are often hidden in impenetrable jungles, swamps, or rugged mountains, and cannot be exploited without extreme costs and difficulties. Production is under the supervision of the Texas Railroad Commission which is divided into eleven districts. The principal gas reserves in Texas are located in the Panhandle (District 10), the Gulf Coast (Districts 2, 3, and 4), East Texas (Districts 5 and 6), and West Texas (District 10).

Within the Texas Panhandle is the largest gas field in the United States and perhaps in the world. Actually, there are two fields, the Panhandle Field to the south and the Hugoton Field to the north, which meet at the northern boundary of Moore County. The chief production from both fields is from dolomites, limestones, and granite wash of Pennsylvanian and Permian ages. The depth is around three thousand feet, and pressures are now less than five hundred pounds per square inch.

The Panhandle Field is some 120 miles long and from 10 to 40 miles wide, with a gas area of one and one-half million acres. From its extreme southeastern limits, it extends northwestward across Collingsworth, Wheeler, Gray, Carson, Hutchinson, Potter, Moore, Oldham, and Hartley counties. The discovery well in northern Potter County was completed on December 13, 1918, and produced only gas. Development of the gas area (oil was found May 19, 1921) was slow initially because there was a lack of markets and prices were low. The chief commercial use of the gas was in making carbon black, used in the manufacture of tires from natural and synthetic rubber. The Texas "Sour Gas" Law of 1933 prohibited the use of sweet gas in this way. By the latter part of 1936 about thirty plants comprising 75 per cent of the world's production at that time were in operation. Some shipping of liquid hydrocarbons was done by gasoline plants from the year 1926 on, and by January 1, 1937, forty-three plants were in operation. The residue gas was being flared. Gradually, however, pipe lines to large consuming centers were constructed, and as the market expanded, exploration and development rapidly extended the proved gas areas of the field.

The Hugoton Field in Texas is about 60 miles long and 30 miles wide. It includes Sherman, Moore, Hansford, and Dallam counties. The Texas "shallow" Panhandle-Hugoton Field had some 4,400 gas wells and 11,000 oil wells as of 1960, and an estimated recoverable gas reserve of about 20 trillion cubic feet. About 25 trillion cubic feet have been produced to date. Since 1950 there has been extensive development of several deeper gas and oil reservoirs in this area, particularly the Atoka and Morrow sands of Lower Pennsylvanian age found at seven to ten thousand feet. Some of the more important discoveries have been Farnsworth, Twin, Hitchland, and Hansford. The deliverabilities from these deeper wells have been large and have resulted in a reduction in the rate of take from the "shallow" pays.

This huge gas area is a good example of the beneficial effects of conservation measures. Largely through the efforts of the Texas Railroad Commission in co-operation with the producers, no flaring—once amounting to an estimated billion cubic feet a day—takes place in the huge Panhandle Field.

In the south and southwest part of Texas there are many gas fields with tremendous reserves. These are located in the Gulf Coast area, which extends from the eastern boundary of Louisiana westward along the coast of the Gulf of Mexico to Mexico and inland from eighty to one hundred miles. Not all of these reserves are available now. Many are gas condensate or distillate reservoirs which are under cycling operations, and the gas from these will not be ready for sale until these operations have become uneconomical and are halted.

The fields in District 2 (Refugio) contain large gas reserves prin-

TABLE 1
ESTIMATED PROVED RECOVERABLE RESERVES OF NATURAL GAS
IN THE UNITED STATES
(Million Cu. Ft.—14.65 psia at 60° F.)

	Reserves as of Dec. 31, 1959	Extensions and Revisions	Discoveries of New Fields and New Pools in Old Fields	Net Change in Underground Storage	Net Production
			CHANGES IN RESERVES DURING 1960		
Alaska	57,975	36,993	13,000	0	30.
Arkansas	1,422,817	83,115	36,360	211	82,79.
California	8,593,447	395,351	324,694	30,875	500,47.
Colorado	2,496,159	(—) 474,828	121,520	565	100,66.
Illinois	175,110	8,900	297	7,461	18,63.
Indiana	35,088	1,001	284	1,692	3,94.
Kansas	19,981,403	128,848	156,452	8,366	666,34.
Kentucky	1,159,381	46,048	9,020	1,918	72,51.
Louisiana	59,853,920	4,333,983	2,254,600	0	3,056,36.
Michigan	515,403	7,549	31,200	56,057	24,45.
Mississippi	2,486,524	31,804	210,390	(—) 581	186,30.
Montana	665,491	(—) 17,245	0	14,126	36,19.
Nebraska	132,719	(—) 3,057	861	0	12,69.
New Mexico	17,912,798	(—)1,654,454	127,457	(—) 3,317	778,76.
New York	106,519	(—) 7,588	420	1,662	4,81.
North Dakota	1,206,542	(—) 35,415	0	0	20,10.
Ohio	748,766	34,297	9,250	12,549	39,30.
Oklahoma	16,651,292	975,342	665,460	1,084	993,97.
Pennsylvania	1,051,972	191,836	18,000	27,448	119,67.
Texas	120,475,783	2,471,209	2,428,403	7,309	5,902,78.
Utah	1,264,250	260,445	63,734	0	62,28.
Virginia	38,632	(—) 3,300	300	0	2,34.
West Virginia	1,593,551	318,967	71,488	37,001	189,88.
Wyoming	3,847,064	199,836	93,719	1,148	207,01.
Miscellaneous	123,987	3,203	100	20,654	7,81.
TOTAL	262,596,593	7,332,840	6,637,009	226,228	13,090,45.

(Source: *Proved Reserves of Crude Oil, Natural Gas Liquids, and Natural Gas*, Vol. XV [December 31, 1960], A.G.A. and A.P.I.)

Total (Columns 7 + 8 + 9 + 10, also Columns + 2 + 3 + 4 Less Column 5)	Non-associated	Associated	Dissolved	Under-ground Storage
107,663	95,811	0	11,852	0
1,459,710	957,514	287,932	209,222	5,042
8,843,895	2,509,684	1,962,792	4,249,526	121,893
2,042,754	1,294,053	258,434	489,538	729
173,135	9,349	0	111,185	52,601
34,120	1,100	1,200	19,875	11,945
19,608,724	18,735,589	527,181	274,886	71,068
1,143,849	1,041,373	0	76,365	26,111
63,386,141	50,527,589	8,956,486	3,902,066	0
585,758	116,015	71,793	56,634	341,316
2,541,830	1,906,135	340,020	290,718	4,957
626,178	465,058	29,138	76,799	55,183
117,828	93,277	8,673	15,878	0
15,603,724	11,214,132	2,753,119	1,592,049	44,424
96,201	36,841	0	138	59,222
1,151,021	9,453	340,400	801,168	0
765,553	326,987	0	89,251	349,315
17,299,203	12,275,573	1,943,428	2,973,501	106,701
1,169,585	714,941	0	22,940	431,704
119,479,915	78,214,180	27,137,031	14,077,131	51,573
1,526,140	1,007,349	31,476	487,315	0
33,290	33,290	0	0	0
1,831,125	1,472,197	0	63,633	295,295
3,934,749	3,197,676	157,435	558,066	21,572
140,129	48,172	0	15,184	76,773
263,702,220	186,303,338	44,806,538	30,464,920	2,127,424

cipally in the sands of Frio, Vicksburg, and Wilcox ages. The depth of the largest reserves varies from three to ten thousand feet. Some of the largest fields are Burnell-Wilcox, Blanconia, Poesta Creek, and Pettus Wilcox in Bee County; Appling and Heyser in Calhoun County; Nordheim and Myersville in DeWitt County; Appling, Mayo, Morales, Texana and West Ranch in Jackson County; Fashing and Burnell in Karnes County; Provident City in Lavaca County; Boyce in Goliad County; Clayton, Huff, Oakville, and Tom Lyne in Live Oak County; Mary Ellen O'Connor and Refugio Area in Refugio County; and Cologne, Heyser, Fuqua, McFaddin, and Placedo in Victoria County. Total gas reserves in this district are estimated at about 15 trillion cubic feet as of December 31, 1959.

This area is for the most part topographically flat and offers no unusual obstacles to pipe-line construction. Reserves from this area played an important part in the first large gas pipe-line construction projects in Texas, and the area has continued to be the locale of "Pipeline Alley."

District 3, which centers around Houston, has extremely large gas reserves. The largest reserves are found at depths of five to twelve thousand feet and are in sands of Frio, Wilcox, and Miocene ages. This district has a gas reserve of thirty trillion cubic feet, and has several fields with reserves in excess of one trillion cubic feet.

The largest field in this district is the Katy Gas Field which is located only thirty miles west of Houston in Waller County. It was discovered in 1935 and has a number of productive Yegua-age sands between 6,500 and 7,500 feet. Its true value was not realized until the advent of cycling, and it was almost a decade before the productive limits were defined and the gas-condensate production of the field fully developed. This was made possible by the installation of the Katy Gas Cycling Plant, one of the world's largest such plants and one of the first for the recovery of liquid hydrocarbons and the storing of the dry or residue gas (from the cycling operations) in the original reservoirs for future sale. The processing capacity of this plant, which is operated by the Humble Company, the principal owner in the field, is over 550 million cubic feet of gas per day. The average daily extraction of products is over 20,000 barrels. Reserves are around five trillion cubic feet. Renowned oil companies with experience of long standing share this great field. They include the Humble Company,

24

Pan American Oil Company (an affiliate of Standard Oil of Indiana), Amerada Petroleum, Sinclair Oil Corporation, Tidewater Oil Company, and Union Producing Company (an affiliate of the United Gas Corporation).

Another sizable field is the Old Ocean Field located in Brazoria County. The discovery well of the Old Ocean Field was completed in 1934 at a depth of 8,600 feet. An important event in the history of efficient production and sound conservation practices occurred here on August 1, 1948, when the Old Ocean Field began operations under a unit agreement, thus becoming one of the largest voluntarily unitized oil and gas fields in the United States. Over 585 of the royalty owners and more than 98 per cent of the leasehold operators agreed to the unit plan of operation. Old Ocean's gas reserves have been estimated at four to five trillion cubic feet. Gas goes from this field to Natural Gas Pipeline Company of America, and thus to the City of Chicago. In 1960 plans were being made to furnish the city of Fort Worth with gas from this field.

Fields in this district with reserves of about one trillion cubic feet are the Chocolate Bayou and Pledger fields in Brazoria County. Other sizable gas fields are New Ulm in Austin County; Red Fish Reef, Mayes, Sea Breeze, and Willow Slough in Chamber County; Sheridan, Chesterville, and Columbus in Colorado County; Madisonville in Madison County; Needville in Fort Bend County; Liberty in Liberty County; Bammel, Fairbanks, North Houston, Aldine and Tomball in Harris County; West Beaumont, Hampshire, Big Hill, Marrs-McLean, Port Arthur, Port Acres, and Lovells Lake in Jefferson County; Bay City, Markham, Wadsworth, Collegeport, and Sugar Valley in Matagordo County; Conroe and Port Neches in Montgomery County; and West Bernard and Magnet Withers in Wharton County.

Deeper drilling daily discloses additional gas reserves. Many of the traps for the gas accumulations are associated with deep-seated and piercement-type salt domes, and drilling on the flanks of these domes frequently adds additional reserves. The abundance of nearby gas reserves has greatly contributed to the growth of Houston as a substantial industrial area and as the site for many petrochemical plants. It was an important factor in Houston's becoming the seventh largest city in the United States in 1960.

25

District 4 is in the extreme southern part of Texas and is adjacent to Mexico. The largest reserves are in sands and sandstones of Frio, Vicksburg, and Wilcox ages from depths of five to twelve thousand feet. This district has gas reserves of 25 trillion cubic feet and several fields in excess of a trillion cubic feet. It has been the starting point for many of the transcontinental pipe lines. An active drilling program is now taking place in the development of its deeper Wilcox reserves.

Two of the largest fields in this district are the Seeligson Field in Jim Wells County and the Agua Dulce-Stratton Field in Neuces County. Each of these fields has reserves of three trillion cubic feet. The LaGloria Field in Jim Wells County has reserves of around two trillion cubic feet.

Other fields in this district having sizable reserves are Fulton Beach and Lamar in Aransas County; Mariposa in Brooks County; Sejita, Government Wells, Piedre Lumbre, and Hagist Ranch in Duval County; Edinburg, McAllen, Tabasco, Donna, Lacy, Hidalgo, La Blanca, and San Carlos in Hidalgo County; Captain Lucy, Tijerina, Canales, and Tom Graham in Jim Wells County; Chevron and May in Kleberg County; Brayton, Red Fish Bay, Flour Bluff, Minnie Bock, Mustang Island, and Saxet in Nueces County; Rooke, Mathis, and White Point in San Patricio County; Rincon, La Reforma, and Sun in Starr County; and Lopeno in Zapata County.

In the East Texas area (Districts 5 and 6) are found sizable gas reserves, particularly in Railroad Commission District 6. The largest field is the Carthage Field, which produces from lime formations at about 5,500 feet. Its reserves are between two and three trillion cubic feet, and its size can be attributed to the large areal extent of the field. The first well was drilled in 1936, but its extent was not realized until several years later.

Other large fields in this area are Willow Springs in Gregg County; Waskom, Hallsville, Lansing, and Woodlawn in Harrison County; Rodessa in Cass and Marion counties; Teague in Freestone County; Long Lake in Anderson, Freestone, and Leon Counties; Buffalo in Leon County; Cayuga in Freestone and Anderson Counties; Grapeland in Houston County; Bethany in Panola County; Joaquin in Shelby and Panola counties; Chapel Hill in Smith County; Trawick in Nacogdoches County; New Hope in Franklin County; and Opelika in Henderson County. In addition, there probably exist more than

26

one trillion cubic feet of gas in the big East Texas oil field, found in Gregg, Cherokee, Smith, and Rusk counties. Most of the reserves are found in sands and limes of Cretaceous age in Districts 5 and 6.

In the past five years an active exploration program has disclosed large gas reserves in the deeper Smackover lime. Such gas is high in sulphur content and is sour. These reserves have a premium location and are closer to eastern markets than any other reserves in Texas. As of 1960 they were probably about 14 trillion cubic feet.

The gas reserves in West Texas (Districts 7-C and 8) are principally found dissolved in oil. However, the magnitude of the oil fields causes this reserve to be sizable—probably consisting of 12 trillion cubic feet. The principal producing formations range from three to twelve thousand feet in depth and are geologically older than the Gulf Coast producing formations. They are Permian, Devonian, and Ordovician in age and are mostly limes and carbonates, although some sands are found.

The largest gas-containing fields in District 8 (most of which are more noted for their oil) are Fullerton, Emma, Fuhrman-Mascho, and McFarland in Andrews County; Block 31 and Waddell in Crane County; Goldsmith, North Cowden, South Cowden, Foster, and TXL in Ector County; Seminole in Gaines County; Levelland and Slaughter in Hockley County; Yates, Payton, and Puckett in Pecos County; Cogdell, Kelly Snyder, and Diamond M in Scurry County; Ward, North Estes, and South Ward in Ward County; Keystone, Emperor, and Kermit in Winkler County; Anton-Irish in Hale and Lamb counties; Arthur and Jo Mill in Borden County; Russell in Gaines County; and Wasson in Yoakum County.

The largest gas containing fields in District 7-C are Big Lake in Reagan County; Dora Roberts in Midland County; Benedum, McElroy, and McCamey in Upton County; Fort Chadbourne in Runnels and Cole counties; Clara Couch in Crockett County; and Sprayberry Trend area in Midland, Glasscock, Reagan, and Upton counties.

There are other gas-producing areas in Texas. One of these is located in the north-central part of the state. Although there are a number of fields, they are characteristically small in gas reserves. There is an extensive gas-containing area, but the total reserve is small as compared to the other areas of Texas.

In the past several years Railroad Commission District 9 has had

27

an important gas development and drilling program in Wise County. Important gas reserves are also located in Grayson and Young counties. In District 7-B gas has been the principal fuel for years. The principal gas-producing counties in this district are Stephens, Eastland, and Coleman.

Louisiana is the second-ranking state in the United States in both gas production and reserves. Its gas reserves in 1960 were estimated at 63 trillion cubic feet of gas, and it produces almost 3 trillion cubic feet annually. In 1950 Louisiana's gas reserves were estimated at about 30 trillion cubic feet. Thus, its rate of development of gas reserves in the past ten years has been the highest in the nation.

Louisiana is divided into North and South Louisiana from a standpoint of geography, politics, topography, and geology. North Louisiana developed its gas reserves first. As early as 1906 gas wells were drilled in the Caddo field, north of Shreveport. This city has become one of the country's foremost gas centers and is the home office for one of the world's largest gas companies, United Gas, as well as a principal office for Texas Eastern Transmission Corporation and Arkansas Louisiana Gas Company. Monroe Field, in northeastern Louisiana, was discovered in 1916 and was the major source of supply for some of the earlier pipe-line companies. Following Monroe many large oil and gas fields were discovered and developed in North Louisiana, such as Haynesville, Homer, Red River-Bull Bayou, and Rodessa.

The largest gas field in North Louisiana is Monroe, in Ouachita and Morehouse parishes. It has a reserve in the neighborhood of two trillion cubic feet. Other fields in North Louisiana having large gas reserves are Hico Knowles and Ruston in Lincoln Parish; Ada, Bear Creek, and Lucky in Bienville Parish; Logansport and Spider in De Soto Parish; Sligo and Benton in Bossier Parish; Cotton Valley and Ada in Webster Parish; Lisbon and East Haynesville in Claiborne Parish; Lake St. John in Concordia Parish; Longwood and Bethany-Longstreet in Caddo Parish, and Delhi in Richland Parish. The total gas reserves in North Louisiana in 1960 were estimated at ten trillion cubic feet.

Oil and gas are found in North Louisiana in sand, chalk, and lime formations from depths of one to eleven thousand feet. The traps responsible for accumulation are both structural and stratigraphic, and the producing formations range from Upper Cretaceous to Juras-

28

sic in age in North Louisiana, and from Eocene to Lower Cretaceous in Central Louisiana.

During the time that the oil and gas fields in North Louisiana were being developed, progress made in South Louisiana was comparatively slow. The topographic mounds, which might indicate hidden salt plugs, were the chief objects of exploration, and the majority of the remaining area was mostly neglected. However, in 1925, new geophysical methods using the torsion balance and the refraction seismograph were introduced and were a spectacular success in the Gulf Coast region. In addition, improvements were made in drilling methods for the swampy areas in South Louisiana.

Late in 1944 the Magnolia Petroleum Company was permitted the use of dynamite for a seismograph survey in Louisiana offshore waters. Much seismic work was done in the Gulf of Mexico, and many possible oil- and gas-bearing structures were located. In 1947, in Block 32 off Terrebonne Parish, the first producing offshore well was completed. Drilling activity has continued in various areas off the coast and has contributed substantially to Louisiana's gas reserve.

The dominant feature of South Louisiana is the flat, marshy topography. The surface outcrops are of Pleistocene and younger Tertiary age, and the sediments form a deltaic wedge. Oil and gas production is from sands at depths of seven hundred to twenty thousand feet that range from Miocene to Eocene in age. The chief traps are related to the occurrence of salt domes and are characterized by faulting.

The reserves in South Louisiana, including those in the offshore waters, are about fifty trillion cubic feet. Several of the fields have more than one trillion cubic feet of reserve. Some of the larger fields are Paradise in St. Charles Parish; Bateman Lake, Bayou Sale, and Horseshoe Bayou in St. Mary Parish; Erath, Live Oak, Tigre Lagoon, West White Lake, and Fresh Water Bayou in Vermillion Parish; Bay St. Elaine, Bayou Penchant, Bourg, Hollywood, Houma, Lirette, Gibson, Caillou Island, and Four Island Dome in Terrebonne Parish; North Elton in Allen Parish; Pecan Lake, Lakeside, Cameron, Deep Lake, Lowery, South Pecan Lake, and East Mud Lake in Cameron Parish; North Tepetate, Tepetate, Bayou Mallet, Church Point, Egan, and Branch in Acadia Parish; Bastian Bay, Delta Duck Club, Grand Bay, West Bay, and Delacroix Island in Plaquemines Parish; Hayes, Bell City, Iowa, East Moss Lake, and Holmwood in

Calcasieu Parish; Bay Marchand, Chacahoula, Delta Farms, Valentine, Lake Long, Thibodaux in LaFourche Parish; Lake Arthur in Jefferson Davis Parish; Lafitte in Jefferson Parish; Krotz Springs and Shuteston in St. Landry Parish; Duck Lake in St. Martin Parish; East Lake Palourde in Assumption Parish; Week's Island and Lake Sand in Iberia Parish; and College Point in St. James Parish. Large offshore fields include Vermillion area, Block 14; Eugene Island area, Block 32; Main Pass area, Block 69; South Pass area, Block 24; Vermillion area, Block 39; Vermillion area, Block 46; West Cameron area, Block 45; and East Cameron area, Block 46. It can be expected that additional large reserves of gas will be developed in the future in the offshore waters.

Today Louisiana is one of the main suppliers for the transmission companies whose pipe lines carry gas to southern, central, and eastern states. Major transmission systems are represented among the carriers of Louisiana natural gas—United Gas Pipeline Company, Transcontinental Gas Pipe Line Corporation, Tennessee Gas Transmission Company, Texas Eastern Transmission Corporation, Interstate Natural Gas Company, Gulf Interstate Company, American Louisiana Pipe Line Company, Mississippi River Fuel Company, and others.

Kansas ranks third in reserves, but fifth in annual production in the United States. This high rating can be attributed to the state's having the major share of the Hugoton gas field, the largest gas field in the United States. Of a proved extent of about 4,250,000 acres, Kansas holds 2,600,000 acres within its borders, Oklahoma 1,000,000, and Texas 650,000 acres. Of the total Hugoton reserves estimated at twenty-seven trillion cubic feet, Kansas' part is sixteen trillion, Oklahoma's about six, and Texas' about five trillion.

The Hugoton Field is so enormous that if superimposed on the state of New Jersey, it would cover about 80 per cent of that state. The two discovery wells were completed about the same time in 1922. The real discovery well is considered to be the Crawford well southwest of the town of Hugoton, from which the field gets its name. Because of a lack of markets, development, as in the case of the Panhandle Field, was slow, and it was not until the thirties that Hugoton's possibilities began to be fully realized and exploited by the pipeline companies. Like the Panhandle, the Hugoton Field is an excellent example of successful conservation. The Hugoton gas area is under

30

proration by the Kansas Corporation Commission, Division of Conservation. Only one well may be drilled on each 640 acres, and allowable production is established on a monthly basis in accordance with nominations made by the pipe-line companies. Some four thousand gas wells produce from this Kansas field. It is also a substantial contributor to the natural gas and LPG industry, since about twenty natural gasoline plants are in operation. Annual production of natural gas from the Kansas-Hugoton is about 400 billion cubic feet. Gas from this field helps to supply the needs of sixteen states. Deeper drilling in the Hugoton area has disclosed sizable reserves at greater depths.

Other gas fields of size in Kansas are Medicine Lodge and Rhodes in Barber County, McKinney in Clark County, Cunningham in Kingman and Pratt counties, and Spivey-Grabs in Kingman and Harper counties. The total gas reserve in Kansas is estimated at 20 trillion cubic feet as of December 31, 1959, and the annual production at 640 billion cubic feet.

The State of New Mexico is the fourth largest state in area in the United States, measuring 121,666 square miles. It also ranks fourth in natural gas reserves, having a reserve estimated at almost 18 trillion cubic feet as of December 31, 1960. The two areas in which oil and natural gas are developed are located in the extreme southeastern and northwestern parts of the state, separated by the Sangre de Cristo Mountain Range, the southern part of the main Rocky Mountain chain, and the irregular isolated tilted mountain uplifts between Albuquerque, New Mexico, and El Paso, Texas.

The oil-and gas-productive area of southeastern New Mexico is the western part of the general Permian Basin area of West Texas. The greater part of the oil and gas production here occurs in the Permian sands and limestones, with important but lesser volumes in the Pennsylvanian, Devonian, and Ordovician sands and limestones. Depths of production range from seven hundred to twelve thousand feet. Much of the production is casinghead gas from oil wells. Some of the larger fields are Eunice-Monument, Eunice South, Langlie-Mattix, Brunson, Maljamar, Jalmat, Artesia, Eumont, Hobbs, Lovington, Bagley, Caprock, Denton, Dollarhide, Drinkard, Gladiola, Saunders, and Vacuum. The greatest amounts of gas production come from Blinbry, Drinkard, Dean, Eumont, Langlie-Mattix, Jalmat,

Tubb, and Vacuum fields, in Lea, Eddy, and Chaves counties in south-eastern New Mexico.

The oil- and gas-productive area of northwestern New Mexico is a geologic province of its own, designated the San Juan Basin. The exploitation of this large area was at first restricted by the availability of markets; however, the opening of markets for this gas in California has led to its exploitation. The major oil- and gas-producing formations are Upper and Lower Cretaceous sandstones and Pennsylvanian limestones. Depths of production range between nine hundred and ten thousand feet. Most of the gas found here is in the non-associated category. Some of the larger fields are Blanco, West Kutz, Fulcher, Tapacito, Aztec, and Ballard.

The earliest report of commercial oil or gas production in Southwestern New Mexico is related to the development of artesian water supplies near Dayton in Eddy County. In 1909, the Old Hammond or Brown well produced up to forty barrels of oil a day from a depth of 950 feet. At some time between 1909 and 1915 another well near Dayton recorded gas production. In northwestern New Mexico in San Juan County both oil and gas were encountered in the Farmington well drilled in 1906–1907. Apparently the first commercial exploitation of natural gas in New Mexico occurred in 1920 when a well drilled near Aztec, San Juan County, began serving the town of Aztec with natural gas. The first commercial exploitation of natural gas in the southeastern area came with the discovery of the Artesia Field, Eddy County, in 1923.

The utilization of the natural gas reserves of New Mexico by long-distance pipe-line transmission began almost simultaneously in 1929 with the El Paso Natural Gas Company transporting gas west from Lea County to Arizona, and with the Southern Union Gas Company bringing gas from San Juan County to the cities of Albuquerque and Santa Fe. Production in New Mexico during 1960 was reported at 778 billion cubic feet. Much of this production goes to El Paso Natural Gas Company. In relation to reserves at current production rates, New Mexico has a twenty-five-year gas supply.

Oklahoma ranks fifth in reserves in the United States, but was third in annual production during 1959. As of December 31, 1960, the gas reserves of Oklahoma were estimated at about seventeen trillion cubic feet, and the annual production was almost one trillion cubic feet.

The discovery of oil and gas in Kansas about 1882 aroused the interest of the Five Civilized Tribes in Indian Territory (Oklahoma). In 1884 the Choctaw Council passed an act forming the Choctaw Oil and Refining Company. In 1891 several small producing wells were completed by the Choctaw Company near Chelsea (Rogers County) and in southeastern Nowata County for the first reported commercial oil production in Oklahoma.

Natural gas was first produced for market in Oklahoma in 1902 in northeastern Oklahoma. Major development of oil and gas fields began in 1904, being confined to the Osage Nation, with development near Muskogee, Chelsea, Red Fork, and Bartlesville. Prior to 1909, piping of natural gas from the state was unlawful, and this prohibition resulted in the waste of vast quantities of gas because the consumption of the state was small. In 1909 the law regarding export of gas was repealed, and activity in gas well drilling and production increased rapidly. In 1910 some five hundred gas wells furnished almost 30 billion cubic feet of gas to consumers, and by 1920 over 150 billion cubic feet of gas was marketed from Oklahoma. This had increased to over 300 billion cubic feet in 1930, to about 500 billion in 1950, and to about one trillion cubic feet in 1960.

Oklahoma is a part of the Mid-Continent oil- and gas-producing region. The fields lie principally in three areas: the Prairie Plains homocline in the northeast, extending along the western edge of the Ozark Mountains; the Central-Southern region, extending south of and between the Arbuckle and Wichita Mountains; and the Anadarko Basin, extending from the south central and southwestern part to the northwestern part of the state. The reservoir rocks are mainly consolidated sandstones, porous limestones, dolomites, and granite wash. Early oil and gas field development exploited the reservoirs of Pennsylvanian age and Mississippian age, but development since 1915 has taken place in both these and the deeper reservoirs. The gas fields in the central-southern and northwestern part of the state have proved to be the greatest source of non-associated gas. The western part of the state appears to offer the best possibility for future major gas discoveries, particularly the Anadarko Basin area.

The largest gas field in Oklahoma is the Hugoton Field in Texas County, which contains an estimated six trillion cubic feet. Other fields containing major gas reserves are Elk City in Beckham County,

East Lindsay in McClain County, West Edmond in Oklahoma County, and Ringwood in Major County. Recently there has been considerable development of the deeper Pennsylvania formations, especially the Atoka and Morrow fields in western Oklahoma in Beaver, Harper, and Woodward counties. These wells are from seven to ten thousand feet deep and usually have sizable deliverabilities.

Many major gas pipe lines either originate in Oklahoma or depend on Oklahoma for a considerable amount of their gas supplies. This is true of Natural Gas Pipeline Company of America, Northern Natural Gas Company, Cities Service Gas Company, Lone Star Gas Company, Oklahoma Natural Gas Company, and Panhandle Eastern Gas Pipeline Company.

CALIFORNIA

California ranks sixth in gas reserves in the United States and also sixth in annual production. As of December 31, 1960, California had almost nine trillion cubic feet of gas reserves and produced about 500 billion cubic feet of gas during 1960. Natural gas produced from an artesian water well near Stockton was utilized initially in California in 1864. Natural gas obtained from oil fields did not assume economic importance until 1900, although oil was produced in California in 1870, or perhaps earlier. In 1907, the Santa Maria Gas Company became the first utility company to supply natural gas to its consumers. A line was laid from Buena Vista Hills to Bakersfield in 1910. Another line from this field to Glendale and Los Angeles was completed in 1913. Although delivery through this line began April 28, 1913, natural gas was not served directly to customers for many years. Instead, it was reformed and blended with artificial gas, resulting in a lower *British thermal unit* (Btu) value ranging from 600 to 850 per cubic foot. The Los Angeles area has been supplied with 100 per cent natural gas since 1927.

Although the initial supply of gas, such as that produced at Stockton, was dry, casinghead gas obtained after the development of the major oil fields of the state, it supplied the needs of the gas companies for many years. Upon the discovery of the Buttonwillow gas field in 1927, dry gas again assumed importance as a source of supply. Natural gas from Kettleman Hills was delivered first to San Francisco in 1929. The production of dry gas has increased yearly since 1937 be-

34

cause of the large reserves of the Rio Vista Field, and all of the principal population centers in California are now served with natural gas.

The reported annual net gas production in California increased from 90 billion cubic feet in 1919 to 371 billion in 1941, and 605 billion in 1948, and was 465 billion in 1959. For the most part the oil and gas fields of this state are located in an area 230 miles long and 100 miles wide, trending northwest-southeast. The principal geological formations producing oil and gas are marine sediments of Middle and Upper Cenozoic age. However, gas in commercial quantities has recently been produced from Cretaceous and Lower Tertiary strata, causing geologists to focus more attention on these older beds. Depths of production range from one to sixteen thousand feet.

The gas reserve provinces are the Coastal region, centering around Ventura County; the Los Angeles region; the North Central region around Sacramento County; and the San Joaquin Valley region. The predominant gas reserves are dissolved gas in oil fields in the San Joaquin Valley and non-associated gas in the North Central region. The largest gas fields are Rio Vista in Sacramento County, which has a reserve between one and two trillion cubic feet; Beehive Bend in Glenn County; and Trico in Kern, Kings, and Tulare counties. Much of the gas reserve is found as dissolved gas in oil fields such as Ventura, Kettleman North Dome, Coalinga, North and South Belridge, Buena Vista, North and South Coles Levee, Elk Hills, Cuyama, San Ardo, Brea O'Linda, Edison, Fruitvale, Kern, Cat Canyon Group, Inglewood, Greeley, Midway-Sunset, Midway East and West, South Mountain, Wheeler Ridge, McKittrick Group, Mount Paso Group, Rio Bravo, Newhall-Potrero, Long Beach, Santa Fe Springs, Wilmington, and Huntington Beach.

California's principal gas-industry role in the past several decades has been that of consumer; and its dramatic growth since the end of World War II has made it a principal market for gas from West Texas, New Mexico, Colorado, and Canada. The rapid growth of the El Paso Natural Gas Company parallels the population growth and increased gas usage in California. Currently there is a proposal to import gas from northern Mexico to meet expanding California needs.

THE ROCKY MOUNTAIN STATES

The Rocky Mountain States—Wyoming, Colorado, Utah, North

Dakota, Montana, and Nebraska—rank in natural gas reserves in the order listed and have an aggregate reserve of almost 10 trillion cubic feet. During 1960 these states had a net gas production of 440 billion cubic feet.

Wyoming has the largest reserve, almost four trillion cubic feet as of December 31, 1960. The first commercial gas well in Wyoming was completed in 1905 on the Torchlight Dome at a depth of four hundred feet in the Mowry shale. Some of the largest gas fields are Big Piney, Church Buttes, Worland, Beaver Creek, Tip Top, and Baxter Basin. The availability of additional gas markets has stimulated drilling and development.

Topography in Wyoming is characterized by rugged mountains and deep basins. The principal basins are the Bighorn in the northwest, the Powder River in the northeast, the Wind River in the central section, and the Washakie and Green River in the southwest. Most of the producing oil and gas fields are found in the Bighorn, Wind River, Powder River, and Green River basins. Leasing and development have been most active in the Wind River and Powder River basins recently. Within the varied topography may be found a complete stratigraphic sequence from Tertiary to Pre-Cambrian in age. The younger Tertiary formations are exposed at the surface in most of the basin areas, with the older Mesozoic and Paleozoic rocks exposed along the mountainward flanks of the basins. Production is obtained from formations ranging from Tertiary to Cambrian age, the most important producing zones being the Wasatch of Tertiary age and the Tensleep Sand of Pennsylvanian age. The Wasatch, Frontier, and Dakota are probably the most important gas-producing horizons. Gas is obtained from depths ranging from a few hundred to fourteen thousand feet.

Colorado ranks second among the Rocky Mountain States in gas reserves, having about two trillion cubic feet. The first natural gas field in the state was discovered in 1898 with the opening of the Garcia gas field from a depth of seven hundred feet in the Pierre formation of Upper Cretaceous age. Recently there has been extensive gas development in the Mesa Verde reservoirs of Cretaceous age from five to ten thousand feet. During 1960 Colorado produced about 100 billion cubic feet of gas. This figure should be greatly increased in the next several years.

Gas and oil accumulations occur in both structural and stratigraphic traps. The most significant producing horizons are the Dakota, Morrison, and Sundance sands of Cretaceous and Jurassic age, and the Weber sands of Pennsylvanian age. The principal basins in which oil and gas occur in Colorado are the Washakie Basin in the extreme northwest, the Piceance Creek Basin in the northwest, the San Juan Basin in the southeast, the North Park Basin in the north, and the Denver Basin in the northeast. In the central portion of these basins, formations predominantly of Tertiary and Cretaceous age are exposed, while formations ranging from Cretaceous through Cambrian in age are generally exposed along the rims of the basins and the bounding mountainward folds.

The fields containing the largest gas reserves are Rangely, Piceance Creek, Ignacio, Adena, East and West Hiawatha, Powder Wash, North and South McCallum, Wilson Creek, and Little Beaver. The principal natural gas pipe-line companies purchasing gas in Colorado are the Colorado-Wyoming Gas Company, El Paso Natural Gas Company, Colorado Interstate Gas Company, Rocky Mountain Gas Company, and the Mountain Fuel Supply Company.

The first completed oil well in Utah was drilled in 1907 to open the shallow Virgin Field. During the latter part of 1924 and the early part of 1925, several minor gas discoveries were made. High-content carbon-dioxide gas was discovered in the Farnham Field. Commercial helium reserves were located in the Woodside Field and the Harley Dome; shallow, low-pressure wet gas was discovered in the Cisco Field and commercial dry gas was found in the Ashley Valley Field. Utah had an estimated gas reserve of one and one-half trillion cubic feet at the end of 1960, and its production for that year totaled about sixty billion cubic feet.

The principal petroliferous provinces in Utah are the Uinta Basin, the Colorado River Salt Basin, and the Black Mesa Basin, all located in the eastern and southeastern parts of the state. The principal gas-containing sediments are the Dakota, Mancos, and Frontier of Cretaceous age and the Morrison of Jurassic age. It is believed that at least twenty thousand feet of sediments are present in the deeper parts of the basin, ranging from Cambrian and Miocene. Oil and gas have been found in this basin from sediments of Cretaceous, Jurassic, Triassic, Permian, and Pennsylvanian ages. Gas rich in helium has been found in the Woodside and Harley fields, and rich in carbon dioxide in the Farnham and Gordon Creek fields. Oil and gas have been found in the Colorado River Basin in sediments of Cretaceous and Jurassic ages. The northern portion of the Black Mesa Basin extends into Utah, and oil and gas have been produced from formations of Permian and Pennsylvanian ages.

Some of the larger fields containing gas reserves are Ashley Creek, Clear Creek, Clay Basin, Bar X West, and Red Wash. Salt Lake City is a principal market. The Mountain Fuel Supply Company, and the Pacific Northwest Pipeline Company are the important pipe lines in the area.

Commercial natural gas was developed in North Dakota in 1907, when a well was drilled south of the town of Westhope in Bottineau County. The next significant event was the development of drilling in the Cedar Creek Field in Montana, which was then extended into North Dakota. (Gas is transported from this field by the Montana-Dakota Utilities Company.) The discovery of the Beaver Lodge Field in 1951, which produces from Madison and Mississippian limes at 8,500 feet and Devonian limes at 10,500 feet, was the most important episode in the state's petroleum history. Subsequent drilling disclosed the Tioga Field, which also produces from Madison lime. Tioga–Beaver Lodge had produced over fifty million barrels of oil through 1959, and is still producing five million barrels annually.

The discovery of this field led to increased exploration and to the discovery of some seventy-five new oil and gas fields. Most of them have been in northwestern and northern Dakota in Bottineau, Burke, Renville, Divide, Williams, and McKenzie counties. The largest gas-containing fields are Tioga, Beaver Lodge, Cedar Creek, Little Missouri, Blue Buttes, and Charlson. North Dakota now has a gas reserve estimated at about one trillion cubic feet at the end of 1960, and during 1960 some twenty billion cubic feet of gas were produced from North Dakota fields.

Other Rocky Mountain States having significant reserves are Montana with a reserve of 600 billion cubic feet and Nebraska with 100 billion cubic feet.

THE APPALACHIAN STATES

The Appalachian States—West Virginia, Pennsylvania, Ohio, and New York—were the birthplace of the natural gas industry in the

United States. They lead the nation in the quantity of underground gas storage, and the prices paid for gas at the wellhead are among the nation's highest—often reaching thirty cents per thousand cubic feet (MCF). The total gas reserves of these states approximate three and one-half trillion cubic feet of which one trillion cubic feet is in underground storage. This represents more than 50 percent of the total underground gas storage in the United States.

West Virginia has a reserve of 1.8 trillion cubic feet. The gas industry here had its start in conjunction with the salt business when William Tompkins used natural gas in his furnace for evaporating salt brine in 1841. Natural gas and oil are now produced from counties comprising at least one-half of the state, all lying west of the Appalachian Structural Front. Production is from formations of Pennsylvanian, Mississippian, and Devonian ages. During 1959 some fifteen thousand gas wells and thirteen thousand oil wells were producing in this state. The counties with the largest volumes of gas reserves are Ritchie, Logan, Mingo, Lewis, Kanawha, Lincoln, Wayne, Gilmer, and Calhoun. The most active counties from a drilling standpoint are Ritchie, Calhoun, Wayne, Logan, Mingo, and Lewis.

Pennsylvania, the birthplace of the petroleum industry, has a gas reserve of approximately one trillion cubic feet. Natural gas was first used here for heating and lighting purposes in the 1860's. In 1872 gas was piped a distance of six miles into Titusville, where it was used for domestic purposes. During 1960 gas was produced by some twenty thousand gas wells and eighty thousand oil wells from formations of Pennsylvanian, Mississippian, Devonian, and Silurian ages. The most important recent developments have been the exploitation of the deeper Oriskany sandstones of Devonian age and the offshore wells in Lake Erie producing gas from the Medina section of Silurian age.

Pennsylvania has been the site of some of the outstanding gas storage projects. The Oakford Storage project, a joint endeavor of Texas Eastern Transmission and New York State Natural Gas Company, provides over 100 billion cubic feet of storage and is an example of the many storage projects planned and operated in Pennsylvania.

Natural gas was known to exist in Ohio as early as 1814. At that time, wells drilled on Duck Creek, north of Marietta, Ohio, encountered natural gas. In 1874 natural gas was used for lighting purposes in the City of East Liverpool, Ohio. The discovery of gas in the Trenton limestone near Findlay in 1884 was the impetus to the development of the gas industry in this northwestern area. The advantages of natural gas led to the rapid expansion of facilities to serve both domestic and industrial consumers in Ohio, and as early as 1900 it was necessary to import gas from other states to meet the Ohio demand. This importation of gas led to the construction of storage projects, and today, Ohio has a reserve of about 750 billion cubic feet of gas, of which almost 45 per cent is represented by gas storage.

It is estimated that some 175,000 wells have been drilled in Ohio in the search for oil or gas and that some four trillion cubic feet of gas have been produced to date. During 1960 gas was produced from about 9,000 gas wells and 13,000 oil wells. The principal gas-producing formations have been the Beria sand of Mississippian age, the Clinton sand of Silurian age, and the Trenton limestone of Ordovician age, with production depths ranging from five hundred to five thousand feet. The formations most likely to be productive with deeper drilling are the St. Peter sandstone and dolomites of Basal Ordovician age.

The major portions of Ohio's gas reserves exist in Medina, Lorain, Coshocton, Meigs, Morgan, Stark, Ashland, Wayne, Muskingum, Tuscarawas, Athens, and Holmes counties. The most active counties from a standpoint of recent gas well drilling have been Wayne, Meigs, Coshocton, and Morgan.

In 1960, New York had a reserve of only 100 billion cubic feet of gas, most of which was stored. It is worthy of mention because of its historical significance, for it was here that the first gas well in the United States was drilled, at Fredonia, in 1821. Gas from this well was used locally for heating and illuminating purposes. In 1870 one of the earliest gas pipe lines in the United States was constructed to deliver gas from a well in West Bloomfield Township, Ontario County, New York, to the city of Rochester, a distance of thirty miles. The line was constructed of hollowed wooden logs. Since that time scores of gas wells have been drilled, and today New York is prominent in the industry as a consuming state, with almost twenty storage fields.

THE MIDDLE SOUTH

Mississippi has a sizable gas reserve estimated at about two and one-half trillion cubic feet in 1960. In addition, deeper drilling is developing additional reserves. The first commercial gas well was completed in 1926 in Monroe County from the Hartselle sandstone of Pennsylvanian age. Then came the discovery of a major gas reserve, the Jackson Field in Hinds County, which has produced more than 100 billion cubic feet to date from the Selma gas rock of Upper Cretaceous age. The discovery of the large Tinsley oil field in 1939 led to an intensified search for both gas and oil. As a result several large fields have been discovered. The largest of these is Gwinville, which is in the one-trillion cubic feet reserve category. Other large gas-containing fields are Cranfield, Baxterville, Bolton, Carthage Point, Hub, Soso, Brookhaven, Pistol Ridge, and Maxie.

The principal producing oil and gas formations in Mississippi are the Wilcox of Eocene age, the Eutaw and Tuscaloosa of the Gulf series of Cretaceous age, and the Comanche series of Cretaceous age. There are excellent markets, the two principal outlets being United Gas Pipe Line Company and the Southern Natural Gas Company.

In 1902 the Choctaw Oil and Gas Company discovered the first commercial gas field in Arkansas with the completion of a gas well near Mansfield in northwestern Arkansas. In 1920 the first commercial gas discovery was made in southern Arkansas from the Nacatoch sand in Union County. Discovery of the prolific Smackover Field in 1922 stimulated drilling, and many large oil and gas fields have been subsequently found.

The principal oil and gas fields have been in southern Arkansas in sands or limes of Cretaceous age. The largest gas accumulations are found in the Reynolds lime of Jurassic age at depths of seven to nine thousand feet. Some of these fields having the largest gas reserves are McKamie-Patton, Magnolia, and Dorcheat-Macedonia. The gas fields in the northwest produce from formations of Pennsylvanian age. The Cecil, White Oak, and Lone Elm fields in Franklin County, and Moreland Field in Pope County are prominent. Development in the northwest has been the most recent activity, with Franklin, Johnson, Logan, and Sebastian counties being outstanding.

In 1960, Arkansas had a reserve of almost one and one-half trillion cubic feet. There have been ample markets for the gas. The Arkansas Louisiana Gas Company, the Arkansas Power and Light Company, the Arkansas Oklahoma Gas Company, and the Arkansas Western Natural Gas Company have been principal purchasers.

Kentucky has a gas reserve in excess of one trillion cubic feet. As early as 1863, natural gas production from a well near Brandenburg, Meade County, was used as fuel in the distillation of salt from brine. Increased demand for gas has resulted in an extensive search for this fuel, and it is estimated that some 40,000 wells have been drilled and at least two trillion cubic feet of gas produced. Almost 95 per cent of the gas production in Kentucky is from the Big Sandy area in the eastern part of the state. This area includes 6,200 gas wells in Floyd, Martin, Knott, Pike, Magoffin, Johnson, Lawrence, Letcher, and Perry counties. Additional gas production is from oil and gas fields in eastern, south central, and western Kentucky. Drilling activity has recently centered around Green County in central Kentucky and Breathitt County in eastern Kentucky.

THE CENTRAL STATES

Michigan, Illinois, and Indiana have a total reserve approaching 750 billion cubic feet, of which almost half is storage gas. It is not likely that future drilling in these states will add significantly to the nation's supply.

ALASKA

In Alaska, oil seeps were reported at Iniskin Bay (across Cook Inlet from Kenai) as early as 1853. The Katalla oil field was discovered in 1903, and had produced 154,000 barrels of oil by 1933 when it was abandoned. The navy conducted exploration activities on Naval Petroleum Reserve No. 4 for a ten-year period ending in 1953 and discovered the Umiat oil field and Gubik gas field.

The completion of an oil well in 1937 at Swanson River on the Kenai Peninsula from the Hemlock formation of Eocene age at about eleven thousand feet was a major stimulus to exploration. Since that time eleven producing wells have been completed and a line laid to the coast. Gas has been discovered in commercial quantities in the Cook Inlet area on the Kenai Peninsula. Many major petroleum operators now have sizable holdings in Alaska, and plans have been made to build a gas pipe line to the city of Anchorage. Since there are 365 million acres in Alaska, several good sedimentary basins, and a growing population, it is likely that Alaska will soon have a large gas reserve of its own.

LOCATION AND SUPPLY

As indicated above, the states having the largest proved gas reserves as of December 1960, are:

	Reserves, Trillion Cu. Ft.
Texas	120
Louisiana	63
Kansas	20
Oklahoma	17
New Mexico	16
Total	236

As of January 1, 1949, the states ranged as follows:

Texas	99
Louisiana	27
Kansas	14
Oklahoma	12
California	10
Total	162

Thus, during a decade natural gas reserves increased by almost one-third, in spite of production during this period equal to one-half of the known reserves at the start of the decade. The 140 per cent increase in reserves in Louisiana can be attributed to the discovery and development of fields in South Louisiana.

The largest gas fields in the United States are as follows:

Field	*State*	*Reserves, Trillion Cu. Ft.*
Hugoton	Texas, Oklahoma, Kansas	27
Panhandle	Texas	15
Katy	Texas	5 plus
Old Ocean	Texas	3 plus
Seeligson	Texas	2–3
Agua Dulce–Stratton	Texas	2–3
Carthage	Texas	2–3

Thus, about 25 per cent of the total United States gas reserves are found in seven fields.

The largest gas reservoirs in the United States are the carbonate rocks of Permian and Pennsylvanian age, the sands of Miocene, Eocene, and Oligocene age, and the sands and limes of Cretaceous and Jurassic ages.

For the past several years in the United States the ratio of oil reserves to annual production has been 12 to 1. For natural gas the ratio of gas reserves to annual production has changed from 32 to 1 in 1946, to a ratio of 21 to 1 in 1960. The history of estimators of total oil resources in the United States is marked by alarmists who thought we would soon be out of oil. The history of estimators of natural gas resources is much shorter, but marked by a similar trend, so that with the passage of time and the advantage of hindsight, each successive estimate is higher than the previous one in regard to ultimate gas resources. There is a finite natural gas reserve, however, and the time required by nature to manufacture this commodity is of such length that each cubic foot produced today subtracts a cubic foot from the total resource. Any estimate of total future gas reserves is at best an educated guess, although the reasoning that Lewis G. Weeks, former Chief Geologist, Standard Oil Company, New Jersey, used in arriving at total ultimate oil resources is logically sound. Since oil and gas exist in marine sedimentary basins, he estimated the volumes of such basins and, by use of several ratios, arrived at an estimate of total oil resources. It should be remembered that as we drill deeper the ratio of gas to oil discoveries increases, and that a cubic foot of pore space at twelve thousand feet contains roughly twice as much gas as at four thousand feet on account of the higher pressures at depths. This fact is somewhat illustrated by the ratio of gas reserves to liquid hydrocarbons in 1947 being 4.1 MCF/barrel; in 1959 it was 7.1 MCF/barrel.

Recent estimates of future gas resources vary from 500 trillion cubic feet to 1,700 trillion cubic feet. Estimates of different experts for maximum future annual gas production rates in the United States vary from 14 to 20 trillion cubic feet. The year 1960 showed an annual production of about 13 trillion cubic feet, and the future growth rate for natural gas is estimated at 3 to 4 per cent a year. This results in an estimate of almost 18 trillion cubic feet for gas production by 1970. It is believed that the maximum future annual production will exceed this figure, and that the total future gas reserves will be at least 1,500 trillion cubic feet.

The finding of these gas reserves, as was pointed out previously, is dependent on an economic incentive of sufficient force to cause the oil and gas companies to search. It is believed that the potential is there. Since natural gas is often discovered in looking for oil, the number of wells drilled annually for both oil and gas is some index of whether the pace of the search is rapid enough. With the slowdown in the search for oil in the United States in the past several years, indicated by a decrease in the number of wells drilled annually from 58,160 in 1956 to 48,328 in 1959, there is some concern. The Federal Power Commission prefers to have a twenty-year supply to approve a certificate for a pipe line. The United States has a twenty-one-year supply presently, if no more wells are drilled and the annual rate of production remains at 13 trillion cubic feet. Over the next ten years it is estimated that some 150 trillion cubic feet of gas will be produced, and we will be producing almost 20 trillion cubic feet annually. To have a twenty-year supply at that time we will have to have a reserve of 400 trillion cubic feet. Since our 1960 reserve is 260 trillion cubic feet and the estimated production for the next ten years is 150 trillion cubic feet, in order to have a twenty-year supply in 1970, we must find almost 300 trillion cubic feet, or 30 trillion feet annually. For the last several years we have added about 20 trillion cubic feet annually. If this rate continues until 1970, we will at that time have a fifteen-year supply. Unless our rate of drilling increases over the 1960 rate, it is doubtful that 20 trillion feet will be found annually.

The most likely sources of future gas resources are under the offshore waters of the Gulf Coast area, particularly the Louisiana and Texas Coastal areas, the Edwards trend in South and Southwest Texas, the Smackover trend in East Texas, various sands at ten to thirty thousand feet along the Gulf Coast of Texas and Louisiana, Lower Cretaceous deep sands and perhaps deep Jurassic limes in Mississippi, the Piceance and Sand Wash basins of northwestern Colorado, the Uintah Basin in Utah, the Foothills Belt in Montana, the Arkansas Valley in western Arkansas and eastern Oklahoma, the Anadarko Basin in Oklahoma, the Warrior Basin in northeastern Mississippi and northwestern Alabama, the Palo Duro Basin of northwestern Texas and Val Verde Basin of West Texas, the Delaware Basin of West Texas and southeastern New Mexico, offshore Lake

Erie, deeper beds in the Appalachian geosyncline, the various basins in Alaska, and the Green River, Washakie, and Wind River basins of Wyoming.

Some people have worried about the purposes for which gas is used. It would seem that economics should determine purpose as long as the gas is not flared. It is quite likely that years before our gas reserves are exhausted, solar and nuclear energy will be replacing gas in household and industrial heating.

ESTIMATING THE RESERVES

There are several methods employed by the American Gas Association in making the estimates of gas reserves discussed above. The *volumetric method* is used in connection with non-associated gas reserves. It utilizes structural and isopachous maps based on data from electrical logs, cores, and drill-stem and production tests. Sand volumes are obtained by planimetering. Core-analysis data and electrical-log interpretation permit reasonable estimates of porosity, connate water, and net productive thickness so that volume of gas-filled pore space may be calculated. Laboratory analysis of the gas for determination of its compressibility at various pressures and temperatures and the determination of reservoir pressure and temperature by recording instruments make it possible to calculate the volume of gas contained in the reservoir with reasonable accuracy.

Calculation of the gas in place in the reservoir may be accomplished by use of the following formula:

$$Q = 43,560 \times \emptyset \ (1-S_w) \ \left(\frac{P}{P_b}\right)\left(\frac{460+t_b}{460+t}\right)\left(\frac{1}{Z}\right)$$

where

Q = cubic feet of gas per acre foot at base temperature and pressure

$43,560$ = number of cubic feet per acre foot

$\emptyset$ = porosity expressed as a decimal fraction

S_w = interstitial water expressed as a decimal fraction

P = reservoir pressure in pounds per square inch absolute

P_b = base pressure in pounds per square inch absolute

t = reservoir temperature in degrees Fahrenheit

t_b = base temperature in degrees Fahrenheit

Z = compressibility factor at pressure P

46

In the event a water drive is not anticipated, the volume of gas which will remain in the reservoir at the expected abandonment pressure may be calculated and deducted from the volume of gas initially in place to determine the volume of recoverable gas. The abandonment pressure to be used depends on the price of gas, the size of the field, its location with respect to market, and the type of market. If the market is a transmission pipe line, the operating pressure of the line may be a controlling factor in the abandonment pressure for small fields. However, in the case of large fields, installation of compressor plants may be economically feasible, thus lowering the abandonment pressure substantially below the operating pressure of pipe lines serving the area.

In the case of water-drive fields, the pressure will be wholly or partially maintained by the movement of water into the reservoir as gas is withdrawn, the magnitude of pressure decline being dependent on the rate of gas withdrawal with respect to the rate of water advancement. Water-advancement rate is a function of the area of the gas-water contact, the permeability of the reservoir, and the pressure differential created by gas withdrawals. Recoverable gas is usually estimated for water-drive reservoirs by applying a recovery factor to the calculated volume in place. The selection of a recovery factor depends on the thickness and homogeneity of the sand, the relative permeability of the sand to gas and water at varying gas saturations, the percentage of the gas-containing portion of the reservoir originally underlaid by water, the dip of the reservoir beds, and the amount of structural closure above the gas-water contact. The recovery factor will be highest when the sand is uniform and homogeneous, the permeability of the sand to gas is high at low gas saturation, the percentage of the gas-containing portion of the reservoir originally underlaid by water is relatively small, the beds are relatively steep, and the amount of structural closure above the gas-water contact is large.

Recovery factors used by different estimators under the same conditions vary widely. Study of the recovery from depleted fields for which volumetric data are available is helpful in selecting a recovery factor.

The *pressure-decline-curve method* is one of the most widely used, and one of the most reliable of the several means of estimating non-associated gas reserves in those reservoirs which do not have a water

47

drive. Several types of pressure-decline curves are used, and one or more of these curves is constructed for each reservoir studied to determine if a water drive is present and its relative importance. Early pressure-decline curves were constructed from closed-in wellhead pressures, sometimes referred to as *rock pressures*. Since the development of methods of measuring and calculating reservoir pressures, most engineers and geologists use reservoir pressures in plotting decline curves. In the event a water drive is not present, wellhead or reservoir pressure plotted against cumulative production may be extrapolated in a straight line to the expected abandonment pressure, and the ultimate recovery read direct. Estimates made in this manner ignore the effect of deviation from Boyle's law. When the accuracy of other data justify refinements, reservoir pressure divided by the compressibility factor (Z) may be plotted against cumulative production to correct for the effect of deviation from Boyle's law.

The *equal-pound-loss method* is a special use of this method, in which a curve is not actually constructed, but the production at the point of intersection of the curve with the abandonment pressure is calculated by assuming a constant slope determined by the initial pressure after a known volume of gas has been withdrawn. This method is not as reliable as a decline curve since only two pressure points are used.

The equal-pound-loss method may be corrected for deviation of gas from Boyle's law by use of the following formula, published by Eugene A. Stephenson in *Geology of Natural Gas* in 1935:

$$R = Q \left(\frac{P_r \, dr - P_a \, da}{P_i \, di - P_r \, dr} \right)$$

where
  R = gas reserve to abandonment pressure
  Q = production of the reservoir during the decline in pressure from P_i to P_r
  P_i = initial pressure of the reservoir
  P_r = reservoir pressure as of the date of appraisal
  P_a = reservoir pressure as of the date of abandonment
  di = deviation factor at P_i
  dr = deviation factor at P_r
  da = deviation factor at P_a

Cumulative pressure drop may be plotted against cumulative production on logarithmic paper. This method of plotting was developed by H. C. Miller of the United States Bureau of Mines. If cumulative production per pound drop is constant, the curve will be a straight line with a slope of 1 (45 degree angle with the horizontal). If water, oil, or gas is encroaching into the known gas area, the slope will be less than 1 (an angle of less than 45 degrees with the horizontal). The effect of deviation from Boyle's law will cause a slight flattening of the curve. If this curve has a slope of 1, or slightly less, the ultimate production may be determined by extrapolating the curve of a pressure drop equivalent to the initial pressure minus the expected abandonment pressure.

Cumulative production per pound decline in closed-in wellhead or reservoir pressure may be plotted against cumulative production or against time. If values for cumulative production per pound pressure decline are constant, the resulting curve is a straight line parallel to the time or cumulative production axis, and it may be assumed that estimates of reserves made by use of the equal-pound-loss method or by extrapolation of the pressure cumulative-production-decline curve will be correct. If the slope of the curve is negative (i.e., values of cumulative production per pound drop increase with cumulative production or time), water, oil, or gas is encroaching into the known gas area. It should be remembered that the effect of deviation from Boyle's law will cause a slight increase in values even if a water drive is not present.

A large error is often introduced by the method of obtaining the average field pressure. If numerical averages of the producing wells are used for each point plotted, the rate of drilling influences the slope of the curve. If only a few wells are drilled in a large reservoir of low permeability, the numerical average of their pressures after considerable gas has been withdrawn may be considerably lower than the average pressure of the reservoir. If the drilling rate is rapid enough with respect to permeability of the reservoir and rate of gas withdrawal, new wells may be completed with closed-in pressures considerably higher than those of wells already producing. The effect of this is a flattening or a reversal of slope of the cumulative production-pressure-decline curve.

Errors of this type can be reduced by constructing isobaric maps and planimetering to obtain the weighted average pressure. The reservoir area used in obtaining the weighted average pressure should be the same for each point plotted. If a reservoir is determined to be larger than previously estimated, all isobaric maps should be corrected and pressures recalculated so that all points on the curve represent the average pressure of the same area. Greater accuracy can be obtained by weighting pressures on the basis of reservoir pore volume rather than on the basis of surface acreage if there are large variations in net productive thickness.

Certain additional problems are encountered in estimating associated gas reserves. First, the volume of gas which may be produced from the gas cap may exceed the original volume of gas contained in the gas cap because of migration of solution gas upstructure with reduction of pressure on the oil zone. Second, the reservoir volume occupied by the gas cap may increase as oil is withdrawn or it may decrease because of movement of oil upstructure. Third, the volume of gas produced from the gas cap may not be known accurately because some oil wells near the gas-oil contact may produce associated gas as well as dissolved gas. Decline-curve methods for estimating the amount of gas remaining in a gas cap are inaccurate since the volume of the reservoir will remain constant only under exceptional conditions, and dissolved gas may migrate into the gas cap. The problem of estimation is simplified if no effort is made to distinguish between associated and dissolved gas. The total original gas reserve may be computed and the cumulative production of associated and dissolved gas subtracted to obtain the total gas reserve remaining at any time.

The principal method of estimating dissolved gas reserves is a *volumetric method*. The original gas in place is determined by estimating the original volume of stock-tank oil in place and multiplying this value by the original solution gas-oil ratio. The recovery factor to be applied depends on the mechanics under which the reservoir will be produced. In the case of reservoirs in which the pressure does not drop below the bubble point, the gas-oil ratio will be constant and the recovery factor for gas will be the same as the recovery factor for oil. The East Texas Field is an example of this type of reservoir. Where the pressure drops below the bubble point, the recovery factor for gas will be greater than the recovery factor for oil. In order to make an accurate determination of the recovery factor, it is necessary to predetermine the pressure history of the field by material balance and water influx calculations, or by extrapolating a curve of pressure against cumulative production if rates of production have been constant. After the pressure history of the field has been estimated, the amount of gas to be recovered can be reasonably approximated by multiplying the volume of recoverable oil by the original dissolved gas-oil ratio and adding an amount equal to the volume of unrecoverable oil times the difference in the original dissolved gas-oil ratio and the amount of gas in solution per barrel of oil at the average pressures at which the reservoir is expected to be produced.

To calculate the amount of recoverable gas in a constant-volume reservoir, it is necessary to calculate the gas originally in place and subtract the gas that is calculated to be unrecoverable at the expected abandonment pressure of the reservoir. This may be calculated by the following equations:

$$R = O_p G_o - U$$

where

R = recoverable gas in cubic feet

U = unrecoverable gas in cubic feet,

$$\text{or } (V - O_u F v_a) \; 5.61 \left(\frac{P_a}{P_b}\right) \left(\frac{520}{t + 460}\right) \left(\frac{1}{Z_a}\right) + O_u G_a$$

V = void space in reservoir in barrels, or $7758 \times \emptyset \times (1 - S_w)$

O_u = unrecoverable oil in barrels at stock tank conditions, or $(O_p - O_r)$

O_p = original oil in place in barrels at stock tank conditions, or $V/F v_o$

O_r = recoverable oil in barrels at stock tank conditions

$F v_o$ = original formation volume factor

P_a = reservoir pressure at abandonment in pounds per square inch absolute

P_b = base pressure in pounds per square inch absolute

t = reservoir temperature in degrees F.

Z_a = compressibility factor at P_a

G_a = cubic feet of gas at base pressure in solution per barrels of stock tank oil at P_a

G_o = cubic feet of gas at base pressure originally in solution per barrel of oil at stock tank conditions.

51

PRODUCING NATURAL GAS

The first step in the production of natural gas is the drilling and completion of wells. Leases must first be obtained that give the producer the right to drill the well, complete it, and produce gas and oil. To obtain these leases usually requires the payment of a cash bonus and an agreement to pay a royalty of one-eighth to one-third of any production obtained to the owner of the mineral rights.

The well is drilled using either a cable-tool or a rotary rig. The former method is employed in hard-rock country and involves pounding the rock with percussion-type blows and bailing out the cuttings. The rotary method is used in softer sediments. A rotating bit with pressure applied to it cuts into the sediments, and the cuttings are removed by a stream of mud that circulates through the drill pipe, bit, and back up to the surface. In some cases air or gas is used as the cleansing medium. The rotary method is the newest and most popular. The deeper wells, ten thousand feet and below, use this method.

In either case a hole is drilled to or through the producing formation, and a string of pipe or *casing* is cemented in the hole. If set through the formation, holes are shot opposite the formation and sometimes the formation is acidized to increase deliverability. The well is controlled by the weight of mud on the formation and by a valve at the surface. A smaller string of pipe, or *tubing* (usually two to two and one-half inches in diameter) is run inside the casing. Tubing enables the well stream to move at a higher velocity and thus to produce more liquids contained in the gas. All of this is connected at the wellhead to a *Christmas tree,* which is an assembly of valves and fittings mounted at the head of the well to control the flow.

The actual rate of flow from the gas well is regulated by the use of a positive choke (a constriction inserted in the flow passage of the Christmas tree) which is finished to a multiple of one-sixty-fourth of an inch, or an adjustable choke which advances or retracts a needle point to increase or decrease the area of the flow passage. Pressure gauges and thermometers are also important pieces of equipment in observing and determining the flow rate.

Upon completion of the well it is necessary to measure the flow capacity. This is usually done by use of the pitot tube, critical flow prover, choke nipple, or orifice meter. There is a relationship between the rate at which a gas well can produce and the pressure differential occurring with the flow at the wellhead. The well is flowed at three rates of flow, and the drop in wellhead pressure for each flow rate is observed. Using these data, an open flow potential, or the maximum rate at which the well could produce unhindered to the atmosphere, is calculated. This is expressed in MCF per day.

The completion of the gas well is merely the first step in getting the gas to the consumer. If the gas well is a considerable distance from a gas pipe line, other gas wells must be drilled and completed in the field until the combined deliverability and reserve make the laying of a gathering line from the main line economically feasible. This sometimes requires several years, and producers will have large sums of money invested in the shut-in wells with no revenue until the gathering line is laid.

Once the gathering line is laid, the producer usually signs a gas purchase contract with the pipe line purchasing his gas. This contract specifies a price, and includes certain specifications for the gas deliveries, such as freedom from sulphur impurities (usually no more than 1.0 to 0.25 grains per hundred feet hydrogen sulphide), a certain heating value (usually 1,000 Btu per cubic foot), and provision for removing hydrates and liquids. Equipment must be provided to accomplish these objectives, and the operator usually installs the following equipment between his gas well and the gathering line:

(1) A free-liquid knockout unit. Gas for transmission lines is limited to a maximum of three to seven pounds of water per million cubic feet. Mechanically all free water and liquids are removed from the flowing gas stream.

(2) A heat exchanger, which changes the temperature of the gas and prevents the formation of hydrates. (Water vapor and hydrocarbon vapors combine to form a snowlike substance, called hydrates, when the gas expands. These hydrates are ices that could stop up the flow line.)

(3) A separator. Separators are usually vertical tanks with tangential inlets and a series of baffle plates, which decrease velocity and separate the heavier hydrocarbons from the methane by gravity. The gas goes out an overhead outlet and the liquids through a port at the bottom. For high-pressure gas-condensate mixtures, multi-stage separators are used to arrive at a stable liquid.

(4) A meter. This is usually an orifice meter, which records con-

tinuously on a chart pressure changes before and after the gas passes through an orifice, from which volume can be calculated. Often the gas wells will be connected to a gasoline plant. In this case, a simple *drip* will be used, which is a section of pipe fitted with hemispherical heads and mounted in a tilted position so that the liquids drain to one end. A *heater* would not be used unless the gasoline plant is a considerable distance away. An orifice meter would be installed somewhere between the gasoline plant, and the well-head. The pipe-line company would buy the gas at the outlet side of the gasoline plant, and here there would probably be a dehydrator, and perhaps a compression plant, whose compressors would raise the pressure of the gas from that at the discharge side of the gasoline plant to that necessary to cause the gas to flow at a required velocity to the next compressor station. The dehydrator would be either a liquid or solid desicant. The liquid type uses glycol to absorb the water vapor, and the solid type uses charcoal as an absorber. Both employ heaters.

When gas is obtained from an oil well, it first passes through a separator, with the oil going to oil storage tanks and the gas flowing to a regulator and a meter before entering the gathering line. The gathering line usually collects gas at low pressures from many oil wells and delivers it to a central point where it must be dehydrated and its pressure increased by the use of compressors.

Sour gas, which contains a large amount of hydrogen sulphide, is sweetened by a process similar to the glycol dehydration unit. The solution used to remove the water vapor and hydrogen sulphide consists of diethylene glycol, monoethanolamine, and water, and is known as the *glycol-amine process*. Corrosion of equipment is a real problem. In recent years, there has been a trend toward the use of chemicals for retarding corrosion of subsurface well equipment and well connections. The quantity of carbon dioxide, hydrogen sulphide, and the flow rates are factors influencing corrosion.

Much has been written about the current supply of natural gas and how best to utilize it now while making provisions for the future. Listed below are some good references used in the writing of this chapter and suggested for additional reading on this subject:

"Alaska Gas Discovery Is Big," *Petroleum Week,* Vol. XI, No. 14 (October 7, 1960), 30.

American Gas Association and American Petroleum Institute, *Proved Reserves of Crude Oil, Natural Gas Liquids and Natural Gas in the United States,* XIV, New York, December 31, 1959.

DeGolyer and McNaughton, *Estimated Natural Gas Reserves by States Available for Synthetic Liquid Fuel Manufacture,* a survey for the United States Army Corps of Engineers, Dallas, Texas, 1951.

DeGolyer, E. L., "The Nation's Reserves of Natural Gas," a speech delivered before the Interstate Oil Compact Commission, Oklahoma City, Oklahoma, 1945.

Elmer, W. M., "The Pipeliner's Viewpoint," an address before the 31st Annual Meeting, I.P.A.A., Dallas, Texas, October, 1960.

Facts About the Oil and Gas Pipe Line Industry, 1960, a pamphlet published by *Pipe Line Industry,* September, 1959.

Foster, Fred K., "Carthage Gas Field Development," *Oil Weekly,* Vol. CXXIV, No. 4 (December 23, 1946), 33–44.

Goldston, W. J., "The Producer's Viewpoint," an address before the 31st Annual Meeting, I.P.A.A., Dallas, Texas, October, 1960.

Golush, W. B., "A Management Look at Natural Gas," paper 1445–G presented before the annual meeting of the A.I.M.E., New York, New York, February 14–18, 1960, and published in the *Journal of Petroleum Technology,* Vol. XII, No. 7 (July, 1960), 11–16.

Gruy, H. J., and John A. Crichton, "A Critical Review of Methods of Estimating Gas Reserves," a paper presented before meetings of the American Institute of Mining and Metallurgical Engineers, Tulsa, Oklahoma, October 8, 1947, and Los Angeles, California, October 23, 1947.

Hill, Kenneth E. and Richard E. Barnett, "The Outlook for Natural Gas," *The Mines Magazine,* Vol. XLIX, No. 11 (November, 1959), 28–30.

Hillard, Hinson, "Guidebook of Houston Geological Society," handed out at the Annual Meeting, A.A.P.E., 1953.

Hinton, C. H., "The Hugoton Field," a paper presented before the Interstate Oil Compact Commission, Wichita, Kansas, December, 1952.

Hubbert, M. King, "The Mineral Resources of Texas," paper presented before the Conference on Texas, Austin, Texas, April 11–12, 1958.

———, "Nuclear Energy and the Fossil Fuels," in *Drilling and Production Practices—1956,* New York, 1957, 7ff.

I.P.A.A., *The Oil Producing Industry in Your State,* special 1959 edition, Washington, D.C.

Institute of Gas Technology, *Natural Gas Production and Transmission,* Chicago, 1952.

Ivers, John L., and Edward Symonds, *Energy from Economic Development,* a booklet published by the First National City Bank, New York, 1961, from a paper presented before the Second Arab Petroleum Congress, Beirut, Lebanon, October 19, 1960.

Kaye, Emley, "Some Factors in the Economics of Recycling," A.I.M.E. *Transactions,* Petroleum Division, Vol. CXLVI, New York, 1942.

McCollum, L. F., "The Effect on the American Consumer of Federal Regulation of Natural Gas," a paper presented at the Annual Meeting of the Independent Petroleum Association of America, Tulsa, Oklahoma, October 26, 1954.

Merriam, Daniel P., "Hugoton Embayment Commands Fresh Look," *Oil and Gas Journal,* Vol. LIV, No. 44 (March 5, 1956), 82–86.

Montgomery, Randall F., "The Oil and Gas Producing Zones of Southeastern New Mexico," Interstate Oil Compact Commission *Bulletin,* Vol. XIV, No. 2 (December, 1955), 20.

"Natural Gas Business in the United States," *The Mines Magazine,* Vol. XLIX, No. 11 (November, 1959).

"Natural Gas in the Southwest," Southwestern Federation of Geological Societies *Transactions,* Vol. I, Abilene, Texas.

Netschert, Bruce C., *The Future Supply of Oil and Gas,* Baltimore, Md., 1958.

Neuner, Edward J., *The Natural Gas Industry,* Norman, 1960.

Noble, Frank G., "Operating Features of the Katy Gas Cycling Plant," *Oil Weekly,* Vol. CIX, No. 9 (May 3, 1943), 17–24.

Payne, James E., "Origin of Oil and Gas," *Steelways* (February, 1953).

Petroleum Extension Service, *Field Handling of Natural Gas,* Austin, Texas, 1954.

Pressler, H. P., Jr., "Legal Problems Involved in Cycling Gas in Gas Fields," *Petroleum Engineer,* Vol. XVII, No. 11 (July, 1946), 151.

Rogatz, Henry, "Geology of Texas Panhandle Oil and Gas Field," A.A.P.G. *Bulletin,* July, 1939.

Searles, David T., "The Problem of Finding Enough Gas," *Petroleum Press Service,* Vol. XXVII, No. 11 (November, 1960), 426–27.

Society of Petroleum Engineers of A.I.M.E. and International Scouts Association, *International Oil and Gas Development Yearbook* (for 1959), 1960, Parts I and II.

Stadnikoff, G., "Parental Substance of Petroleum," *Erdöl und Kohle* (August, 1958).

Stephenson, Eugene A., "Valuation of Natural Gas Properties," *Geology of Natural Gas, A.A.P.G., a Symposium,* 1935.

Stormont, D. H., "Northwest Gas Out of Toddler Stage," *Oil and Gas Journal,* Vol. LVII, No. 36 (August 31, 1959), 27–28.

Terry, Lyon F., and John G. Winger, *Future Growth of the Natural Gas Industry,* New York, 1957.

Whittelsey, C. C., "Future Holds Great Potential for Natural Gas," *Gas Age,* Vol. CXXII, No. 7 (October 2, 1958), 65.

Wolfe, J. Theodore, "The Natural Gas Distributor," an address before the 31st Annual Meeting, I.P.A.A., Dallas, Texas, October, 1960.

World Oil, Forecast-review Issue (February, 1960).

Wyer, Samuel S., "Natural Gas: Its Production, Service and Conservation," *U.S. National Museum Bulletin 102,* Washington, D.C., 1918.

3

FROM FIELD TO MARKET

by John C. Jacobs

GEOGRAPHICALLY the supply of gas in the United States has always been located some distance from the market for gas, in spite of the fact that gas tends to be consumed in the vicinity of its production. This geographical disparity between supply and market is greater today than ever before, with major sources of supply located in the southwestern United States and major markets in the northeastern and Pacific Coast regions of the United States. The solution to this problem of geographical disparity—the method for converting a nuisance to a natural resource[1]—has been the long-distance, high-pressure pipe line.

In the United States, where the distance between gas supply and demand areas often comes close to one thousand miles, the cheapest way to move large volumes of fluids is by pipe line. This is true for both crude oil and natural gas although a designated pipe line can transport about four times as much energy in the form of oil as in the form of gas, and the physical characteristics of gas dictate its transportation under pressure in a pipe line. The only alternatives to pipe-line transportation are the ocean shipment of liquefied natural gas and the conversion of gas to electricity at the point of production, with the subsequent transportation of electrical energy in high lines. Ocean shipment of liquefied natural gas cannot now, or in the immediate future, compete with pipe-line shipments of natural gas in large volumes,[2] and studies have shown that, at distances of up to 240 miles, it is cheaper to move

---

[1] Emmette S. Redford (ed.), *Public Administration and Policy Formation*, 55.

[2] L. J. Clark, "Sea Transport of Liquid Methane," *Transactions* of the World Power Conference (1960), VI, 3153; *Petroleum Press Service*, Vol. XXVII, No. 7 (July, 1960), 246.

gas by pipe line than to transmit electricity made from gas at the point of production, unless the gas is available at very low pressures and requires considerable compression for pipe-line delivery.[3] Against this broad economic background the long-distance, high-pressure transport of natural gas from field to market has developed, and there is no satisfactory alternative method available in the foreseeable future.[4]

The increasingly efficient solution to this problem stands as a monumental contribution to the public welfare by the equipment manufacturers, design engineers, pipe-line constructors, and others, who have developed the modern low-cost, large-volume, safe, and highly dependable long-distance natural gas pipe line. The rapidity and magnitude of this astonishing development is best illustrated through a consideration of the type of natural gas transportation facilities being constructed in 1930, in 1948, and in 1960,

Although the first pipe line was the wooden one which moved gas to Fredonia, New York, in the 1820's, and the first iron line was that which supplied Pittsburgh in the 1890's, long-distance, high-pressure transport of natural gas really began in the 1930's. By this time the fundamental elements of long-distance, high-pressure pipe lining were developed.[5] High-pressure, thin-walled pipe was available in large quantities, suitable compressors were being manufactured, welding procedures for joining the pipe had been developed, and the ditching machine for placing the pipe in the ground was proved. In 1930 the new model pipe line operated at pressures of 500 psig, was built of pipe

---

[3] Gastone Falomo, "Economics of Long-Distance Fuel Transportation and Electric Transmission," *Transactions* of the World Power Conference 1960), VI, 3007; *Petroleum Press Service,* Vol. XXVII, No. 7 (July, 1960), 246; W. N. Foster and K. W. Finch, "Relative Costs of Transmitting Energy as Electricity or as Natural Gas," *Transactions* of the World Power Conference (1960), VI, 2299.

In general it costs about three times as much to transport gas by pipe line as it does to transport a calorific equivalent of oil. See M. E. Hubbard, "Pipelines in Relation to Other Forms of Transport," *Transactions* of the World Power Conference (1960), VI, 3245.

[4] The movement of natural gas in a liquefied state may be an economic reality shortly; however, it would appear that such movement would complement and not displace pipe-line movement in the gaseous state. See the discussion of ocean shipment of liquefied natural gas in Chapter 11 of the present work.

[5] Baxter D. Goodrich, "Natural Gas—The Pipeline Industry," paper number 60–WA–43, contributed by the Petroleum Division for presentation at the Winter Annual Meeting of the American Society of Mechanical Engineers, New York, New York, November 27–December 2, 1960.

which would withstand a stress of 37,000 psig, was available in diameters up to twenty inches, was welded by the electric arc method, and which used reciprocating compressors for boosting the gas in units of 800 hp. Some 250,000 miles of gas pipe lines were then in operation and almost two trillion cubic feet of gas were marketed.

By 1948 the gas pipe-line network had expanded to 346,000 miles in the United States and marketed production exceeded five trillion cubic feet. The newest pipe line operated at 800 psig, while the pipe used could withstand stresses of 46,000 psi. The pipe was joined by the electric-arc method of welding, was available in diameters up to twenty-six inches, and boosting was done by gas compressors with 1,250 hp electric drivers. Construction methods were improved to highest efficiency.

The 1960 model pipe line was made of pipe in diameters up to thirty-six inches, operated at 1,000 psig, and could withstand stresses of 52,000 psi. Manual electric arc welding was still used to join pipe, but some automatic welding was done in *double jointing* (machine welding of joints before stringing pipe on the right-of-way). Reciprocating compressors were three times as large as in 1948, and centrifugal compressors driven by electricity, steam and gas turbines, and jet aviation engines were available in sizes up to 15,000 hp. The national gas pipe-line network measured over 500,000 miles, and marketed production for 1960 was nearly 13 trillion cubic feet.

THE MANUFACTURE OF PIPE

The continually changing variety of materials and equipment available for the transportation of natural gas exemplifies, in a manner equaled in few other American industries, a rapidly changing technology based on research, competition in a free market, and continual review of actual field experience. One of the most important of the contributions which made possible modern pipe lining is the pipe manufacturer's development of thin-walled, large-diameter, high-operating-pressure steel pipe which can be produced in large quantities. Metallurgically pipe is made of steel which meets the specifications set forth in Table 2. The most important specification is tensile strength, or, more correctly, yield strength. High tensile strength is obtained by controlling the chemical composition (carbon, manganese, silicone) of the steel plate from which the pipe is made and by *cold working* the steel, which amounts to expanding a finished pipe joint slightly by the use of internal water pressure. Chemical-composition control produces tensile strengths up to grade X-46. Welding difficulties increase with the chemical compositions necessary for higher tensile strengths, and X-52 grade is made only through cold working.

As shown in Table 2, pipe is available in ordinary grades A, B, and C, which are covered by API standard 5L, and high tensile strength grades X-42, X-46 and X-52 covered by API standard 5LX. As tensile strength increases, the required pipe wall thickness decreases for a given operating pressure. This factor and its effect on the cost of pipe are shown by the use of indexes in Table 3, which indicates that a twenty-four-inch diameter line built of X-52 pipe would require less than half the investment of a similar line built of grade-A pipe. A Canadian authority describes the advantages of thin-walled pipe in these words:

> To obtain increased yield strength the composition of the steel was changed from that formerly used. The tensile properties of this material exceed those of finished grade B pipe except for elongation. After forming high test pipe the yield strength is further increased by cold working.
>
> The reduced steel tonnage required for a given line size and operating pressure results in lower freight and field handling costs. The slightly higher cost ($6.00 per ton) for 52,000 lb. yield strength material over grade "B" pipe is more than repaid by the saving in weight. For example 100' of 24" diameter cross country gas line pipe operating at 790 p.s.i. using grade "B" pipe requires ⅜" wall material to withstand the hoop stress. If 52,000 pound material is used ¼" wall pipe is satisfactory. The approximate saving in weight and dollars per 100' is as follows:

	Tons per 100'	Mill Value $ per Ton	Total Cost per 100'
100'—24" O.D. x ⅜" Wall Gr B	4.731	$186.50	$882.33
100'—24" O.D. x ¼" Wall 52,000 lb. y.s.	3.215	$192.50	$681.81
SAVING	1.516 tons		$200.52

Although the dollar saving is great some disadvantages are encountered. Welding fittings must be designed to withstand the higher working pressure in the areas adjacent to the circumferential weld. Dents and

TABLE 2

STEEL SPECIFICATIONS FOR TUBES IN U.S.A. (*Ordinary and High Yield-strength Steels*)

Quality of Steel	PHYSICAL CHARACTERISTICS				STRESS RATE FOR SHOP HYDRAULIC TEST				CHEMICAL SPECIFICATIONS (% Maximum Contents)			
	Yield-Strength (kg./mm2)	Fracture Limit (kg./mm2)	Elongation (in %) According to Thickness	Ratio of Yield Strength to Fracture Limit	Outside Diameter <8⅝ in. (220 mm.) (kg./mm2)	% of Yield-Strength	Outside Diameter >10¾ in. (270 mm.) (kg./mm2)	% of Yield-Strength	Carbon	Manganese	Phosphorus	Sulphur
ORDINARY STEELS												
Grade A	30,000	48,000	21 to 35	0.625	18,000	60	18,000	60	0.3	0.3 to 0.9	0.045	0.06
Grade B	35,000	60,000	18 to 30	0.58	21,000	60	21,000	60	0.3	0.35 to 1.5	0.045 to 0.11	0.06
Grade C	45,000	75,000	20	0.6	27,000	60	27,000	60	0.3	0.35 to 1.5	0.045 to 0.11	0.06
HIGH YIELD-STRENGTH STEELS												
X. 42	42,000	60,000	20 to 25	0.7	31,500	75	35,700	85	0.3	1.25	0.045 to 0.11	0.06
X. 46	46,000	63,000	17 to 22	0.73	34,500	75	39,100	85	0.3	1.25	0.045 to 0.11	0.06
X. 52	52,000	66,000	15 to 20	0.79	39,000	75	44,200	85	0.3	1.25	0.045 to 0.11	0.06

(Source: OEEC, *Long Distance Gas Transport*, 48.)

NOTES—*Elongation*—For a steel of given quality, the necessary elongation increases with the thickness of the tube.

Hydraulic test pressure—is limited by API standards to a maximum of 2,500 psi (176 kg.cm2) for ordinary steel tube and to a maximum of 3,000 psi (211 kg/cm2) for high yield-strength steel tube.

Maximum diameter of ordinary steel tube—ordinary steel tubes do not exceed 24 in. (600 mm.) in diameter.

Courtesy A. O. Smith Corporation, Milwaukee, Wis.

PLATE I.—Welded Pipe Manufacture.

Courtesy Cooper-Bessemer Corporation, Mount Vernon, Ohio

Plate II.—Reciprocating Compressor.

Courtesy Cooper-Bessemer Corporation, Mount Vernon, Ohio

PLATE III.—Pipe-Line Centrifugal Compressor.

Courtesy Texas Eastern Transmission Corporation, Houston, Tex.

PLATE IV.—Interior of a Reciprocating Compressor Station.

Courtesy Texas Eastern Transmission Corporation, Houston, Tex.

PLATE V.—Cylinder-operated Automatic Valve.

Courtesy Texas Eastern Transmission Corporation, Houston, Tex.

PLATE VI.—VHF Radio Receiving Tower at a Compressor Station.

gouges must be cut out of the line or special full encirclement repair patches installed. Field welding repairs such as filling of holes and longitudinal welding in the parent metal cannot be tolerated. Even with the shortcomings of the higher strength material some of which are noted above, High Test Line Pipe is economically sound.[6]

Manufacturing processes produce welded pipe in diameters from five inches to thirty-six inches and seamless pipe in diameters up to twenty-six inches.[7] Welded pipe is made from flat steel plates in a process which involves separation of sheets, shaping the tube, making the longitudinal weld, cold expansion of the tube (one-half-inch expansion for thirty-inch pipe), finishing the ends of the pipe joints, hydraulic testing for acceptance, and visual inspection of the finished joint of pipe prior to loading for shipment. Welded pipe manufacture is illustrated in Plate I. Seamless pipe is made from steel billets which, at forging temperature, are pierced to form a tube. No welding is required.

Tubes of all tensile strengths from grade A through X-52 are available in seamless, electric-resistance seam welding, and electric flash welding. The X-42, X-46, and X-52 grades are available with submerged arc-two passes welding, and grades A, B, and C are available in lap or butt welding. Pipe is made in joints from twenty to forty feet in length. Double lengths of forty and eighty feet produced by welding are commonly used, as are triple lengths of twenty feet long joints.

Recently a mobile German pipe-making machine has been introduced which makes spiral welded pipe on the right-of-way from steel coils.[8] The machine produces a thin-walled, high-pressure, spiral, double-welded pipe in diameters up to forty inches. Other piping advances include the use of corrosion-free aluminum pipe and of plastic pipe[9] which does not require joint-by-joint welding. These new materials can be formed into pipe lines capable of operating at 500 psig.

[6] R. D. Walker and A. B. Jones, "Economic Trends of the Transportation of Fuel by Pipeline," paper presented at the Canadian Sectional Meeting of the World Power Conference, Montreal, Canada, September 7–11, 1958.

[7] OEEC Technical Assistance Mission, *Long Distance Gas Transport in the United States*, 46–59; Chapter XIV, "The Strength of Pipe," in *Natural Gas*, edited by Eugene A. Stephenson; Chapter X, "Transmission," *Natural Gas*, home study course published by the Institute of Gas Technology, 134–37.

[8] "New Machine Can Make Line Pipe on Right-of-way," *Oil and Gas Journal*, Vol. LVIII, No. 7 (February 15, 1960), 60.

[9] *Oil and Gas Journal*, Vol. LIX, No. 3 (January 16, 1961), 62.

TABLE 3

INDEXES OF THIN WALL PIPE

Quality of Steel	DIAMETER UNDER 10 IN.				DIAMETER 10 IN. AND ABOVE			
	Stress Rate on Shop Hydraulic Test	Index of Thickness	Index of Price per Ton	Index of Price per Linear Unit	Stress Rate on Shop Hydraulic Test	Index of Thickness	Index of Price per Ton	Index of Price per Linear Unit
A. 37 STEEL (FRANCE)								
		205	168	345		230	168	386
ORDINARY STEELS (UNITED STATES)								
Grade A	12.7	217	90	195	12.7	245	90	220
Grade B	14.8	185	92	170	14.8	210	92	193
Grade C	19.0	145	94	136	19.0	164	94	154
HIGH-TENSILE STEELS (UNITED STATES)								
X. 42	22.2	124	95.0	118	25.2	123	95.0	117
X. 46	24.3	113	98.5	111	27.5	113	98.5	111
X. 52	27.5	100	100.0	100	31.1	100	100.0	100

(Source: OEEC, *Long Distance Gas Transport*, 50.)

COMPRESSING THE GAS

Compressors are necessary in long-distance gas transmission to restore the pressure lost in friction between the pipe and the moving gas. This pressure loss is the measure of the loss of gas-transporting ability in the line. The compressor, engine, and turbine manufacturers have made available a wide range of gas-compressing machines. Most gas compression is done with reciprocating piston compressors driven by internal combustion engines fueled with natural gas.[10] Plate II represents such a machine which is available in sizes from 250 to 4,000 hp. These machines are desirable because of their great flexibility of operation and are particularly useful where the quantity of pressure of the gas being handled is subject to wide changes. Although investment and operating expense are greater than for the alternative centrifugal machines, the cost of fuel to drive the reciprocating compressor is lower than that required to drive the centrifugal compressor. The engine driving the reciprocating compressor may use any type of fuel, and the compressor may be driven by any type of engine, including electric motors as well as internal combustion engines. However, nearly all installations are driven by gas engines, and the cost of gas for fuel has been increasing over the past fifteen years faster than has the price of electricity, which is often used to drive centrifugal compressors. The reciprocating compressor can be used over a wide range of compression ratios (outlet gas pressure divided by inlet gas pressure) up to 5.0.

The centrifugal compressor is particularly adaptable to steady output conditions at compression ratios up to 1.3. Steady conditions at this compression ratio are typical of long-distance, large-volume, high-pressure gas transmission. In this type of compressor the low pressure gas is introduced at the center of a high-speed rotating turbine, and the high-pressure gas is taken off the periphery of the machine as shown in Plate III. The compressor may be rotated by an electric motor, steam turbine, gas turbine, or jet aviation engine. Investment and mainte-

---

[10] OEEC Technical Assistance Mission, *Long Distance Gas Transport in the United States,* 79ff; Chapter XVII, "Gas Compression," in *Natural Gas,* edited by Stephenson; Chapter XII, "Compression of Gas," in *Natural Gas,* published by the Institute of Gas Technology, 163ff.; "Compression of Natural Gas," *American Gas Journal,* Vol. CLXXVII, No. 7 (December, 1952), 19; Arnold B. Tuer and Charles H. Swartz, "Economics of Field Compressor Stations," *Oil Week,* Vol. X, No. 24 (July 31, 1959), 28.

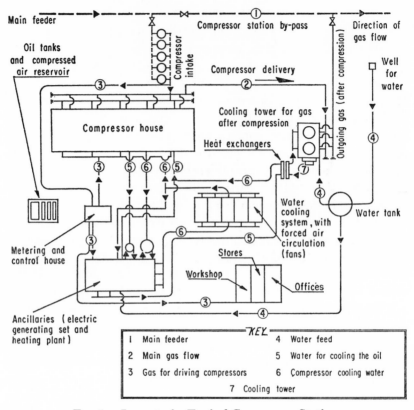

FIG. 1.—Layout of a Typical Compressor Station.

nance charges are lower than for reciprocating compressor, but fuel costs are higher. Table 4 compares investment and operating costs for different types of compressor units. Centrifugal compressors come in units (compressor and driver) rated at up to 15,000 hp and operate at speeds from 3,600 to 6,500 rpm.

Compressors are installed on the pipe lines inside buildings and, together with the necessary auxiliaries, are called *compressor stations*. The layout of a typical station is diagrammed in Figure 1. Plate IV shows the interior of a reciprocating station. Compressor stations are spaced to give the most economical balance between investment in pipe and in compressors, but the station spacing will usually range from sixty to one hundred miles on a modern long-distance pipe line.

TABLE 4

COMPARISON OF INVESTMENT AND OPERATING COST
FOR DIFFERENT TYPES OF COMPRESSORS
(Index of Capital Outlay and Annual Costs per Housepower)

	Piston Compressors with Gas Engine	Centrifugal Compressors*		
		Electric Motor	Steam Turbine	Gas Turbine
Capital Outlay	100.00	66.60	89.00	78.00
Annual Cost†				
Running and maintenance	6.50	3.55	8.15	2.45
Power consumption	3.90	16.00	6.85	5.00
TOTAL	10.40	19.55	15.00	7.45
Financial cost (9 per cent)	9.00	6.00	8.00	7.05
Total Annual Cost	19.40	25.55	23.00	14.50

(Source: OEEC, *Long Distance Gas Transport*, 84.)

* Power costs for centrifugal compressors could be scaled down if compression ratios were less than 1.25–1.30.

† Power costs are calculated on the basis of present average price of the natural gas used for this purpose, and of electricity rates (per kwh) for heavy power consumers.

FITTING AND JOINTING

The methods of joining lengths of pipe have progressed, as operating pressures have increased, from the early threaded joint to the bolted flange coupling, through the Dresser type coupling to the modern welded joint, which is now used almost exclusively in long lines.[11] Acetylene welding was introduced in 1916 and electric-arc welding in 1928. In the field, welding of pipe is accomplished by lining up the two joints with internal and external clamps so that the joints are about 1/16 to 1/32 of an inch apart. A first crew makes tack welds for a temporary joint and *stringer beads* which go all around the pipe to close the several joints. A second crew makes the *filler beads* necessary to completely fill the double opening between the joints. The problem is to get penetration and fusion of the weld metal to the bot-

[11] OEEC Technical Assistance Mission, *Long Distance Gas Transport in the United States*, 93ff.; Chapter XIV, "Strength of Pipe," in *Natural Gas*, edited by Stephenson, 23ff.; Chapter X, "Transmission," in *Natural Gas*, published by the Institute of Gas Technology, 136ff.

tom of the beveled opening without burning through the pipe. Welds are inspected by cutting test pieces of the weld and by taking x-ray pictures of the welds. Recently machine welding of joints in the fields has been satisfactorily tested.[12] Also, double jointing of pipe is now an accepted procedure to reduce by one-half the required manual welding in the field.[13]

Both gate valves and plug valves are used in pipe lines. Gate valves do not have the pressure tightness of plug valves, but can be opened and shut more gradually. Therefore gate valves are used in compression-station suction lines where close control of small volume is important. Gate valves are also used where *pigs* must pass, since gate valves can be opened to the full diameter of the pipe. Lubricated plug-type valves have good pressure tightness and are the most common type of pipe-line valves. Cut-off valves are usually placed in a pipe line at intervals to segregate sections of the pipe line in case of line breaks. Plate VI illustrates such a valve. Pipe-line valves may also be equipped for opening and closing by remote control. Drips are built into the line at low spots to permit the withdrawal of liquids.

It has been proved that pipe-line pressure loss can be reduced by frequent brushing of the interior of the pipe line to remove foreign matter. This operation is called *pigging* and involves passing a *pig* or *go-devil* through the line. The pig is driven by the gas moving through the line and brushes the wall of the pipe as it rotates. Appropriate piping connections are provided for the introduction and expulsion of the pig. Plastic coating of pipe interiors is also used to increase efficiency, as well as to protect against corrosion.

MEASURING THE VOLUME

Most readers are acquainted with the bellows-type gas meter (see Figure 2) commonly used to meter gas to the individual household consumer. However, gas measurement on long-distance pipe lines and

[12] *Oil and Gas Journal,* Vol. LIX, No. 5 (January 30, 1961), 84. Paul Reed, pipe-line editor of the *Oil and Gas Journal,* has played an important role in the development of the automatic welding machine. See the *Oil and Gas Journal,* Vol. LIX, No. 6 (February 6, 1961), 6.

[13] Paul Reed, "Double-jointing Came Long Way '60 . . . And Greater Progress Foreseen for '61," *Oil and Gas Journal,* Vol. LIX, No. 7 (February 13, 1961), 70. This article authoritatively reviews the progress made to date in double-jointing and discusses the economics of this process. See also H. C. Price, "Gas Pipeline Construction Brought Up to Date," *The Mines Magazine,* Vol. XLIX, No. 11 (November, 1959), 55.

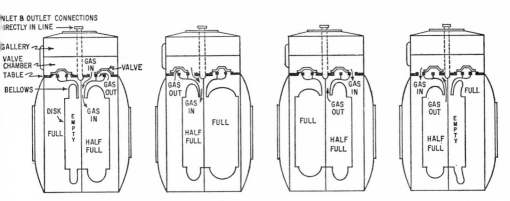

Fig. 2.—Operation of the Bellows Gas Meter.

in the field where gas is produced is done almost entirely with the orifice meter. The principles of orifice measurement were developed by the Italian physicist B. Ventura (1797) and the New England engineer Clement Herschel (1886). The orifice meter as evolved from the Pitot tube and designed by H. B. Cooper and John G. Pew of Hope Natural Gas Company, Hastings, West Virginia, was first used in 1911 to measure large volumes of natural gas. In the following year, R. Weymouth introduced his formula for computing the flow of natural gas in pipe lines in a paper read before the Society of Mechanical Engineers.[14]

The orifice meter, which is highly accurate (far less than 1 per cent error) and adaptable to a wide range of volumes, operates on the principle that the loss of pressure across the *orifice plate,* a restriction in the pipe line, is proportional to the amount of gas flowing through such restriction. The principle is illustrated in Figure 3. The orifice meter is devised so that the pressure differential across the orifice plate is continually recorded on the chart. The charts are usually changed daily and are forwarded to the pipe-line measurement center for calculation of the gas volume indicated. Pipe-line measuring stations also include devices for measuring and recording the temperature, heat content, moisture content, and the specific gravity of the gas passing the point of measurement.

[14] Rockwell Manufacturing Company, *The Orifice Meter for Measurement of Flow of Gases and Liquids;* Chapter XI, "Metering," in *Natural Gas,* published by the Institute of Gas Technology, 149–62; "Principles of Orifice Measurement," *American Gas Journal,* Vol. CLXXVII, No. 6 (November, 1952), 23.

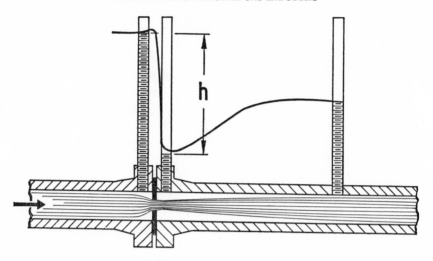

FIG. 3.—Principle of Orifice Measurement.

PURIFYING THE GAS

Gas is treated prior to its transmission to meet marketability specifications. There are four common types of gas treatment: gasoline plant processing, dehydration, removal of chemical impurities, and removal of physical impurities.

The condensable hydrocarbon liquid content of pipe-line gas should not exceed 0.2 gallons per one thousand cubic feet of gas (GPM) to prevent condensation of hydrocarbon liquids in the pipe line during transmission. Gasoline plant processing, the removal of condensable hydrocarbons, prevents the condensation of liquids in the pipe line and provides natural gasoline and LPG. Recovery is accomplished by refrigeration or by placing the gas in contact with an absorbing oil (see Figure 4). The facilities involved are called *gasoline plants* and represent investments of about $30 to $40 per gallon per day of products recovered. A recovery of 100,000 gallons a day is typical of a medium-sized plant. The product, natural gas liquids, has a larger rate of increase in use than either crude oil or gas. The output of natural gas liquids in 1960 was 11.75 per cent of that of petroleum.

Dehydration, the removal of water, is accomplished by temperature reduction in a low-temperature separator (see Figure 5) or by passing the gas through a bed of material such as alumina or silica gel

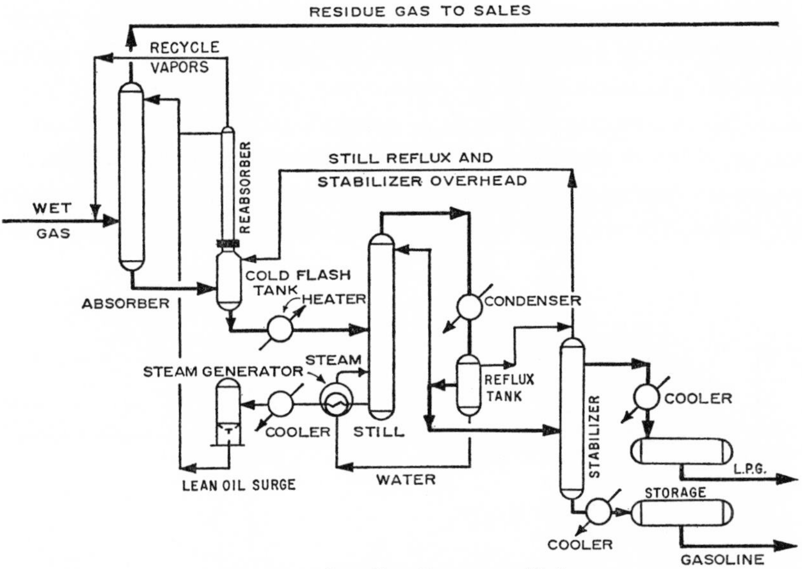

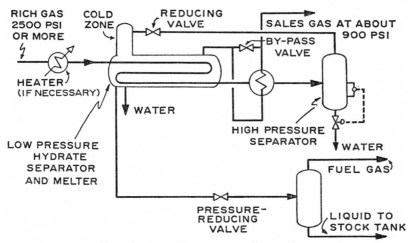

RESIDUE GAS TO SALES

RECYCLE VAPORS

STILL REFLUX AND
STABILIZER OVERHEAD

WET GAS

REABSORBER

COLD FLASH TANK

HEATER

ABSORBER

CONDENSER

STEAM GENERATOR

STEAM

REFLUX TANK

COOLER

COOLER

STILL

STABILIZER

L.P.G.

LEAN OIL SURGE

WATER

STORAGE

COOLER

GASOLINE

FIG. 4.—Gasoline Recovery Unit.

which adsorbs water. Water content should be less than seven pounds per million cubic feet (MMCF) of gas to prevent freezing, hydrate formation, in the transmission lines. Passing gas through a contactor countercurrently with glycol is another way of removing water. The glycol is regenerated through use of heat and can be recirculated.

RICH GAS 2500 PSI OR MORE

COLD ZONE

REDUCING VALVE

SALES GAS AT ABOUT 900 PSI

BY-PASS VALVE

HEATER (IF NECESSARY)

WATER

HIGH PRESSURE SEPARATOR

WATER

LOW PRESSURE HYDRATE SEPARATOR AND MELTER

FUEL GAS

PRESSURE-REDUCING VALVE

LIQUID TO STOCK TANK

FIG. 5.—Low-Temperature Separation.

71

The removal of chemical impurities—sulphur, mercaptans, or carbon dioxide—is necessary to protect the pipe from corrosion and to make the gas marketable. A sulphur-free gas is required for acceptance into a pipe line. The impure components are removed by circulating a liquid absorbing medium between a gas-liquid contactor, where the gas impurities are absorbed in the liquid, and a still, where the impurities are stripped from the liquid by heating. This process

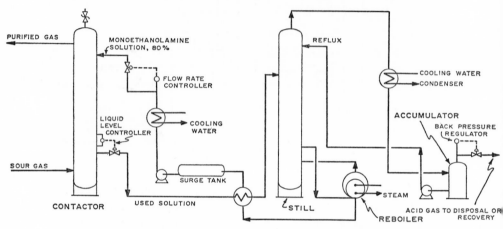

FIG. 6.—Gas-sweetening Process.

is illustrated in Figure 6. Liquid ethanolamine is circulated for the removal of sulphur compounds and carbon dioxide. Carbon dioxide may also be removed by circulating a caustic solution. It is not economically feasible to remove nitrogen from natural gas.

The removal of physical impurities is accomplished by passing all gas through separators before introducing it into the pipe line. Separation usually takes place at each gas well. In the separation process, gas is passed through a drum in which the lessening of velocity permits the dropping out of all water, hydrocarbon liquids (called condensate or distillate), mud, and dust.[15]

Since natural gas is odorless, it is odorized in the long lines prior to delivery from these lines to the distributing companies in order that

[15] OEEC Technical Assistance Mission, *Long Distance Gas Transport in the United States,* 17ff.; Chapter IX, "Gas Conditioning," in *Natural Gas,* published by the Institute of Gas Technology, 121–30; "Gas Conditioning," *American Gas Journal,* Vol. CLXXV, No. 6 (November, 1951), 31.

leaks may be detected by smell. Small amounts of mercaptan are continuously injected into the gas stream.[16]

PIPE-LINE CORROSION

Pipe lines corrode externally through an electro-chemical process in which tiny electric currents flow from an anode to a cathode through an electrolyte. The currents may arise because of dissimilar metals in a common electrolyte or because a common metal is in dissimilar electrolytes. Both of these causes of corrosion are illustrated in Figure 7.

External corrosion is controlled by the use of excessive wall thickness, by pipe coating, by cathodic protection, and by the use of rectifier units. Employing excessive wall thickness is very costly, and coating the pipes is more common. The pipes are painted, wrapped, and coated before they are buried in the ground. The coatings are carefully inspected and any breaks are hand-repaired before the pipe is finally lowered into the ditch. Nevertheless, breaks in the coatings occur from time to time. Cathodic protection involves the burying of metallic anodes close by the pipe line and the connecting of such anodes to the line by a wire. The buried metal anode preferentially corrodes, setting up a current in which the pipe is the cathode, thus protecting it from corrosion. The use of rectifier units involves taking alternating current from a power line, converting it to low voltage direct current, and introducing the positive side of this direct current into the ground and the negative side to the pipe line. The resulting electric current cathodically protects the pipe line. Internal corrosion control in pipe lines is obtained by removing acid gases such as hydrogen sulfide and carbon dioxide from any gas prior to its being introduced into the line and by the use of internal pipe coatings.[17]

TAPPING UNDER PRESSURE

It is often convenient to *tap*—connect a branch line—to a pipe line

[16] Chapter IX, "Gas Conditioning," in *Natural Gas,* published by the Institute of Gas Technology, 130.

[17] OEEC Technical Assistance Mission, *Long Distance Gas Transport in the United States,* 103–107; Chapter X, "Transmission," in *Natural Gas,* published by the Institute of Gas Technology, 140–45; Chapter XIV, "Strength of Pipe," in *Natural Gas,* edited by Stephenson, 24–29; *Petroleum Engineer,* Vol. XXXIII, No. 2 (February, 1961), Special Pipeline Handbook Issue, section on pipe protection, H–60; "Corrosion and Pipe Protection," *American Gas Journal,* Vol. CLXXVI, No. 4 (April, 1952), 25.

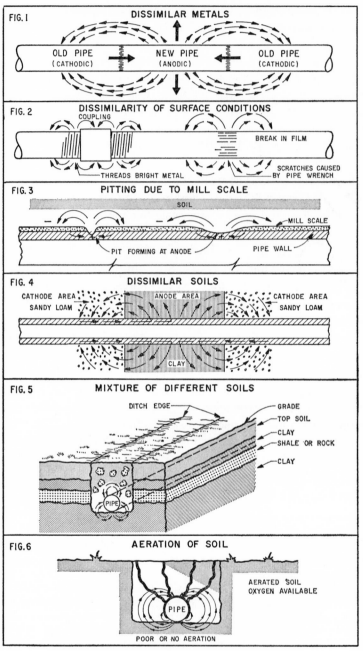

FIG. 7.—Types of Corrosion.

operating under high pressure. An ingenious tapping machine (see Figure 8) has been developed to accomplish this connecting of branch lines up to twelve inches in diameter on main lines operating at pressures up to 1,000 psig. A joint consisting of a steel flange coupling is first welded to the pipe line. The valve which will control the connection is then mounted on the coupling. The pipe-line tapping machine is bolted to the opposite flange of the valve, and the main-line

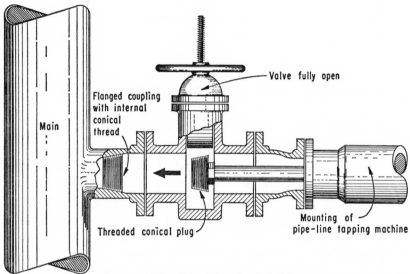

FIG. 8.—Pipe-Line Tapping Machine.

pipe is drilled through the valve and coupling. The tapping machine is rotated either by hand or by a compressed-air motor. After the opening has been drilled in the main line, the drill is removed and the valve closed. The tapping machine is disconnected, and the branch line is connected to the valve. When the valve is opened, gas can flow from the branch line into the main line, all without any cessation of the high-pressure usage of the main line.[18]

REMOTE CONTROL

In its continuing efforts to achieve uninterrupted high-load-factor operation of the gas transmission network, the natural gas industry

[18] OEEC Technical Assistance Mission, *Long Distance Gas Transport in the United States,* 140–41.

has made use of all the modern electronic marvels in communication and automatic control and continues the search for improvements.

In a system operating over an area of several hundreds of miles with variations in volume and pressure at the numerous points of gas supply and with constant changes in the amounts of gas required at the different points of delivery, the control of flow and pressure throughout the pipe-line system is a most complicated problem. Handling this problem requires the very best in rapid communication. Consequently, pipe-line companies are extensive users of leased telephone lines, teletype, and especially microwave radio. Plate VI shows a typical very high frequency (VHF) radio receiver at a compressor station. Radio receivers and transmitters are located at the central dispatching office, at all compressor stations, at all district offices, and in all automobiles and trucks.

In addition to its use of the latest electronic systems, the gas pipe-line industry also uses the latest electronic means of telemetering and of automatic remote control of valves and compressors. Compressor stations are operated from distant points by remote control. Such stations can be started and stopped and the throughput varied by an operator located miles away in a central office. The saving in labor costs is obvious. Short pipe-line systems are today completely subject to remote control. Control includes telemetering whereby pressures, temperatures, and volumes measured at points on the pipe line are immediately indicated at a central control panel in the central office. In addition, such data are recorded in typed form by an automatic printing machine. In some instances the telemeter data are automatically fed into a computing machine, which, in turn, produces information concerning what changes should be made in pipe-line operations to maximize throughput and minimize costs. This information may even be automatically fed back to the compressor stations and automatic control valves and applied to line operation without human intervention.[19]

[19] "The Automatic Pipeline," *Oil and Gas Journal*, Vol. LV, No. 27 (July 8, 1957), 89; "Main-line Block Valves Are Remotely Controlled," *Oil and Gas Journal*, Vol. LIX, No. 6 (February 6, 1961), 132; "Pipeline Built in 1929 Is Automated," *Petroleum Week*, Vol. XII, No. 2 (January 31, 1961), 49.

DESIGNING THE TRANSMISSION SYSTEM

Design has as its aim the specifying of a pipe-line system which will carry out the desired gas transportation at minimum cost. It is necessary that the following items be explained to the designer:

(1) Route and length of lines. This involves an aerial survey of the routes followed by personal reconnaissance of questionable parts of the route.[20]

(2) Character of markets to be served, now and in the future. This includes anticipated load factor (average day requirements divided by maximum day requirements) and availability of storage for peak shaving. The pressure at which gas must be delivered must also be designated.

(3) The selling price of gas from the pipe line.

(4) The cost of gas supply and the point and pressure at which it will be available.

With these data, his formulae, and experience, the design engineer will determine the optimum (at lowest operating cost) working pressure for the line, diameter and thickness of the pipe to be incorporated into the line, horsepower of compressors required, and the distance

[20] J. W. Stanley, "Pipeline Surveying and Mapping, a Breakdown of Costs," *Pipe Line News,* Vol. XXV, No. 10 (October, 1953), 43–44. Mr. Stanley estimates the cost of surveying and mapping a pipe line at $625 and gives the following breakdown for this amount:

1. Preliminary Maps and Scouting	$15.00
2. Aerial Surveys and Photographs	15.00
3. Ownership and Miscellaneous Maps	15.00
4. Steroscopic Study	10.00
5. Scouting	10.00
6. Permission to Survey	20.00
7. Preliminary Surveys	125.00
8. Preliminary Alignment Maps	25.00
9. Abstractor's Fees	35.00
10. Condemnation Surveys and Plats	25.00
11. River Crossings and Permit Plats	15.00
12. Station Site Surveys and Plats	25.00
13. Survey Inspection	20.00
14. Re-routes and Line Changes	20.00
15. Re-staking Lines for Construction	75.00
16. Miscellaneous Drafting	25.00
17. Final Survey	125.00
18. Final Maps	25.00
	$625.00

and spacing between stations.[21] From these determinations he will estimate the investment required for the pipe line and the cost of transporting gas in cents per thousand cubic feet (MCF).

The flow of gas through a pipe is caused by pressure differential. The pressure becomes lower as the gas moves from the inlet towards the outlet of the pipe. The greater the differential the greater will be the quantity of gas flowing. To state the matter another way, as gas moves through a pipe, the pressure is reduced because of friction between the moving gas and the pipe walls. Weymouth's formula expresses the relationship:

$$Q = 670.8 \, d^{8/3} \sqrt{\frac{P_1^2 - P_2^2}{GL}}$$

[21] The calculation of optimum compressor station spacing involves an interesting economic balance between investment in larger diameter pipe or in additional compressor horsepower. An example of such a calculation is set forth in Walker and Jones, "Economic Trends of the Transportation of Fuel by Pipeline." The object in making the economic balance is to select the combination which will operate at the lowest over-all costs.

See K. B. Nagler, "Transportation and Storage of Gaseous Fuels," *Transactions* of the World Power Conference (1960), VI, 3183. Mr. Nagler points out that:

1. For a given pipeline diameter the transportation cost per unit of gas volume increases almost directly with the length of the line.

2. The volume capacity rises more rapidly with increasing pipe diameter than the increased costs per mile; therefore, the larger the line diameter, the lower the transportation cost per unit of gas volume at the optimum capacity of the larger diameter line.

3. The transportation costs per unit of gas volume vary inversely with the percentage changes in load factor. The percentage variation in unit costs is approximately the same for any given percentage change in load factor for any given length pipeline, regardless of diameter. In the design of a pipeline transportation system, approximately equal costs per unit volume delivered might be realized by a line of given length of 24″ diameter and compressor stations less than 100 miles apart, as for 30″ line with compressor stations 200 miles apart, but the latter system would, in most cases, lend itself to more economic expansion. A modest increment of expansion can generally be obtained more cheaply by additional compressors than by building a parallel pipeline (looping). With a given amount of compression horsepower, a 50 per cent loop between compressor stations only provides about 20 per cent additional capacity.

See also A. Bolzinger and H. Descazeaux, "Developpement et Technique des Grands Transports de Gaz par Pipelines en France, *Transactions* of the World Power Conference (1960), VI, 3201; *Petroleum Press Service*, Vol. XXVII, No. 7 (July, 1960), 246. This paper describes the use of operational research methods in solving pipe-line design problems and points out that, for long-distance lines of sixteen-inch diameter, the optimum design is one in which a line is constructed today capable of carrying expected requirements for the next six to eight years and plans are made for the building of parallel lines when future expansions are needed.

where

Q = cubic feet per 24 hours measured at 14.7 lbs. per sq. in. absolute and 60° F.

Flowing temperature of gas = 60°

P_1 = pressure at starting point, pounds per square inch, absolute

P_2 = pressure at terminal, pounds per square inch, absolute

d = internal diameter of pipe, inches

G = specific gravity of gas

L = length of line, miles

In pipeline design the formula used is the Panhandle formula, a variation of the basic Weymouth formula which is expressed as:

$$Q = 812.36 \frac{(P_1{}^2 - P_2{}^2)^{0.5394}}{L} d^{2.6182}$$

Another basic formula is that of Barlow which is used to determine the proper wall thickness of steel pipe. This formula is:

$$T = \frac{d \times p}{2 \times f}$$

where

T = thickness of wall, inches

d = outside diameter of pipe, inches

p = internal fluid pressure, pounds per square inch

f = working fiber stress, pounds per square inch

To understand the fundamentals of pipe-line design, consider the examples shown in Figure 9. The example entitled line No. 1 assumes that gas is available in the field at 700 psi, and that a market exists at City B which is 200 miles away for 115,000 MCF/D of gas at a delivery pressure of 50 pounds per square inch. By applying the Weymouth formula we calculate that a twenty-inch-diameter pipe line is required, if no compressor stations are included.

The next example, which is illustrated by line No. 2, assumes that a 1,000-mile pipe line with a daily capacity of 90,000 MCF is required. Gas is available at 700 psi and is to be delivered at the market at 50 pounds per square inch. Since the capacity of a 1,000-mile, 20-inch pipe line is less than 90,000 MCF/D, it will be necessary either to increase the diameter of the pipe or to install compressor stations. The example shown in line No. 2 assumes that we design compressor stations at 200-mile intervals, or that we would include four compressor stations on a 1,000-mile line. Our calculations show that

TABLE 5

Theoretical Pipe-Line System Cost-of-Service

Plant Investment (Original Cost)	$195,750,600
Fixed Charges	Per cent of Plant
Depreciation (3.3% of depreciable property)	3.234
Ad valorem taxes	1.250
Interest (5½% on 65% of plant)	3.575
Balance to Capital Stock	2.925
Federal Income Taxes (52%)	3.169
Total Fixed Charges	14.153
Operation and Maintenance	
Compressor Stations	
Pipeline	
Measuring and Regulating Stations	
Supervision and Engineering	
Administration and General	
Fuel Gas	
Gas Loss and Company Use	
Total Operation and Maintenance Cost	
Total Cost of Transportation	
Cost of Gas for Resale	
Total Cost-of-Service	
Cost of Transportation (Cents per MCF per 100 Miles)	

STATISTICS

Miles of 30" O.D. × ⅜" W.T. Pipe	1,000	Miles
Maximum Throughput per Day	608,000	MCF
Annual Deliveries At 95% Load Factor	210,680,000	MCF
Number of Compressor Stations	14	
Total Horsepower Installed	175,000	

Annual Costs Dollars	Annual Costs Cents/MCF	Relative Component Cost of Transport Per cent	Relative Component Cost-of-Service Per cent
6,330,900	3.00	17.60	7.31
2,447,000	1.16	6.80	2.85
6,998,400	3.32	19.45	8.08
5,726,000	2.73	15.91	6.61
6,203,700	2.96	17.24	7.15
27,706,000	13.17	77.00	32.00
1,327,600	0.63	3.69	1.53
569,300	0.27	1.58	0.65
120,000	0.06	0.34	0.14
334,100	0.16	0.93	0.38
1,714,400	0.81	4.77	1.97
3,692,500	1.76	10.27	4.24
510,700	0.24	1.42	0.59
8,268,600	3.93	23.00	9.50
35,974,600	17.10	100.00	
51,068,800	24.24		58.50
87,043,400	41.34		100.00
	1.71		

if the outlet pressure of the 200-mile section of twenty-inch-diameter line is set at 400 pounds, the line capacity is 95,000 MCF/D for the 700-pound inlet pressure. This capacity fits our market requirement of 90,000 MCF/D. Consequently compressor stations will be included at 200-mile intervals with an inlet pressure of 400 pounds and an outlet pressure of 700 pounds.

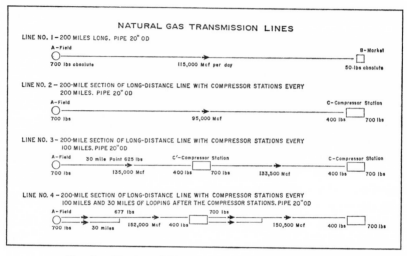

Fig. 9.—Design of Natural Gas Transmission Lines.

The example shown as line No. 3 indicates how the capacity of a pipe line can be increased by the installation of additional compressor stations following the initial construction of the line. In line No. 3 we have inserted a new compressor station between each of the existing compressor stations in line No. 2 with the consequence that compressor stations are located 100 miles apart. Under these conditions calculations indicate that the line has a capacity of 135,000 MCF/D, as compared with the 95,000 MCF/D capacity for a 200-mile compressor station spacing.

Example line No. 4 is included to show the effect of *looping*, the construction of parallel pipe lines over part of the distance of the original line. In example No. 3 the pressure at a point thirty miles from a compressor station is calculated to be 625 pounds. In example No. 4 the pressure at the same point will be increased to 677 pounds with a greater volume (152,000 MCF/D) flowing through the line. The greater

TABLE 6

THE TREND OF PIPE-LINE CONSTRUCTION COSTS
(Dollars per Mile Reported to FPC in Fiscal 1954, 1959, 1960)

Diameter Inches	Minimum	Maximum	Total	Average R/W	Material	Labor	Misc.	Year
2	$4,976	$11,754	$6,088	$484	$2,544	$2,704	$356	1954
	------	------	------	-----	-----	-----	----	1959
	------	------	6,356	107	3,047	3,015	187	1960
3	4,992	6,624	5,232	510	2,523	2,169	30	1954
	13,935	17,718	14,955	2,412	5,106	6,396	1,041	1959
	13,272	16,325	14,827	2,956	5,977	4,928	966	1960
4	7,624	8,208	11,304	500	5,312	4,196	1,296	1954
	8,404	22,772	10,092	476	5,316	4,180	120	1959
	10,830	44,969	19,645	1,107	6,218	11,136	1,184	1960
6	12,312	19,686	17,232	660	9,468	6,408	696	1954
	15,750	52,962	24,414	1,422	8,634	12,720	1,638	1959
	17,858	36,806	21,096	2,156	10,128	7,557	1,255	1960
8	11,880	36,464	20,256	784	9,472	8,736	1,264	1954
	13,088	45,872	28,952	1,224	13,464	12,712	1,552	1959
	15,760	86,564	35,859	3,041	13,534	17,635	1,649	1960
10	15,310	23,440	20,040	810	12,760	5,720	750	1954
	25,580	55,620	40,380	1,580	17,460	19,710	1,630	1959
	30,840	85,114	63,588	4,659	17,564	38,659	2,706	1960
12	40,404	145,596	40,404	1,272	20,832	17,400	900	1954
	38,904	72,360	50,280	2,244	21,276	23,880	2,880	1959
	25,339	60,278	36,637	1,243	21,985	11,694	1,715	1960
16	27,824	269,120	30,800	1,408	18,688	9,904	800	1954
	40,576	74,720	55,888	1,295	33,184	19,456	1,952	1959
	39,347	61,908	44,553	1,790	28,882	12,283	1,598	1960
20	44,060	49,720	46,200	1,580	28,040	15,080	1,500	1954
	42,220	63,060	54,300	1,400	33,600	16,360	2,940	1959
	51,217	77,373	68,813	2,777	34,797	28,658	2,581	1960
24	63,120	64,176	64,128	2,664	36,672	21,408	3,384	1954
	60,432	72,792	65,688	2,040	42,120	18,744	2,784	1959
	66,853	166,037	88,642	2,932	56,575	26,687	2,448	1960
26	------	------	73,424	3,068	37,232	31,330	1,794	1954
	60,970	113,412	68,510	2,314	43,524	18,174	173	1959
	77,707	112,104	93,419	2,333	60,576	26,890	3,620	1960
30	70,200	83,610	77,970	1,530	57,570	15,150	3,720	1954
	78,270	137,670	86,760	2,220	55,410	24,780	4,498	1959
	78,913	166,919	112,242	4,101	67,637	35,479	5,024	1960
36	------	------	------	-----	-----	-----	----	1954
	131,904	135,324	133,056	3,456	89,100	21,888	5,868	1959
	------	------	199,364	11,508	82,560	96,180	9,116	1960

(Source: *Oil and Gas Journal* [June 27, 1960], 109.)

TABLE 7

COMPRESSOR-STATION INVESTMENT AND OPERATING DATA

RECIPROCATING STATIONS

Company	Number Employees	Plant Cost (Thousand Dollars)	Expenses (Thousand Dollars) Fuel or Power	Other	Compressor Fuel (MMCF)	Total Hp	Investment per Hp (Dollars)	Number Driving Units	Number Compressor Units	Expenses per Hp (Dollars)	Number Stations	Year Installed
1	9	1,795	9	16	24	4,000	449	2	4	6.31	1	1958
2	97	15,349	396	800	2,017	58,000	265	29	29	20.64	5	1956
3	67	9,508	248	335	1,363	46,870	203	50	50	12.45	11	1911–58
4	457	31,578	1,189	2,828	8,967	152,230	207	180	405	26.39	30	1913–58
5	75	2,546	109	368	732	16,325	156	60	60	29.29	10	1927–52
6	70	20,816	700	927	3,633	70,000	297	35	35	23.25	5	1954–57
7	374	24,134	2,318	3,070	7,296	109,210	221	122	252	49.34	31	1902–47
8	104	7,591	158	697	1,624	35,570	213	117	117	24.06	22	1920–58
9	32	3,433	175	370	652	15,700	219	13	13	34.75	1	1946–55
10	375	34,167	1,546	2,687	8,241	151,330	226	97	97	27.98	15	1949–58
11	10	1,694	22	114	111	5,280	321	4	4	25.97	1	1943–56
12	466	43,090	1,875	4,041	14,578	202,500	212	129	129	29.21	13	1948–58
13	1,059	99,632	3,474	6,631	23,164	421,160	237	280	280	23.99	24	1931–58
14	110	27,855	231	922	1,427	89,900	310	55	143	12.83	16	1956–58
15	738	61,439	3,247	6,031	3,360	316,660	194	228	630	29.30	23	1932–58
16	182	20,367	403	1,061	3,360	70,410	289	51	51	20.80	7	1953–57
17	495	42,322	1,798	3,254	9,688	183,394	231	173	486	27.55	28	1940–58
18	1,136	163,500	5,283	10,156	39,708	582,270	281	453	453	26.51	37	1945–58
19	326	68,069	2,409	2,636	12,107	272,100	250	180	180	18.54	24	1948–58

Company	Number Employees	Plant Cost (Thousand Dollars)	Expenses (Thousand Dollars)		Compressor Fuel (MMCF)	Total Hp	Investment per Hp (Dollars)	Number Driving Units	Number Compressor Units	Expenses per Hp (Dollars)	Number Stations	Year Installed
			Fuel or Power	Other								
20	443	47,232	1,835	3,195	10,550	198,980	237	155	155	25.28	22	1929–56
21	276	47,468	908	2,208	7,528	130,000	365	65	65	23.97	11	1951–53
22	484	71,221	2,473	4,183	19,862	308,460	231	141	141	21.58	23	1950–58
23	219	20,857	690	1,496	4,601	76,000	274	34	34	28.77	10	1951–56
24	316	15,994	1,210	2,346	3,904	78,315	204	97	173	45.41	20	1909–58
25	248	37,227	567	1,942	5,161	140,790	264	191	191	17.82	30	1925–57

CENTRIFUGAL STATIONS

Company	Number Employees	Plant Cost (Thousand Dollars)	Expenses (Thousand Dollars)		Compressor Fuel (MMCF)	Total Hp	Investment per Hp (Dollars)	Number Driving Units	Number Compressor Units	Expenses per Hp (Dollars)	Number Stations	Year Installed
			Fuel or Power	Other								
Gas Engine												
1	50	24,938	607	1,069	3,149	70,000	356	20	20	23.95	5	1957
Gas Turbine												
1	97	41,221	1,352	1,553	11,102	179,600	230	32	32	16.18	12	1952–58
2	38	12,003	523	268	3,488	56,400	213	8	8	14.03	2	1953
3	48	5,697	226	308	1,507	18,900	301	3	3	28.30	3	1956
4	50	13,869	304	389	2,279	38,500	360	6	6	18.02	4	1955–58
5	174	49,811	1,398	1,011	7,430	250,400	199	34	34	12.19	13	1956–58
Electric Motor												
1	11	2,246	186	72	-----	12,500	179	1	1	20.93	1	1958
2	6	1,905	43	37	-----	4,500	423	3	3	18.07	1	1958
3	203	30,077	7,848	1,373	-----	210,500	143	68	68	43.80	22	1948–58
Steam Turbine												
1	75	10,601	671	459	5,391	53,200	199	11	11	21.23	3	1951–52

(Source: *Oil and Gas Journal* [June 27, 1960], 109.)

pressure results from the fact that the gas is flowing through two pipes over the thirty-mile section, instead of one pipe, and the lower resistance results in a higher terminal pressure. Our calculations indicate that the installation of the thirty-mile loops after each compressor station increase the capacity of the line from 135,000 MCF/D to 152,000 MCF/D.[22]

It should be noted that the design engineer's freedom is limited by the safety standards established by the governmental authorities in the different areas through which the pipe line will pass.[23] These standards regulate such things as pipe-line thickness and maximum working pressure, depth of burial, and permissible proximity to buildings in populated areas.

Table 5 sets forth the results of a design study of a 1,000-mile pipe line from southern Louisiana to southwestern Pennsylvania. Total operating expenses of 1.7¢/MCF/100 miles are indicated. Another authority cited a figure of 2.705¢/MCF/100 miles as the cost of transportation in the Trans-Canada gas pipe line. This figure is expected to fall to 1.790¢/MCF/100 miles by 1963 because of increases in throughput from 90 to 210 billions of cubic feet per year.[24]

Table 6 shows the trend of investment in pipe lines as a function of the diameter of the line, and is based on data reported to the Federal Power Commission. A recent paper[25] indicates that, for the United States, twenty-nine projects submitted to the Federal Power Commission in 1956 ranging from two- to thirty-six-inch pipe and from one to 260 miles in length averaged $3,916 per inch-mile (cost per inch-mile is the cost of a line exclusive of compressor investment divided by the mileage and again by the outside diameter of the line), with a range of from $7,445 per inch-mile for metropolitan area construction to $3,746 per inch-mile for cross-country work. In Canada, the cost

[22] "Transmission of Natural Gas," *American Gas Journal*, Vol. CLXXV, No. 1 (July, 1951), 29; OEEC Technical Assistance Mission, *Long Distance Gas Transport in the United States*, 37ff.; Chapter XVI, "Transportation of Natural Gas," in *Natural Gas*, edited by Stephenson; L. W. A. Campbell, "When Do You Build a Gas-transmission System?," *Oil and Gas Journal*, Vol. LVII, No. 3 (January 19, 1959), 81.

[23] Such safety regulations are generalized in the American Standards Association Code for Pressure Piping, B 31.8–1958. Also see Nagler, "Transportation and Storage of Gaseous Fuels."

[24] R. B. Toombs, "Methods Used in Canada to Achieve Economic Transportation of Fuels by Pipeline," *Transactions* of the World Power Conference (1960), VI, 3117; *Petroleum Press Service*, Vol. XXVIII, No. 7 (July, 1960), 246.

of a 122-mile 30-inch gas line amounted to $4,300 per inch-mile.[26] In another Canadian project the cost of 33 miles of 12¾-inch pipe line was equivalent to $3,360 per inch-mile. A 12¾-inch gas pipe line in Trinidad was estimated to require an investment at 1960 prices of $3,060 per inch-mile.[27]

Table 7 shows compressor station investment and operating expenses as reported to the Federal Power Commission. A recent report describes compressor station investment as follows:

> The construction costs of pipeline compressor stations are frequently expressed in dollars per brake horsepower (bHP). A 1951 pipeline compressor station project of 10,000 HP at each station resulted in an average of $372 per bHP—composed of $200 for material and equipment, $82 for contract labor and materials, $52 for engineering and supervision, the balance being overhead and tools and equipment. A recent expansion project on the same system again involving 10,000 HP stations resulted in an average cost of $350 per bHP, reflecting larger engines with improved auxiliaries requiring less operating personnel and thus decreased facilities for personnel. Where such factors do not apply, recent construction, of course, has been substantially higher.[28]

Figure 10 shows the drastic effect of reduced throughput (low load factor) on operating expenses. This chart illustrates the reason for operating gas pipe lines at the highest possible throughput.[29]

PIPE-LINE CONSTRUCTION

Operating in a highly competitive market the pipe-line construction people have, on the basis of much field experience and with the exercise of great ingenuity, developed the essentially piece work business of joining the many joints of pipe together and placing them into a highly efficient continuous operation. Pipe-line construction costs

[25] Nagler, "Transportation and Storage of Gaseous Fuels," 4–5.

[26] Toombs, "Methods Used in Canada to Achieve Economic Transportation of Fuels by Pipeline."

[27] Foster and Finch, "Relative Costs of Transmitting Energy as Electricity or as Natural Gas."

[28] Nagler, "Transportation and Storage of Gaseous Fuels."

[29] Figure 10, illustrating the effect of throughput on the unit cost of operating a pipe-line system, is based on Exhibit 34 of Federal Power Commission Docket G-4769 in which the fixed capital costs were representative of an interstate pipe-line system in 1954 with 13 per cent accrued depreciation. The figure is included here to show the order of magnitude of the effect of changes in throughput on unit operating costs and not for use in estimating 1962 gas transportation costs.

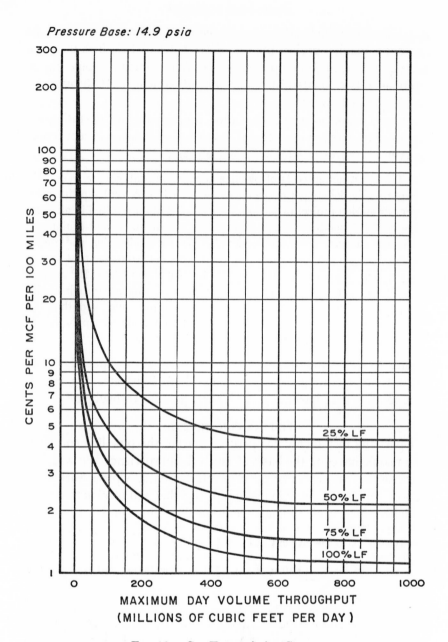

Pressure Base: 14.9 psia

CENTS PER MCF PER 100 MILES

25% LF

50% LF

75% LF

100% LF

MAXIMUM DAY VOLUME THROUGHPUT
(MILLIONS OF CUBIC FEET PER DAY)

Fig. 10.—Gas Transmission Costs.

are low, and new methods permit the construction of pipe lines in all types of terrain—whether montainous or sandy and whether under water or on land—and under all types of weather conditions.

The following discussion of pipe-line construction assumes that an aerial survey of the route has been completed, and a ground reconnaissance made to select the best route in questionable areas. It further assumes that the pipe-line facilities have been designed and the materials ordered have been delivered at the designated points along the pipe-line route. Finally it assumes that the necessary governmental authorizations have been obtained from the Federal Power Commission, that financing has been arranged, and that firm contracts exist to provide a gas supply to the line and to provide sales from the line.[30]

Assuming that these things have been done, the actual construction of the line begins with obtaining the right-of-way by entering into contracts with the surface owners, who grant the natural gas company the right to lay and maintain a line or lines over an easement from seventy-five to one hundred feet wide across the owner's land. The easement carries with it such right of ingress and egress as may be necessary in building and maintaining a pipe line. Payments for right-of-way range from one dollar to three dollars per lineal rod. Pipe-line companies usually are classified as public utilities, and this classification carries with it the right of eminent domain. This right permits the pipe-line company to condemn, under either state or federal statutes, the land needed for the construction and operation of the pipe line when agreement cannot be reached with the landowner. Right-of-way agreements often provide that the pipe-line company will place a tap on its line for the use of the landowner. Pipe-line companies also obtain in fee, or by long-term lease, such surface rights as may be necessary for the construction of compressor stations and measuring stations.

After the right-of-way contracts have been executed, several engineers survey and stake the exact pipe-line route. A crew then clears

[30] OEEC Technical Assistance Mission, *Long Distance Gas Transport in the United States,* 59ff., 135ff.; Chapter X, "Transmission," in *Natural Gas,* published by the Institute of Gas Technology, 137–140; Chapter XV, "Pipe-line Construction," in *Natural Gas,* edited by Stephenson; W. R. Quarles, "Trans-Canada Rushes 34" Line!," *Pipe Line News,* Vol. XXIX, No. 8 (August, 1957), 27; Eric Ford, "Constructing Long Distance Pipe Lines," *Public Works and Muck Shifter* (March, 1958), 199.

the right-of-way of rock, trees, brush, and other obstructions. Fences are carefully cut and gates installed to permit the entrance of pipe-line trucks and machinery.

After the right-of-way has been cleared, the pipe-stringing crew picks up the pipe at the yards to which it has been delivered by rail and moves the pipe in trucks to the right-of-way, where the pipe is unloaded on the ground next to the ditch line. Holes are drilled and dynamite blasting is used to loosen hard formations in the ditch line. Ditching is done by a machine (see Plate VII) which moves along the ditch line on tractor treads while the ditch is dug by a revolving wheel on which are located a number of buckets with teeth. A conveyor belt dumps the dirt to one side of the trench. The operator of the machine follows a staked line previously marked by engineers. In muddy areas where the ditching machine cannot traverse a crane or back-hoe is used for ditching.

The width and depth of the ditch varies considerably with different companies. Generally the line is buried deep enough to permit culti-vation of the surface, to avoid vandalism, and to give some tempera-ture protection. Usually a cover of thirty inches is provided, although it may be reduced to twenty-four inches in rocky country. Ditch widths will vary from twenty-eight inches for a sixteen-inch line to forty inches for a thirty-inch line.

When a pipe line must cross a railroad or highway, safety regula-tions usually require that the line be encased in a pipe of larger diame-ter (usually six inches larger than the outside diameter of the gas pipe line) which is sealed and vented to the air. This safety casing is placed under the highway or railroad by means of a machine-driven auger which bores a hole through an embankment of sufficient size that the casing may be pushed through. Also pipe with a greater wall thickness than that used in other parts of the line is often specified for highway and railroad crossings. This special pipe will be unloaded at the proper places by the pipe-stringing crew.

Next a pipelaying crew measures and numbers each joint of pipe and places appropriate stakes, which are numbered in sequence with the pipe, in the ground along the ditch. A pipe-bending machine (see Plate VIII) is moved to appropriate places on the right-of-way to per-mit the cold bending of pipe as may be necessary to fit ground con-tours. The pipe joints are then raised by tractors with sidebooms (see

Plate IX) and placed on *skids* (6"x 6"x 4' timber pieces) alongside the ditch.

After the pipe has been set on skids, the pipe ends are cleaned for welding by a portable gasoline-engine-driven buffing machine. Next the pipe gang lines up the two joints of pipe to be welded through the use of specially developed internal and external clamps so that the joints are from 1/16 to 1/32 of an inch apart. The pipe ends to be welded are cleaned and beveled at 30 degrees. The pipe gang is assisted by a sideboom tractor in lining up the pipe for welding. The pipe crew also sees that the pipe seams are located in the top one-fourth circumference of the pipe in a staggered position. This practice makes for easier repair of a seam leak. Two welders, one working on either side of the pipe, then make the first weld, which is called the *root weld* or *stringer bead*. Then a second group consisting of four welders makes the additional or filler beads that are necessary to complete the weld. All welding is done with the pipe stationary, and is started at the top of the pipe and finished at the bottom. (See Plate X.) Portable electric welding machines accompany the welders. Welds are tested by the cutting of samples and by X-ray. Automatic welding is extensively used in the double pointing of pipe prior to stringing, and an automatic welding machine has been successfully tested which welds pipe alongside the ditch on the right-of-way.

The pipe is welded in sections of approximately 4,000 feet. Following welding the pipe is cleaned by a self-propelled motor-driven machine containing steel cutters and brushes. This machine rides on the pipe which is suspended by a sideboom tractor moving in front of the cleaning machine. Following the cutters and wire brushes of the cleaning machine are two priming rugs which apply a coat of primer to the pipe for corrosion control. After the primer has dried (up to 72 hours), the pipe is coated with an enamel and wrapped either with a felt or fiberglass material. The enameling and wrapping is done by a self-propelled machine which moves along the suspended pipe (see Plate XI). It is essential that the coating and wrapping of the pipe be perfect for corrosion control. The coating and wrapping is tested for defects by a *holiday tester*. This machine (see Plate XII) is moved along the pipe and produces a spark between the machine and the pipe whenever a defect is crossed.

Next the welded and wrapped line is carefully lowered into the ditch

91

by several sideboom tractors (see Plate XIII). Any defects in the coating and wrapping which may have been caused by the skids or by the lowering-in are carefully repaired by hand. The sections in the ditch are then tied in by a pipe gang and welders using the methods described above. At the completion of welding, the line is internally cleaned by blowing a sweeping pig through the line.

The line is tested in sections by the use of either gas or water, and any leaks detected are found and repaired. Test pressures usually exceed the anticipated operating pressure of the line. After the line has been tested and cleaned, the ditch is filled and the excess dirt carefully placed on top of the ditch. The right-of-way is minutely cleaned, and settlement is made with the surface owner for any damages to crops or other property.

Large rivers are crossed by weighting the pipe (see Plate XIV) and placing it in a ditch on the river bottom. The pipe may be pulled across the river from shore to shore, or may be lowered off of barges by means of sidebooms. A wooden covering is used to protect the pipe-coating against scratches if the river bottom is rocky. Suspension bridges (see Plate XV) carry the pipe line across small streams. One of the more spectacular feats of the pipe-line construction industry lies in the laying of lines in deep water to serve offshore gas fields.

4

FINANCIAL ASPECTS
OF TRANSMISSION

by John C. Jacobs

FROM a functional standpoint the natural gas industry of the United States may be divided into three parts, production, transmission, and distribution. This chapter is concerned with the financial aspects of those gas industry operations involved in moving gas from the field where it is produced to the market where it is consumed.

The size of gas transmission operations in the United States is impressive from any standpoint, and is especially so when we consider that the first long-distance, all-welded pipe line was constructed as recently as 1924.[1] At the end of 1959 there were 599,910 miles of gas pipe line in the United States, of which 174,360 miles were used for transmission and the balance for either gathering or distribution. About 11.479 trillion cubic feet of gas were marketed through these lines in 1955, which represented 26.8 per cent of the nation's consumption of all energy fuels for that year.[2] Investment in gas utility and pipe-line facilities in the United States stood at $19,200,000,000 at the end of 1959. Of this amount, $8,105,000,000 was invested in investor-owned natural gas pipe lines.[3] This investment made the gas industry—a relative newcomer among industries—the fifth largest in the United States.[4]

One of the principal characteristics of the United States gas indus-

[1] This line was built by the Magnolia Gas Company of Dallas, Texas, from northern Louisiana to Beaumont, Texas. Hilt, "Chronology of the Natural Gas Industry," *American Gas Journal*, Vol. CLXXII, No. 5 (May, 1950). 29–30.

[2] American Gas Association, *1960 Gas Facts*, Tables 13 and 14.

[3] American Gas Association, *1960 Gas Facts*, Tables 183 and 185.

[4] U. S. Department of Commerce, *Census of Manufacturers*. In 1956 more pounds of natural gas were marketed than pounds of steel were produced in the United States.

FIGURES IN THOUSAND MILLION MEGAWATT HOURS ELECTRICITY EQUIVALENT

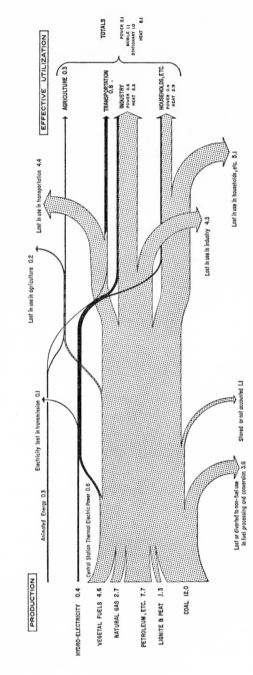

FIG. 11.—Origin and Utilization of the World's Energy in 1952.

Courtesy Texas Eastern Transmission Corporation, Houston, Tex.

PLATE VII.—Ditching Machine.

PLATE VIII.—Pipe-bending Machine

Courtesy Texas Eastern Transmission Corporation, Houston, Tex.

Courtesy Texas Eastern Transmission Corporation, Houston, Tex.

PLATE IX.—Sideboom Tractor.

Courtesy Texas Eastern Transmission Corporation, Houston, Tex.

PLATE X.—Welding Pipe.

Courtesy Texas Eastern Transmission Corporation, Houston, Tex.

PLATE XI.—Coating and Wrapping Pipe.

Courtesy Texas Eastern Transmission Corporation, Houston, Tex.

PLATE XII.—Holiday Tester.

Courtesy Texas Eastern Transmission Corporation, Houston, Tex.

PLATE XIII.—Lowering-in.

Courtesy Texas Eastern Transmission Corporation, Houston, Tex.

PLATE XIV.—Weighting Pipe.

Courtesy Texas Eastern Transmission Corporation, Houston, Tex.

PLATE XV.—The Suspension Bridge Type of River Crossing.

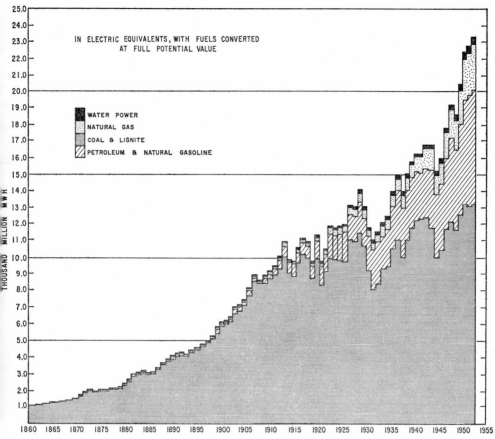

FIG. 12.—World Production of Commercial Sources of Energy, 1860–1952.

try is an unbelievably rapid growth.[5] As an aid to comprehending and evaluating the past growth, present operations, and future problems of the natural gas industry, this section sets forth an over-all summary description of the industry as it is.

One result of the increasing social centralization and electronic collation so epidemic in today's world is a great new fund of information on present and future energy supply and demand at all political

[5] There exists a strong metaphysical basis for the importance of the natural gas industry. Despite years of relativist romanticizing to the contrary, our physical *Weltanschauung* is Newtonian in that we conceive the world in the fundamental terms of energy and matter. Natural gas, of course, represents energy.

95

TABLE 8

Marketed Production of Natural Gas by Countries, 1955–59

(Million Cu. Ft. at 60°F. and Normal Atmospheric Pressure)

Country*	1955	1956	1957	1958	1959
North America					
Barbados	133	125	108	98	96
Canada	150,772	169,153	220,007	337,804	433,183
Mexico†	126,590	132,258	173,262	277,587	329,363
Trinidad	17,590	19,319	21,202	23,403	34,850
United States	9,405,351	10,081,923	10,680,258	11,030,298	12,046,115
South America					
Argentina†	39,372	42,834	52,782	61,721	------‡
Bolivia	224	262	299	224	------‡
Brazil†	2,309	3,130	5,866	11,213	15,948
Chile	17,407	21,913	29,723	49,858	67,746
Colombia†	20,153	23,287	23,736	29,557	------‡
Peru†	29,435	29,914	37,510	33,762	------‡
Venezuela	102,577	111,749	135,241	146,692	156,435
Europe					
Austria	28,595	27,801	28,307	30,613	42,098
Belgium	------‡	------‡	3,247	------‡	------‡
Czechoslovakia	6,454	10,238	28,805	46,486	------‡
France	10,231	12,335	20,630	39,540	94,196
Germany, West	8,941	13,683	13,328	12,832	14,465
Hungary†	20,340	16,868	15,338	13,996	12,360
Italy	135,369	166,645	186,118	193,156	228,307
Netherlands	5,412	6,307	6,196	7,763	10,768
Poland	14,678	16,287	15,641	14,334	15,834
Rumania	148,243	163,235	172,895	189,410	215,798

U.S.S.R.	335,168	450,345	693,524	1,048,117	1,324,864§
Yugoslavia	1,257	1,437	1,550	1,719	1,866
Asia					
Burma	120§	231	225	325	178
Brunei	2,867	3,054	2,824	2,757	-----‡
Indonesia†§	71,207	76,320	80,910	77,775	-----‡
Iran	-----‡	15,552	25,578	26,288	32,055
Japan†	5,804	6,598	9,092	13,730	18,831
Pakistan	1,376	10,441	15,349	19,308	22,365
Saudi Arabia	4	-----‡	-----‡	-----‡	-----‡
Taiwan	969	1,015	1,073	979	983
Africa					
Algeria (Sahara)	-----	-----	-----	4,083	6,699
Gabon, Republic of	-----	-----	75	729	1,498
Morocco	282	273	126	69	154
Tunisia	165	218	225	217	236
Union of South Africa	9	6	-----‡	-----‡	-----‡
Oceania					
New Zealand	5	8	7	5	6

(Source: United States Department of the Interior, Bureau of Mines, II, *Minerals Yearbook* [*Fuels*] [1960], 300. Compiled by Pearl J. Thompson and Berenice B. Mitchell.)

NOTE: The data relate, as far as possible, to natural gas actually collected and utilized as fuel or raw material. They exclude gas used for re-pressuring, as well as gas flared, vented, or otherwise wasted whether or not it has first been processed for extraction of natural gasoline. For countries reporting in the metric system, the following conversion factor will be used:

$$m^3 \text{ at } 32° \text{ F. } (0° \text{ C.}) \times 37.32 = ft.^3 \text{ at } 60° \text{ F.} \qquad (ft.^3 \text{ at } 60° \text{ F. } \times 0.026795 = m^3 \text{ at } 32° \text{ F.})$$

* Natural gas is produced in China but there is no recent information available.
† Total production.
‡ Data not available.
§ Estimate.

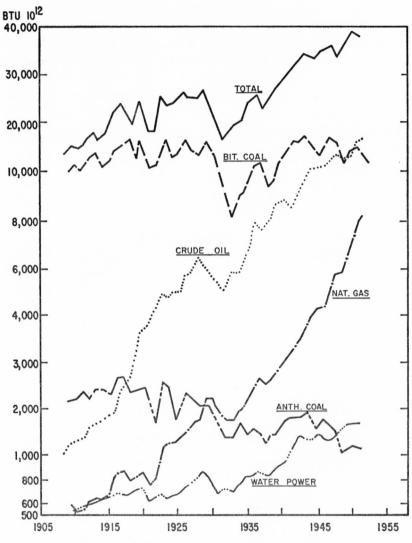

Fig. 13.—United States Energy Supply, 1905–55.

levels, including the world.[6] Figure 11, an encomium to these efforts, shows the source and use of the world's energy in 1952 and emphasizes

[6] The statistics of the natural gas industry are set forth primarily in three publications. The most comprehensive statistics are published by the American Gas Association in its annual volume, *Gas Facts*. Each year the Bureau of Mines of the United States Depart-

the fact that energy conversion is an inefficient process. Only 35 per cent of the world energy input is utilized as heat or power.

Figure 12 illustrates the sources of world energy from 1860 to the present and indicates a rapidly increasing input from oil and natural gas, a phenomenon common also to the United States. Natural gas supplied 9.3 per cent of the world energy requirements in 1952. The graph represents a long-term annual increase in world energy input of 3 to 3.5 per cent per year. For the ten-year period beginning in 1943 and ending in 1953, the rate of increase has been about 5 per cent a year.

Table 8 points out that, for all practical purposes, the United States is the only sizable gas user in the world.[7] In 1959, 81 per cent of the world natural gas consumption occurred here.

Figure 13 represents the annual consumption of energy in the United States of America since 1905. The high per capita energy consumption of the United States has resulted in the use of 34 per cent of the world's energy by only 5 per cent of the world's population.

AN ADEQUATE SUPPLY OF NATURAL GAS

The United States has an adequate supply of natural gas. There was, in 1960, a proved reserve of 262 trillion cubic feet which repre-

ment of the Interior publishes its *Minerals Yearbook*. Volume II of the *Minerals Yearbook* is concerned with fuels, and each year one chapter of this fuels volume is devoted to natural gas. The American Gas Association and Bureau of Mines publications contain statistics concerning the production, transportation, and consumption of natural gas. In addition, the Federal Power Commission publishes an annual volume entitled *Statistics of Natural Gas Companies,* which summarizes data submitted to the Federal Power Commission each year by the natural gas companies under its jurisdiction. The summary data in the Federal Power Commission publication are primarily of a financial nature.

In 1961 the Bureau of Statistics of the American Gas Association published, in loose-leaf binder form, its comprehensive *Historical Statistics of the Gas Industry,* a complete compilation of all statistics of the gas industry.

[7] The statistics which the Communist government of the U.S.S.R. supplies to the world are so incomplete and unreliable that it has been necessary to use an estimated marketed production in 1959 of 1.3 trillion cubic feet, which is about one-tenth of the consumption in the United States. After forty years of the Marxist-Leninist approach, per capita energy consumption in the U.S.S.R. has just about reached the level it would have reached in the same length of time under czarist rule. See Palmer C. Putnam, *Energy in the Future,* 94; Colin Clark, *The Real Productivity of Soviet Russia;* "You Can't Trust Communist Production Figures," *Oil and Gas Journal,* Vol. LX, No. 36 (September 3, 1962), 88.

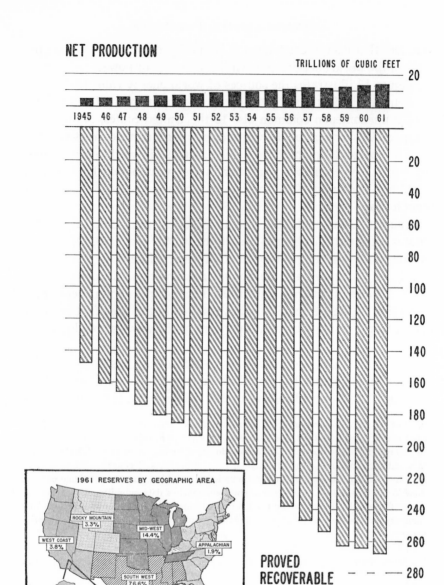

NET PRODUCTION

TRILLIONS OF CUBIC FEET

1961 RESERVES BY GEOGRAPHIC AREA

ROCKY MOUNTAIN 3.3%
MID-WEST 14.4%
WEST COAST 3.8%
APPALACHIAN 1.9%
SOUTH WEST 76.6%

DECEMBER 31, 1961

PROVED
RECOVERABLE
RESERVES

Fig. 14.—Proved Recoverable Reserves and Net Production
of Natural Gas in the United States.

100

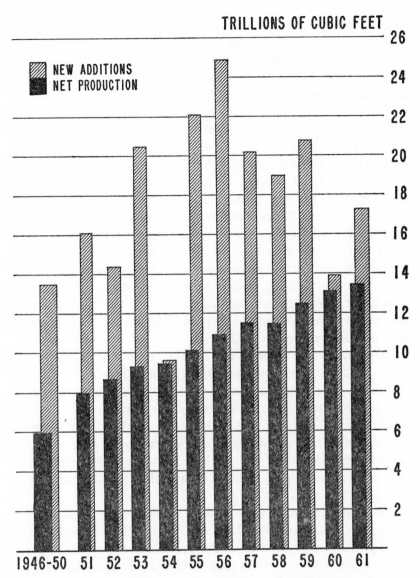

TRILLIONS OF CUBIC FEET

NEW ADDITIONS
NET PRODUCTION

DURING THE LAST SIXTEEN YEARS, NEW ADDITIONS TO PROVEN RECOVERABLE RESERVES HAVE EXCEEDED NET PRODUCTION BY NEARLY 118 TRILLION CUBIC FEET...EQUAL TO AN ADDITIONAL 8 3/4-YEAR SUPPLY AT PRESENT PRO-DUCTION RATES

FIG. 15.—Net Production and New Additions to Gas Reserves.

101

sented a twenty-year supply at the current production rate of 12 trillion feet per year. (See Figure 14.) The *reserve life index* has been approximately twenty years for the last five years. Additions to proved reserves over the past decade have amounted to about 1.8 cubic feet per cubic foot produced. (See Figure 15.) Adding reserves at this rate will maintain a twenty-year reserve life for an annual increase in production of approximately 4 per cent per year. Most future estimates indicate increases in natural gas consumption of 3 to 4 per cent per year. These reserves are developed under a drilling program in which some 3,500 gas wells and 30,000 oil wells are completed each year. About 70 per cent of the United States gas production comes from gas wells and 30 per cent from oil wells.

In the United States, natural gas is sold at reasonable wellhead prices that average about 12.9¢/MCF. In terms of real dollars, the wellhead price of natural gas is about two-thirds that of 1910. Natural gas sells for less on a Btu basis at the well than does crude oil, but it costs about three times as much to transport.[8] The control of wellhead prices under the Natural Gas Act should prevent any excessive price increases above the 1960 level.

There is available to the user of natural gas who purchases it from a pipe line a *net marketed production* of only 70 per cent of the gas produced—after deductions are made for the gas used in repressuring, that lost in underground storage changes, that lost in the field and in transmission, and that used in the field.[9] A principal pre-pipe-line consumption is *field use,* which accounts for about 15 per cent of production. Repressuring, the reinjection of gas into underground reservoirs to increase the production of hydrocarbon liquids, accounts for another 12 per cent.

The 85 per cent which was marketed (including field uses) in 1959 represented 12.046 trillion cubic feet. Over the 1955–59 period, marketed production of natural gas has increased at an average rate of 5.75 per cent a year. This is a much higher rate than that of 3 per per cent per year for all marketed energy and indicates the consumer preference for natural gas. Natural gas has made great inroads into the total energy consumption of the United States (see Figure 16.)—

[8] On the subject of monopoly and competition in field markets of natural gas, see Edward J. Neuner, *The Natural Gas Industry.*

[9] American Gas Association, *1960 Gas Facts,* Table 20.

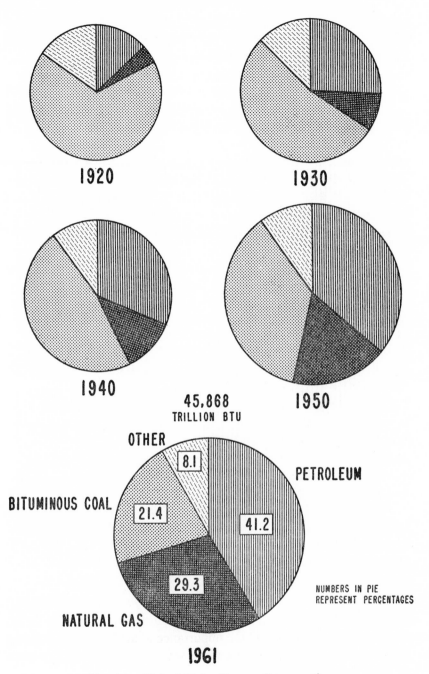

1920

1930

1940

45,868
TRILLION BTU

1950

OTHER

8.1

PETROLEUM

BITUMINOUS COAL

21.4

41.2

29.3

NUMBERS IN PIE
REPRESENT PERCENTAGES

NATURAL GAS

1961

FIG. 16.—United States Energy Consumption.

103

primarily at the expense of coal—and supplied 26.8 per cent of the total United States energy requirement in 1959.

PATTERNS OF NATURAL GAS CONSUMPTION

Figures 17 and 18 illustrate the patterns of natural gas consumption. About 70 per cent of the natural gas produced goes to industrial

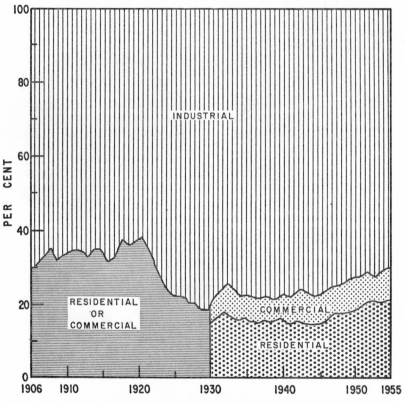

FIG. 17.—Natural Gas Consumption Pattern, Selected Years, 1906–55.

uses, 7 per cent to commercial uses, and 23 per cent to residential consumption. Figure 18 shows the types of consumers making up the industrial usage and indicates the importance of field use and of central power station consumption. Figure 19 sets forth similar data in terms of cubic feet consumed.

104

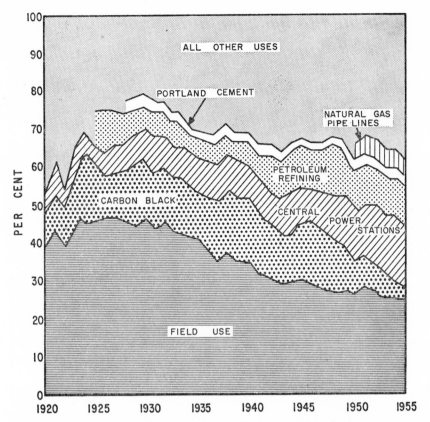

Fɪɢ. 18.—Industrial Use Pattern of Natural Gas, 1920–55.

Although industrial users take the largest volume of natural gas, first priority goes to residential users, and industrial supplies may be curtailed whenever residential needs expand. This not only makes gas available for house heating on cold days but also allows pipe-line facilities to operate at a higher load factor with a resultant lower cost for residential sales. However, the bulk of industrial sales represent sales made in the vicinity of natural gas production rather than an answer to the peak-shaving problem. For example, in 1959, the states of Texas, Oklahoma, Arkansas, and Louisiana provided 76.5 per cent (9.241 trillion cubic feet) of the nation's marketed production. These states, with less than 10 per cent of the nation's population, accounted for 48.9 per cent (3.882 trillion cubic feet) of the nation's industrial

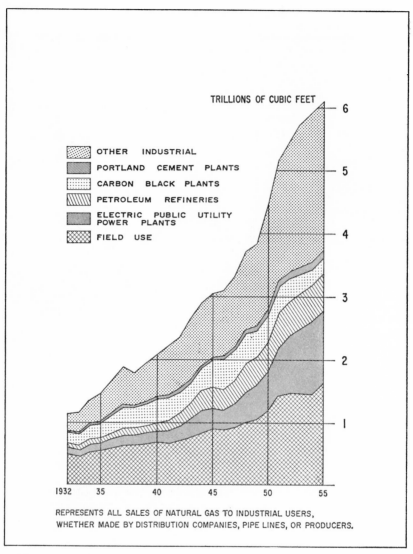

FIG. 19.—Industrial Consumption of Natural Gas in the United States.

gas consumption in the same year. The same states accounted for only 12.2 per cent (0.471 trillion cubic feet) of the nation's residential and commercial usage in that same year.[10]

[10] U.S. Department of the Interior, Bureau of Mines, *1959 Mineral Yearbook* (II: Fuels), Tables 10 and 12; Frank J. Gardner, "Natural Gas Is Texas' Industrial Life-blood," *Oil and Gas Journal,* Vol. LIX, No. 11 (March 13, 1960), 167.

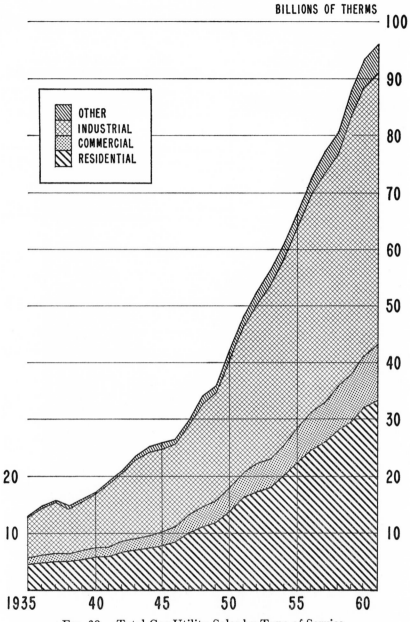

BILLIONS OF THERMS

OTHER
INDUSTRIAL
COMMERCIAL
RESIDENTIAL

Fig. 20.—Total Gas Utility Sales by Type of Service.

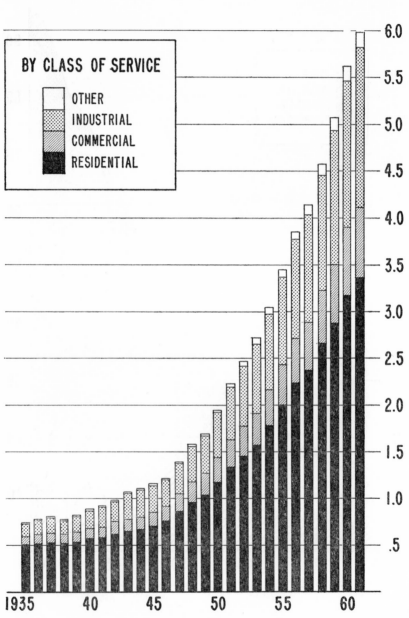

BILLIONS OF DOLLARS

BY CLASS OF SERVICE

- OTHER
- INDUSTRIAL
- COMMERCIAL
- RESIDENTIAL

Fig. 21.—Gas Utility Revenues.

108

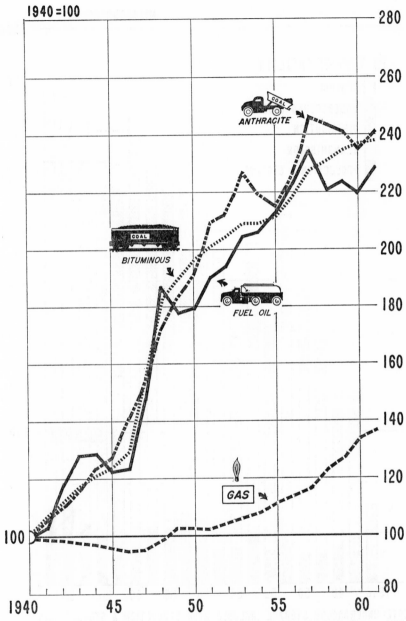

FIG. 22.—Gas Price Compared with Other Principal Fuels.

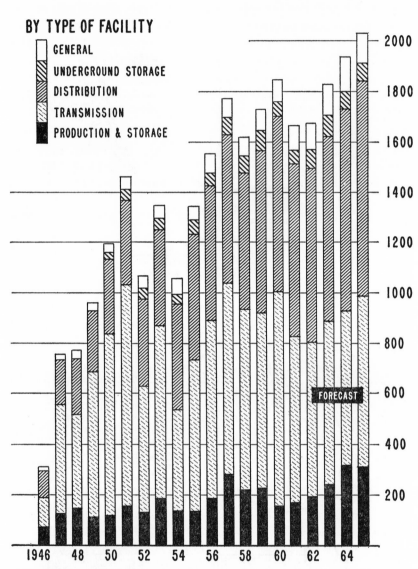

MILLIONS OF DOLLARS

BY TYPE OF FACILITY

- ☐ GENERAL
- ▨ UNDERGROUND STORAGE
- ▨ DISTRIBUTION
- ▨ TRANSMISSION
- ■ PRODUCTION & STORAGE

FORECAST

NOTE: UNDERGROUND STORAGE INCLUDED WITH PRODUCTION & STORAGE DATA PRIOR TO 1950.

FIG. 23.—Gas Industry Construction Expenditures.

110

Figures 20 and 21 represent the volume and dollar value of gas utility sales and introduce a gas sales measure, the *therm,* which is equal to 100,000 Btu's or approximately 100 cubic feet of natural gas. These figures point out the relatively higher value of residential sales, which provided more than one-half of total revenues from one-third of total sales volume. Gas was sold to 32,000,000 customers in 1959.

Figure 22 shows that the price of gas has been stable compared to other fuels. Speaking very generally gas sells for 13¢/MCF in the field, 35 to 40¢/MCF in the wholesale market at the outlet of long-distance pipe lines, and at 100 to 200¢/MCF to residential consumers. Industrial sales prices will vary from 20 to 40¢/MCF. These are rough averages and prices at any particular sales point may vary widely from them. American Gas Association estimates for the city of New York in 1959 show a cost per million Btu's to the residential consumer of 186.9 cents for heating with oil, 168.8 cents for natural gas, and 152.8 cents for coal. These estimates assume efficiencies of 57 per cent for oil-burning equipment, 62 per cent for coal, and 80 per cent for gas.[11] Federal Power Commission data reporting the cost of fuel for electricity generation for 1959 show, per million Btu's, 35.2 cents for fuel oil, 26.5 cents for coal, and 22.3 cents for gas as averages for the entire United States.[12]

Natural gas is moved from the gas-producing wells to the consumer through an extensive, rapidly growing, network of expensive high-pressure pipe lines. Construction expenditures for the expansion of this system amount to approximately $2,000,000,000 a year. (See Figure 23.)

Although substantial quantities of natural gas are used in the field where they are produced and large amounts are used within the states where production takes place for industrial and other purposes, one of the most impressive facts of the industry since World War II has been the growth of pipe lines for the interstate movement of natural gas. In 1959 interstate shipments constituted 60 per cent of marketed production.

FINANCIAL CHARACTERISTICS OF THE INDUSTRY

Financially, the natural gas industry shows the characteristics of large size and rapid growth. Net investment in plant facilities by the

[11] *Petroleum Press Service,* Vol. XXVIII, No. 3 (March, 1961), 98–99.
[12] *Ibid.*

natural gas pipe-line companies was about six times greater in 1958 than in 1945 with an increase from $700,000,000 in 1945 to $4,200,-000,000 in 1954 and $6,300,000,000 in 1958.[13] Similarly, revenues multiplied 5.5 times, from $293,000,000 in 1945 to about $1,600,000,-000 in 1954 and $2,700,000,000 in 1958. The natural gas pipe-line companies' sales volume was 1.77 trillion cubic feet in 1945 but 3.5 times higher in 1954 and up to 8.5 trillion cubic meet in 1958.[14] Gross plant investment in the interstate natural gas transmission industry increased from just over $1,000,000,000 at the end of 1945 to over $5,000,000,000 at the end of 1954 and $8,000,000,000 in 1958. This impressive growth is made even more graphic by comparative figures of individual transmission corporations. Two systems which operated in the decade following World War II, Tennessee Gas Transmission Company and El Paso Natural Gas Company, are being compared by the FPC. Both companies have assets exceeding $1,000,000,000.[15] Tennessee had a gross plant investment of $64,100,000 in 1945 and $751,000,000 in 1954—11.7 times the 1945 figure. By 1958 gross plant investment had increased to $1,349,000,000—more than twenty times the 1945 figure. El Paso's figures are no less impressive. The 1954 investment was 18.6 times that of 1945 and showed an increase

[13] See the financial review of the natural gas pipe-line companies in the annual reports of the Federal Power Commission and in the *Statistics of Natural Gas Companies,* also published by the commission. The comprehensive and representative *Annual Report* of 1955 is particularly interesting because it deals with the growth era of the transmission industry between 1945 and 1954. However, the latter year does not mark the end of gas industry development. On the contrary, the years 1955–59 show further growth.

The annual volumes entitled *Statistics of Natural Gas Companies* deal with so-called "natural gas pipe-line companies." This term usually designates companies which transport natural gas in excess of 250 miles and sell it for resale in excess of 50 per cent of total sales. The FPC also includes several companies which, although they do not meet the foregoing specifications entirely, have the characteristics of pipe-line companies. The FPC's report affords, as it says, "essentially full coverage" of interstate natural gas transmission.

[14] Of these total sales, a large percentage are sales for resale, as opposed to sales for ultimate consumption. It is these sales for resale in interstate commerce which are covered by the Natural Gas Act. See Chapter 12 below.

In 1945 sales for resale totaled 1.249 trillion cubic feet. In 1954 the total was 5.402 trillion cubic feet. In 1958 it was 6.984 trillion cubic feet.

[15] The third interstate system with assets in excess of one billion dollars is United Gas Corporation.

Until 1960, when Transwestern Pipeline Company commenced operations, El Paso was the sole supplier of interstate natural gas to California.

from $33,000,000 to $614,700,000. In 1958, El Paso's gross plant investment was $1,482,000,000. Operating revenues, too, mirror growth. Tennessee experienced a tenfold increase from $14,300,000 in 1945 to $142,995,000 in 1954. By 1958 operating revenue had climbed to $256,400,000. El Paso's operating revenue advanced sixteenfold, from $8,900,000 in 1945 to $143,800,000 in 1954. In 1958, El Paso's operating revenue was $264,400,000.

Such growth of the industry could not have been achieved without a corresponding increase in capitalization. In 1945 the combined capitalization of the natural gas pipe-line companies was $802,034,000.[16] Of this amount, debt constituted some 40 per cent of $318,422,000.[17] Total capitalization at the end of 1954 was about $5,100,000,000 of which capital stock—common plus preferred—and surplus amounted to $1,800,000,000 (34 per cent) and long-term debt to $2,900,000,000 (61.6 per cent). At the end of 1958 capital stock and surplus had increased to $2,800,000,000 and long-term debt to $4,300,000,000 which defines a long-term debt ratio of 60.9 per cent.[18]

DETERMINING COST-OF-SERVICE

Figure 24 shows the growth and present magnitude of the income and expenses of investor-owned gas pipe-line companies. In 1959 total operating revenues were $2,762,000,000 which resulted in a net income of $268,000,000 after deducting $1,818,000,000 to cover such operating expenses as the cost of purchased gas and maintenance, $518,000,000 to cover income and other taxes and depreciation, and $178,000,000 to cover other deductions—primarily interest. Since the gas industry is subject to governmentally imposed public utility controls, this income is received under rate schedules which have been publicly approved in accordance with the *cost-of-service formula*.

[16] Federal Power Commission, *Annual Report* of 1955, 27. By the end of 1958 the figure had increased to $7,980,024,000. By 1959 it stood at $8,845,421,000. See Federal Power Commission, *Statistics of Natural Gas Companies* (for 1960) and prior editions.

[17] Note that 1945 marked the end of a period of limited expansion in the industry. Practically the only outstanding event of the period had been the start of operations by Tennessee Gas on October 31, 1944. With the end of World War II, a period of rapid development began. It was officially heralded by Texas Eastern Transmission Corporation's opening of the Big Inch and Little Inch lines for operation on May 7, 1947.

[18] See the discussion of debt ratio below on pages 122ff., and see Table 9 which sets forth 1960 debt ratios ranging from 53.4 to 69.6 per cent for nine representative natural gas transmission companies.

113

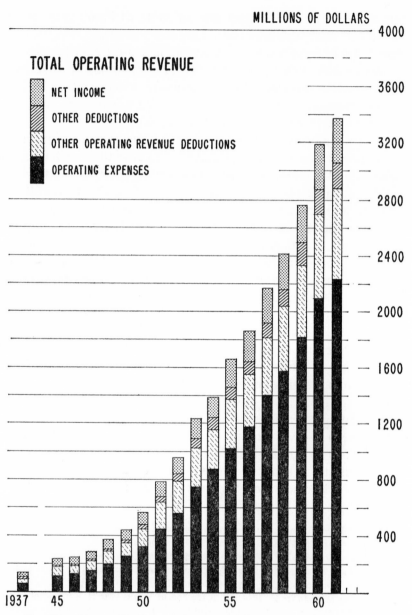

FIG. 24.—Composite Income Account of Gas Pipe-Line Companies.

This formula may be expressed as:
$$R = E + r(I-D) + d + T$$
where

R = total amount of money the gas company is entitled to receive from sales each year

E = annual operating expenses

r = annual rate of return, expressed as a percentage

I = original dollar investment in facilities

D = accumulated depreciation

d = depreciation for a given year

T = taxes for a given year

and $\dfrac{R}{\text{anticipated volume of sales}}$ = ¢/MCF rate to be charged for gas sold.

Operating expenses are spoken of as *variable charges*, while depreciation, return, and taxes are considered the *fixed charges* in pipeline accounting.[19] Under the cost-of-service formula, a pipe line's operating expenses and taxes are equal to the pipe line's obligations to others for these items and only depreciation and return are left to pay interest, meet debt amortizations, pay dividends, and plowback capital into the business.

A determination of a company's cost-of-service may be publicly made as often as the company requests it or when the regulatory agency orders an investigation. Such a determination is a rate-making process and is based upon estimates of all items in the cost-of-service formula. Obviously actual experience with operating expense and volumes sold may differ from the estimates used in making the rates and the gas companies may earn more or less than anticipated.[20] The maintenance of earnings is one of the primary challenges faced daily by people in the industry. Gas companies have the opportunity, but no guarantee, to earn the publicly assigned cost-of-service.

[19] In 1961 total fixed charges were usually estimated at about 14.4 per cent of total plant investment. Of this amount, 6.5 per cent represented return allowed on the depreciated plant investment, 3.5 per cent represented federal income tax on the return calculated at corporation rates after the deduction of interest (5 per cent interest on 65 per cent debt is assumed), 3.3 per cent represented depreciation, and 1.0 per cent represented ad valorem taxes.

[20] In practice the limitations of gas handling capacity in the gas company's pipe-line system will limit the possible increase in earnings, whereas there is no limit to the downside of reduced earnings.

THE VANISHING RATE BASE

A corollary problem to the determination of cost-of-service is that of the *vanishing rate base*. Under cost-of-service rates, pipe-line securities must be serviced out of depreciation and return on a depreciated rate base. Once a facility is fully depreciated (which occurs in about thirty years), there is no return or depreciation to the investor, and the pipe line is continued in service on a basis under which there is no profit to the operator. The vanishing rate base is not a serious problem to the gas industry at present because large additional investments are made in gas pipe lines each year. The problem will become serious if gas industry investment ceases to expand. At present there is one pipe line, between the fields of northeastern Louisiana and the markets of Saint Louis, Missouri, which is fully depreciated and on which no return is earned. It has been suggested that gas companies will be forced to become investment trusts with interests in many industries in order to protect gas company investors against the implications of depreciated rate base utility accounting.[21] The diversification programs featured in many pipe-line company annual reports are a manifestation of this answer to the vanishing rate base problem and represent the search for greater rates of return in higher-risk businesses not subject to utility-type controls.[22]

[21] Charles I. Francis, "Rate Regulation of the Natural Gas Companies by the Federal Power Commission," *Law and Contemporary Problems*, Vol. XIX, No. 3 (Summer, 1954), 413.

[22] "Diversification is the keynote of the future," says an overprint on the cover of the 1955 *Annual Report* of Tennessee Gas Transmission Company. Tennessee has made sizable petrochemical and oil industry investments. In 1958, 40 per cent of its gross income came from sources other than its gas business. El Paso also has entered the petrochemical field and engages in refining and producing oil and gas. Texas Eastern Transmission Corporation is a producer of oil and gas, and its Little Big Inch pipe line has been reconverted to a carrier of petroleum and LPG products with large underground liquid products storage facilities.

A smaller natural gas company, Arkansas Louisiana, which is primarily a distributor, has been quite active in diversification. In less than eight months of 1957, it added three subsidiaries to its operations. One manufactures natural gas air conditioning units in a plant formerly owned by Servel. Another is a large cement plant, and the third is a pipe-line construction firm.

It is the opinion of the large bondholders such as the life insurance companies that "there should be no objection (to these 'related' industries) so long as they can be engaged in within the confines of the indenture restrictions protecting our securities."

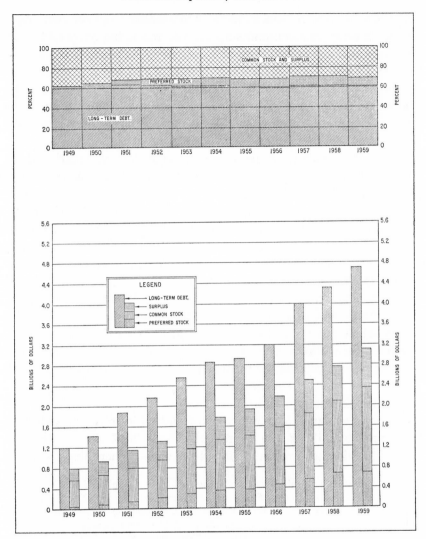

FIG. 25.—Capitalization of Natural Gas Companies, 1949–59.

RATE OF RETURN

In 1959 natural gas companies had total assets of $8,845,421,000 of which $4,707,661,000 (60.2 per cent of total capitalization and surplus) represented long-term debt, $696,337,000 (8.9 per cent) represented preferred stock, and $2,416,936,000 (30.9 per cent) represented common stock and surplus. The remaining $1,024,487,000 represented current liabilities and miscellaneous reserves. (See Figure 25.) These figures show a rapid increase over the 1945 total asset figure of $878,627,000, of which $319,514,000 (36.5 per cent of total capitalization and surplus) was represented by long-term debt. From the standpoint of assets the gas industry is the fifth largest in the United States of America.[23]

One billion dollars of gas company securities were marketed in 1959. The desirability of gas industry securities depends on a number of factors which include stability of income, outlook for future growth, and return on the investment.[24] The utility nature of the gas industry provides comparatively great security of income. The prospects for future growth will be discussed later. As described above, return depends upon standards used by public authorities in setting return in a rate proceeding and upon the ability of gas company management thereafter. Gas companies realized a return to 6.7 per cent in 1959. By way of comparison, five-year averages for the 1952–57 period show returns of 19.8 per cent for the aircraft industry, 15.6 per cent for the automotive industry, 11.3 per cent for the steel industry, 10 per cent as the median for twenty-five industry groups, 8.6 per cent for the retail trade, and 6.5 per cent for natural gas distributing companies.[25]

For the guidance of administrative authorities charged with setting rates of utilities, the Supreme Court of the United States has defined a fair rate of return as one which, among other things, will en-

[23] In connection with this and the following sections, see John F. Childs, *Long-term Financing;* Richard W. Hooley, *Financing the Natural Gas Industry: The Role of Life Insurance Investment Policies;* James C. Bonbright, *Principles of Public Utility Rates;* James W. Hargrove, "Money for the Man in the Middle," address before the American Association of Petroleum Landmen, Houston, Texas, 1961; Richard Austin Smith, "The Unnatural Problems of Natural Gas," *Fortune,* Vol. LX, No. 3 (September, 1959), 120, 261; and James W. Hargrove, "Characteristics and Problems of Interstate Natural Gas Transmission," in *Economics of the Gas Industry, q.v.,* I, 25.

[24] Edward P. Lebens, "Preferred Stock as a Medium for Gas Utility Company Financing," address before the General Management Section of the American Gas Association, Pittsburgh, Pennsylvania, 1960.

[25] Jerome C. Hunsaker, Jr., "The Institutional Investor Looks at the Gas Business," address before the General Management Section Conference of the American Gas Association, Pittsburgh, Pennsylvania, 1960.

able the utility "to attract the capital necessary for the proper discharge of its public duties."[26] The Court has also approved the Federal Power Commission's allowance of 6 per cent annual rate of return in the depreciated rate base.[27] As shown below, assuming a 75 per cent debt ratio and 3 per cent interest on bonds, the 6 per cent return on total capitalization is equal to a 12 per cent return on common stock, or equity.

Type Security	Per cent of Rate Base	Interest Rate	Per Cent
Bonds	75	3.0	3.0
Common Stock	25	12.0	3.0
TOTAL	100	6.0	6.0

The foregoing figures are representative of the 1938–1945 period when return was set by the FPC on the over-all basis at rates or 5.75 to 6.25 per cent. The 6 per cent rate was chosen by the Commission on the basis of its "judgment" and "experience," with the consequence that no quantitative measure of a "fair" rate of return was involved. In answer to pressure demanding that questions as fundamental as rate of return be decided by some better method than hunch, the Federal Power Commission adopted the *cost-of-money method* of determining rate of return in 1954.[28] Under this method the gas company is allowed its actual cost of debt financing plus a rate of return on the equity which the FPC considers adequate. For example, in a recent case[29] the return was set as follows:

[26] *Bluefield Waterworks and Improvement Company v. Public Service Commission of West Virginia*, 262 U.S. 679 (1923).

[27] *Natural Gas Pipeline Company of America v. Federal Power Commission*, 315 U.S. 575 (1942); *Federal Power Commission v. Hope Natural Gas Co.*, 320 U.S. 591 (1944). See the discussion of the Hope Gas case on page 278.

Also see Eli Winston Clemens, *Economics and Public Utilities*, 150–51, 227, 241; Emery Troxel, *Economics of Public Utilities*, 379–86; and Glaeser, *Public Utilities in American Capitalism*, 370, 389, 402.

[28] *In the Matter of Northern Natural Gas Company*, 11 FPC 123 (1952).

[29] *In the Matter of Panhandle Eastern Pipe Line Company*, 25 FPC 787 (1961), Opinion No. 344, issue April 27, 1961, in Docket Nos. G–1116 and G–2506. Those parts of Opinion 344 concerning rate of return follow:

The examiner concluded that the rate of return of 5¾ per cent was fair, reasonable and adequate for Panhandle and should be used in this proceeding. The determination of rate of return here has a rather involved history. In Opinion 269, issued April 15, 1954 [13 FPC 53], we determined that a 5¾ percent rate of return was proper for

Debt at Cost $60.7\% \times 2.90\% = 1.76\%$

Preferred Stock at Cost $6.7\% \times 4.02\% = .27\%$

Common Equity at
  Rate Set by FPC $32.6\% \times 11.41\% = 3.72\%$

Over-all Rate of Return
  (Calculated as shown above) 5.75%

Panhandle. We did not apply this rate of return to the well mouth properties, for we determined the allowances for Panhandle's produced gas on the basis of field prices. When the hearings in the present proceeding opened in October of 1954, Panhandle presented evidence and claimed a higher rate of return. Motions to dismiss were made at the hearing with respect to Panhandle's showing on rate of return and certain other matters. By order of December 13, 1954 [13 FPC 1570], we granted these motions finding that Panhandle had not shown any changed conditions to justify a rate of return above the 5¾ percent allowed in the prior proceeding, but attempted to reassert the theories previously rejected. Upon review by the Third Circuit Court of Appeals our order was affirmed. [*Panhandle Eastern Pipe Line Co.* v. *FPC*, 236 F. 2d 606 (C.A.S.)], and the court said that it was satisfied that the Commission's action was neither arbitrary nor unreasonable and was an entirely permissible exercise of the Commission's judgment.

As a result of this history we find in the present proceeding that the rate of return issue as applied to Panhandle's properties other than its well mouth properties has been settled. The examiner properly adopted 5¾ percent as the rate of return to be used. We may note that we are not applying this rate of return in the present or the future but to the January 1, 1955, to August 31, 1958, past period. If Panhandle, as this period elapsed, had found that 5¾ percent was not compensatory or fair and reasonable, it was, of course, entitled to make a further rate filing. As it was, it did not make an additional rate filing until its filing in Docket No. G-14755, effective September 1, 1958.

It is with respect to the proper rate of return on the well mouth properties that a further determination is necessary, for we are not employing a commodity allowance on Panhandle's own produced gas, but are including its well mouth properties in the rate base. For the purpose of making this determination we have available our findings in Docket No. G-1116 which we have already used in this proceeding with respect to a rate of return on properties other than production. We have a rate of return study presented by Panhandle in the present proceeding and the staff rate of return study and other studies presented in Docket No. G-1116 and incorporated by reference into the record here. We also have the evidence in the present proceeding with respect to Panhandle's financial needs for exploration and development.

In Opinion No. 269, in arriving at the 5¾ per cent return we said that the 5¾ per cent rate was sufficiently high to take care of the shortcomings of earnings-price ratios affected by ownership of natural gas reserves as well as contingencies [13 FPC at p. 100]. In other words, we indicated that the ownership of natural gas reserves tended to depress earnings-price ratios because investors preferred to invest in companies with their own reserves. In fact, the record in the Docket No. G–1116 case showed that those companies with substantial gas reserves had lower earnings-price ratios than those companies with none. Therefore, apart from any necessary incentives, if 5¾ percent is a fair return for Panhandle in this past period on its pipeline investment, it is an ample return on its well mouth properties.

We think, however, that this takes a too narrow and somewhat unfair view of the situation. We are, in effect, providing for rates on the basis of an October 31, 1954,

120

Unfortunately the cost-of-money method is also not quantitative, since there is no definitive standard for proper equity earnings. In fact the rate of return assigned to equity in the above calculation can even be arrived at by working backward from an assumed over-all rate of return of 5.75 per cent. In general the cost-of-money method has depressed over-all return to natural gas companies. Today, using the cost-of-money method, the FPC allows over-all rates of return to

test year for a period which would represent the indefinite future if we had been able to complete the whole proceeding in that year. This "future" is, of course, terminated on August 31, 1958, by the filing of new rates, but nevertheless we must look to the refund period from the standpoint of the test year and the record. We have already found that Panhandle's evidence as to their hypothetical exploration and development program during the refund period is an insufficient basis for using the commodity value of the gas. Nevertheless the record shows that Panhandle had a continuing need for additional gas reserves and did actually undertake certain exploration and development during the years after the test year. The record shows that for actual capital expenditures, including non-productive gas well drilling for developing its owned reserves Panhandle spent $2,910,477 in 1955, $5,058,202 in 1956, $2,828,560 in 1957 and $2,649,911 for the first eight months of 1958. The testimony shows that while Panhandle has large reserves in the West Panhandle Field of Texas and the Hugoton Field of Kansas, Oklahoma and Texas, the production rate from these fields cannot be maintained indefinitely, and Panhandle must develop additional reserves. Not considering the testimony as to hypothetical expansion plans said to be necessary to enable Panhandle to maintain production, it would seem that some incentive was appropriate in addition to the usual rate of return. In the *Phillips* case [*Phillips Petroleum Co., supra.*] we added two percentage points to the 10 per cent allowance for common equity in order to provide this incentive. In our judgment some addition would be reasonable here.

Our allowance of a 5¾ percent rate of return that has been adopted here from the Docket G-1116 proceeding was stated by us in that case to represent an allowance of 11.41 percent on common euity. The computation would be as follows in accordance with our Opinion No. 269 (13 FPC at p. 100):

Debt	60.7%*	×	2.90%	=	1.76%
Preferred Stock	6.7%	×	4.02%	=	.27%
Common equity	32.6%	×	11.41%	=	3.72%
					5.75%

This column represents the capitalization as of December 21, 1952, as shown in Panhandle's annual report for 1952. The Commission's Opinion (13 FPC at p. 100) leaves the column blank.

As an additional incentive we think that the allowance for common equity with respect to the well mouth properties should be 12 per cent as a matter of judgment. This would actually represent a greater increase than the difference between 11.41 and 12 percent because those companies with substantial reserves of their own were shown in the G-1116 record to have earnings-price ratios lower than the purely pipeline companies. Thus, apart from incentive, they would be granted a lower allowance for common equity than the 11.41 percent which we determined as applicable to Panhandle's properties other than well mouth. Since we are recomputing the rate of return for the well mouth properties, we should note in accordance with our Opinion No. 342 in *Northern Natural Gas Co.,* ——— FPC ———, Docket No. G-19040, issued March 7, 1961, the fact that Panhandle, as of December 31, 1952, had an accumulation

natural gas companies ranging from 5.75 to 6.25 per cent per year, depending upon such factors as per cent of capitalization represented by debt, interest rate on bonds, and amount of higher risk producing (well-mouth) properties involved.

The foregoing calculations illustrate the *leverage* by which equity return may be greater than 10 per cent under a so-called 6 per cent rate of return. The greater the percentage of debt to common stock, the greater the leverage and the greater the return to common stock. At the same time, the greater the *debt ratio,* the greater the risk to the common stock owners in that, if the enterprise cannot meet its fixed obligation, there is a greater risk of losing the common equity. Therefore the value of natural gas company common stock as a security depends upon the relationship between interest rates and the over-all rate of return. The upward trend in interest rates of the 1950–1960 decade (see Figure 26) means that over-all return to natural gas companies must be increased if the securities necessary for an expanding gas industry are to be marketed.[30]

The rapidly increasing cost of senior capital by all borrowers including the pipe-line industry obviously can result in a serious squeeze on the common stock equity component of the capitalization and can produce *reverse leverage* unless the FPC allows a compensatory increase in the over-all rate of return. Note that in 1956 a natural gas company preferred stock issue was sold at a money cost of 6.03 per cent to the company, which exceeded the 6 per cent rate of return cur-

---

of deferred taxes in the amount of $1,051,718. However, the effect of this factor here is de minimis with respect to rate of return. The rate of return on Panhandle's well mouth properties would be computed as follows:

Debt	60.35% $\times$	2.90% $=$	1.75%
Accumulated deferred taxes	.54% $\times$	1.50% $=$	.01%
Preferred stock	6.67% $\times$	4.02% $=$	.27%
Common equity	32.44% $\times$	12.0% $=$	3.89%
			5.92%

Rounding off, we think that 6 per cent is a reasonable rate of return on Panhandle's well mouth properties.

[30] See Hargrove, "Money for the Man in the Middle"; James N. Land, Sr., "Future Trends of Interest Rates and Their Significance for the Gas Industry," address before the General Management Section Conference of the American Gas Association, Pittsburgh, Pennsylvania, 1960; Paul G. La Grone, "Financing the Expansion Program of the Natural Gas Transmission Industry," *Public Utilities Fortnightly,* Vol. LXVI, No. 8 (October 13, 1960), 535–49; Paul G. La Grone, "Accounting for Gas Line Expansion Project," *Public Utilities Fortnightly,* Vol. LXVII, No. 3 (February 2, 1961), 158–73.

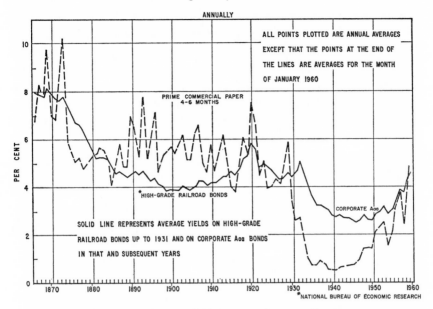

FIG. 26.—Long- and Short-term Interest Rates.

rently allowed. Reflecting these circumstances, a number of pipe-line companies have applied for rates of return of 7 per cent.[31]

CAPITAL STRUCTURE

Figure 25 shows 60 per cent of the capitalization of natural gas companies is in the form of debt (bonds and debentures). By condi-

[31] In its November, 1959, issue *Gas* magazine reports an "important plea" the FPC was then hearing. "Francis H. Crissman, Vice President for the Columbia Gas System," writes the journal, "recently told FPC that rising interest rates, insufficient return, and delay in settling rate cases threaten to block future construction needed to meet grow-ing consumer demand. The hearings involved a Columbia subsidiary which has compro-mised for a 6.5 percent return instead of the 6.75 percent asked. FPC in 1953 set 6.25 percent for the Columbia group. Mr. Crissman said the 1953 figure is no longer ade-quate nor is the 6.5. He showed that Columbia must have almost 7 percent to do noth-ing more than meeting earnings requirements of the Indenture for 1959–63."

Also Tennessee Gas Transmission Company and its subsidiaries have introduced tes-timony before the Federal Power Commission in support of a 7 per cent return. In fact, Board Chairman Gardiner Symonds of Tennessee Gas Transmission Company has been quoted to the effect that Tennessee Gas is unwilling to proceed with more construction unless given firm indications that a higher rate of return will be allowed.

In Docket No. G-19983 certificate proceedings of Tennessee Gas Transmission, L. Emery Katzenbach, II, general manager of White, Weld and Company, an investment brokerage firm specializing in financing of gas transmission companies, testified, in Feb-

tioning certificates of public convenience and necessity under which new gas facilities are placed into operation, the FPC has maintained an upper limit of 75 per cent debt.[32] In the electric utility field the debt ratio is 50 per cent. In comparing the natural gas and electric financing patterns, four differences can be noted. Natural gas company bond and debenture issues are amortized, through relatively high payments by the natural gas company to a sinking fund, in a comparatively short time (ranging from 12 to 20 years). Natural gas companies receive no sinking fund credit for property additions. The indentures covering natural gas company debt provide for annual determinations of dedicated gas reserves and for an acceleration of sinking fund requirements in case of a less than specified reserve life. Natural gas transmission companies do business under firm long-term (20 years) supply and sales contracts. The supply contracts provide for annual reserve determinations and an adjustment in the volume of

ruary, 1960, that the rates of return at that time did not enable, as the Supreme Court laid down in its decision in the Hope case, "the industry to attract capital necessary for the purpose of discharging its public duties." Mr. Katzenbach introduced evidence to show that the private electric utility industry of the United States had earned just under 11 per cent on the common stock equity. This contrasts with recent FPC decisions allowing only 10 per cent on the common stock investment of gas transmission companies whose business is more speculative than the electricity business, as reflected in the fact that buyers insist on a higher rate of return for senior securities of the gas transmission company and a substantially higher sinking fund.

In its decisions, the FPC has not discussed current interest rates, stating, instead, its opinion that "a consideration of the whole matter leads to the conclusion that a rate of return of 10% on the common stock is fair and equitable."

It should be pointed out that in Canada utilities have always been allowed 7 per cent or more because interest rates have traditionally been higher there than in the United States. This was recognized by statute and by the gas purchase contracts of the Trans-Canada Pipe Line Company which contain provisions whereby the rates to the pipe-line company may be adjusted upward in the event that the company is earning more than 7 per cent.

On the other hand, see William R. Connole, "Rate of Return—The Utilities' Most Tilted Windmill," *Public Utilities Fortnightly,* Vol. LXIV, No. 8 (October 8, 1959), 594–600. Mr. Connole, a former member of the Federal Power Commission, writes that "neither reckless tilting of the windmill of the rate of return nor tilting of rate components provides the answer. Rather it will be found in careful examination of cost allocation methods, sensible use of pricing principles once costs are determined, and a reasonable restrained policy of producer pricing."

[32] See, for example, the certificate of public convenience and necessity issued by the Federal Power Commission to the new line to California. *In the Matter of Transwestern Pipeline Company,* 22 FPC 391 (1959). See also Hargrove, "Characteristics and Problems of Interstate Natural Gas Transmission," *Economics of the Gas Industry,* I, 255.

gas to be delivered which will maintain the twenty-year life of the reserve. The sales contracts also contain a twenty-year term and provide for the purchase of minimum quantities of gas each year.

The discussion above points out the importance of a higher debt ratio to the common stock owner. At the same time higher debt ratios are advantageous to the consumer in that such a ratio produces a lower price of gas to the consumer and provides the return necessary to encourage expansion of the gas industry to provide the added amounts of gas the consumer needs. If all-equity financing is assumed, the consumer would have to pay a fourfold increase in the 6 per cent return (12 per cent return and 12 per cent income taxes on return) in order to provide the necessary 12 per cent return after taxes to the purchaser of gas company common stock.[33]

The rapid amortization feature and other safeguards plus the excellent past performance of the industry have made natural gas company debt an attractive security. On September 30, 1950, United States life insurance companies held $1,150,000,000 of natural gas pipe-line securities ($1,130,000,000 in bonds and $20,000,000 in stocks), as compared with holdings of $175,000,000 of such securities in 1945 ($170,000,000 in bonds and $5,000,000 in stocks).[34] The insurance companies, with large amounts of money to be invested each year,[35] consider an investment proper if it provides safety of principal, maximum return commensurate with safety, and an investment in the public interest. Natural gas company debt securities meet all these requirements in that even with higher debt ratios, the more rapid amortization and other safeguards provide safety of principal, a comparatively attractive rate of return, and an opportunity to provide natural gas for public use. In addition pipe-line companies have proved to be well managed in that sales have been increased, reserves replenished, and earnings maintained.

Table 9 sets forth pertinent financial data on nine representative natural gas transmission companies.

[33] Hargrove, "Money for the Man in the Middle."

[34] On the basis of a private communication to the authors, it is estimated that Metropolitan Life Insurance Company, the largest in the world, held $664,908,000 in natural gas securities at the end of 1955 and over $900,000,000 worth at the end of 1956.

[35] Robert Sheehan, "Life Insurance's Eighty-four Billion Dollar Dilemma," *Fortune*, Vol. LI, No. 2 (February, 1955), 112. According to this article, 880 life insurance companies had ten billion dollars available for investment in 1954 and eight billion dollars available in 1959.

TABLE 9

Comparison of Nine Gas Transmission Companies
(May 23, 1961)

	Colorado Interstate Gas Company	El Paso Natural Gas (Consolidated)	Northern Natural Gas (Consolidated)
Capitalization including bank loans, Dec. 31, 1960 (Dollars)	137,895,849.00	1,384,661,413.00	479,296,465.0
Per cent of Debt	58.40	69.60	55.1
Per cent of Preferred	16.10	9.80	12.6
Per cent of Minority Interest		.50	
Per cent Common and Surplus	25.50	20.10	32.3
Number of Common Shares, Dec. 31, 1960	2,472,198	22,746,018	8,544,655
Common Stock Equity, per Share, Dec. 31, 1960 (Dollars)	14.23	12.25	18.1
Net Income Available per Common Share during			
the Year Ended Dec. 31, 1960 (Dollars)	1.96	1.92	2.2
Increase in Revenues 1950–60 (Per cent)	278.00†	1121.80	470.0
Increase in Net Income 1950–60 (Per cent)	124.10†	705.30	280.7
Indicated Current Annual Common Stock Dividend (Dollars)	1.25	1.30	1.4
Estimated Owned and Controlled Gas Reserves, Dec. 31, 1960			
(Billion Cu. Ft.)	7,500.00§	37,700.00§	12,700.0
Gas in MMCF Sold in 1960	298,086	1,270,779	463,245
Estimated Gas Reserves Times MMCF Sold, 1960	25.20	29.70	27.4
Market Price Common Stock (Dollars)	41.50	27.38	41.5
Ratios			
Market Times Estimated 1960 Net per Common Share	21.2	14.3	18.9
Yield on Indicated Annual Dividend	3.0	4.8	3.4
Per cent Indicated Dividend of 1960 Net Income	63.7	67.7	63.6
Market Times Equity per Common Share	2.9	2.3	2.3

Panhandle Eastern Pipe Line	Southern Natural Gas	Tennessee Gas Transmission	Texas Eastern Transmission (Consolidated)	Texas Gas Transmission (Consolidated)	Transcontinental Gas Pipeline
64,004,597.00	266,861,391.00	1,478,807,588.00	795,342,832.00	226,280,765.00	570,050,594.00
53.40	62.60	58.60	64.90	62.60	65.70
3.40		11.60	14.40	12.60	13.80
	.30				
43.20	37.10	29.80	20.70	24.80	20.50
6,765,920	4,965,881	39,368,354	18,210,038*	2,958,582	12,762,983
16.83	20.28	11.21	9.04*	18.95	9.17
3.05	2.28	1.35	1.03*	2.59	1.18
167.60‡	382.70	940.10	328.50	331.80	335.70‡
99.60‡	111.70	386.00	190.80	112.10	227.60‡
1.80	2.00	1.12	0.80*	1.50	1.00
14,000.00§	6,750.00§	18,000.00§	13,808.00§	6,951.00§	9,100.00§
409,639	369,251	894,164	663,218	402,645	414,314
34.20	18.30	20.10	20.80	17.30	21.90
44.50	46.75	23.88	19.25	35.25	23.63
14.6	20.5	17.7	18.7	13.6	20.0
4.0	4.3	4.7	4.2	4.3	4.2
59.0	87.7	83.0	77.7	57.9	84.7
2.6	2.3	2.1	2.1	1.9	2.6

* Adjusted for 2 for 1 stock split, May 5, 1961.
† Increase is from 1952.

‡ Increase is from 1951.
§ Estimated by company.

5

A GLANCE AT
NATURAL GAS COMPANIES

by Alfred M. Leeston

SINCE 1955, the number of residential natural gas customers has increased from 20 million to 34 million. "In just seven years, during a period when most of the postwar boom has leveled off in other areas of our economy, natural gas went ahead to increase by 70 per cent. . . . I forecast gas will hold its share of the total national energy market well into the 1980's if not beyond that," commented Clarence Unnevsher chief of the Federal Power Commission's Bureau of Natural Gas.[1] The 1962 edition of *Gas Facts*,[2] the voluminous statistical record of the gas utility industry, reports that the net production of natural gas reached 13.5 trillion feet in 1961 and that proved recoverable reserves attained a peak of 267.7 trillion cubic feet at the end of that year. Natural gas consumption in 1961 represented 29.3 per cent of the total energy consumption in the United States.

In addition to remarkable growth and expansion in markets and gas consumption, the natural gas industry can point to noteworthy accomplishments in the field of natural resource conservation over the ten-year period which began in 1952. The ultimate capacity of underground storage fields reached 3,121 billion cubic feet in 1961, an increase of 1,829 billion cubic feet over the 1952 figure, 1,292 billion cubic feet. Additional storage facilities now permit more complete year-round utilization of pipe-line capacities and make distributing-company sales to house-heating customers easier. Thus, by increasing underground storage capacity, natural gas companies have reduced waste. This achievement in conservation was accomplished entirely

[1] As quoted in an Associated Press dispatch by Max B. Skelton and carried in the *Dallas Morning News* on Sunday, September 2, 1962.

[2] *Gas Facts* is published annually by the American Gas Association. The reference here is to *1961 Gas Facts,* 1.

through private financing on the part of the natural gas industry—especially the transmission phase of it—and the existence and effectiveness of private effort seems to be a decisive difference between the United States natural gas industry and that of foreign countries.

The following brief discussion of some outstanding natural gas companies shows strikingly the enormous development that has taken place in the natural gas industry and has aptly been called "one of the major industrial phenomena of our age."[3] For the purposes of this discussion, the companies are divided into three broad categories: integrated companies, pipe-line companies, and others. Writes Dero A. Saunders, senior editor of *Forbes* magazine, "The distinction I prefer is between pipe lines on one hand, and integrated and distributing companies on the other. Pipe lines may be defined as primarily transporters of natural gas, either from their owned supplies or from reserves leased from other producers. Integrated and distributing companies are those that gain most of their revenues from sales to the ultimate user, be he industrial or residential. To the extent that they also have gas supplies (either owned or leased) and transport their own requirements, they would classify as integrated; but they are in any event retail distributors."

SOME INTEGRATED COMPANIES

United Gas Corporation

We begin our brief survey of natural gas companies with United Gas Corporation, Shreveport, Louisiana. United Gas is particularly interesting for several reasons. It holds the largest supply position of any individual company, has the largest volume of sales, and is "the world's largest handler of gas."[4] Its promotion of industrial activities within its sales region, the "Gulf South," is one of the most rapidly progressing economic developments in the country. The personality

[3] Clemens, *Economics and Public Utilities*, 303.

See Figure 31 on page 273. This is a map showing the location of the pipe-line systems described in this chapter. Also see Table 9 for a summary of the data pertaining to nine natural gas transmission companies.

[4] These words were spoken by Mr. McGowen in an address about the history of the natural gas industry and the development and growth of the United Gas Corporation which he delivered in New Orleans on December 13, 1951. The address was published by the Newcomen Society in North America in 1951 under the title "Natural Gas, the Gulf South's Symbol of Progress."

129

of its builder, Norris Cochran McGowen, "long recognized as one of the outstanding leaders in the natural gas industry,"[5] commands attention, and "United's is a story of high importance to the economy of the South and the Southwest."[6]

The company emerged from five major groups as the nucleus of more than forty associated companies which all were welded into United Gas in 1930. By the end of 1937 it became essentially the same as it is now, with only minor subsequent consolidations and changes. The era of the holding companies in the utility business was over. Reminiscent of this period are the company's diversifications. Electric Bond and Share Company owns 50 per cent of Escambia Chemical Corporation, one of the diversified interests of United Gas. Escambia is a petrochemical company with a three-plant chemical operation in Pensacola, Florida, and a modern research laboratory at Wilson, Connecticut. United Gas holds 75 per cent interest in Duval Sulphur and Potash Company which mines sulphur, potash, and copper. It also owns about one-third of Atlas Processing Company in Shreveport, Louisiana, which upgrades raw gasoline received from plants in East Texas and northwestern Louisiana.

Earlier than most companies, United entered into considerable gas production of its own, acquiring acreage with productive possibilities. Exploration and production were carried out by Union Producing Company, a subsidiary of the huge concern. This subsidiary company produced 18 per cent of the total gas requirement in 1958 and 16 per cent of the sales which United Gas Pipe Line Company, the transmission company of United Gas, made in the same year.

United's long-term debt of 57 per cent is moderate in comparison with that of other gas companies. Its reserves-in-place, both owned and under purchase contracts, were estimated by its geologists at 36.8 trillion cubic feet of which the company calculates 28.9 trillion to be recoverable. This is over 11 per cent of the United States total, 254 trillion cubic feet, at the end of 1958. The improvement in reserves under contract during 1958 amounted to a net increase of 1.9 trillion. These figures demonstrate the sound reserves policy of United Gas which gives it an estimated twenty-one-year supply. The company has

[5] This statement was made by the Newcomen Society of North America in its introduction to "Natural Gas, the Gulf South's Symbol of Progress."

[6] McGowen, "Natural Gas, the Gulf South's Symbol of Progress."

consistently maintained one of the strongest gas supply positions in the industry owing to its extensive gathering lines and its development activities.

A most interesting activity of United Gas is its forest improvement program. This program is concentrated in northeastern Louisiana on fee lands and more than pays for itself in the sale of wood and in the improvement and increase of forest reserves. It is also an ideal soil conservation project which controls erosion. But the main business is selling gas which is transported by United Gas Pipeline Company. Sales are made to the distribution division of United Gas, other distribution systems and pipe-line companies, power plants, and a wide range of industries in Texas, Louisiana, Mississippi, Alabama, and Florida. The pipe line purchases all of its natural gas requirements from the Union Producing Company and from other producers in 409 fields.

The United Gas system serves major portions of Texas, Louisiana, and Mississippi, and extends to Mobile in southern Alabama, to Pensacola in northwestern Florida, and to the international boundary at Laredo, Texas. "This is the area termed (by United Gas) the 'Gulf South,' a great and growing industrial empire, an area which has unbounded opportunities for continued growth." . . . "United Gas customers include great brick and tile companies, cement and lime producers, chemical plants, gas plants, oil refineries, power plants, pulp and paper mills, sugar refineries, synthetic rubber plants, and a host of other manufacturing enterprises."[7]

In 1958 gas sales reached a total of 1.3 trillion cubic feet, which may be compared with 1931 sales of 154.7 billion cubic feet. No other gas company sells this amount. At the same time, the average price per MCF for natural gas purchases increased between 1931 and 1958 from an all-time low price of 3.14¢/MCF in 1943 to 13.40¢/MCF in 1958.[8] Both production and purchases of natural gas continued at a high rate, further strengthening the supply position of United Gas.

Industrial purchases comprise the bulk of its natural gas sales (673,300,000,000 cubic feet including power plant fuel in 1958) and provide a revenue of $123,000,000. These industrial sales are not subject to direct regulation and are one important factor in United's

[7] This material was gleaned from several annual reports of the United Gas Corporation.
[8] See the financial data of United Gas covering the years 1930–58.

strong returns. "In the aggregate, it is United among the integrated gas companies these last five years that has top showing under the careful hand of Norris Cochran McGowen. Thanks to its well-planned diversification and the large proportion of non-regulated gas sales that go to industrial users, United boasts the heftiest return on book value in the group."[9]

The man who led United Gas during its years of growth is its former president and present chairman of the board, Mr. McGowen. A native of Chicago, he came to Shreveport as a young man to audit the books of the oil and gas properties owned by the Potter Palmer interests of Chicago. Like the man who came to dinner, he stayed and literally grew up with the oil and gas industry in Louisiana. He advanced to the post of vice-president and general manager of the Palmer properties, and, when the Palmer Natural gas holdings were consolidated with those of Electric Power and Light Corporation, Magnolia, Moody, Seagraves, and others in 1930, Mr. McGowen was made president of United's operating subsidiaries. He was in charge of all the operations of the largest natural gas system in the world. He was elected president of United Gas Corporation in 1944.

One of the most important positions he occupied was that of chairman of American Gas Association's Committee on Natural Gas Reserves. The annual reserves estimate made by that committee is one of the most widely circulated reports of its type made by any industry. In 1958, he was succeeded in this office by the current president of United Gas, Ed Parkes. Mr. Parkes is a highly experienced gas executive who, in 1928, joined a company which later became a part of the United Gas system. Mr. McGowen became chairman of the board of United Gas in 1958. His career has helped to establish the high reputation the natural gas industry enjoys on analysis-minded Wall Street today.

American Natural Gas Company

American Natural Gas Company, serving the Wisconsin-Michigan area, is located in New York on Broadway near Wall Street as is Panhandle Eastern. A holding company, American Natural Gas was organized in 1901. Through wholly-owned subsidiaries it operates an interconnected natural gas system. The principal subsidiaries

[9] *Forbes*, Vol. LXXXIII, No. 1 (January 1, 1959), 112. This issue was *Forbes'* Eleventh Annual Report on American Industry.

are two natural gas distributors, Michigan Consolidated Gas Company and Milwaukee Gas Light Company and two operators of interstate gas transmission lines, Michigan Wisconsin Pipe Line Company and American Louisiana Pipe Line Company.

Approximately 80 per cent of the sales of the pipe-line companies are made to the system's two distributing subsidiaries. These two companies have served the public for more than a century. They presently provide gas service for about 1,133,000 customers in important areas in Michigan and Wisconsin, including the highly industrialized cities of Detroit and Milwaukee. The two transmission companies, one of which was completed in 1949 and the other in 1956, operate extensive pipe-line facilities. At present these lines are transporting about 300 billion cubic feet of natural gas annually from producing areas in Texas, Oklahoma, Kansas, and Louisiana to northern markets. Other subsidiaries of the company are American Natural Gas Production Company, organized late in 1957 to engage in exploration for and acquisition and development of gas reserves; Milwaukee Solvay Coke Company, engaged in the manufacture and sale of coke and by-products; and American Natural Gas Service Company, which furnishes services at cost to system companies.

In 1959 the Michigan Wisconsin subsidiary completed construction of pipe lines to the Laverne Field in Oklahoma which increased deliveries from that supply to 80 million cubic feet a day. At the end of that year, Michigan Wisconsin filed an application with the FPC to construct facilities to take an additional 100 million cubic feet of gas a day from this field and the adjacent area. It is expected that additional volumes of gas will become available as development continues in this prolific region. The recent authorization for Trans-Canada Pipelines by the Canadian Government to export 204 million cubic feet daily will benefit Michigan Wisconsin which will receive 158 million cubic feet daily at a point near Marshfield, in central Wisconsin. Michigan Wisconsin also reached an agreement with Northern Natural Gas Company late in 1959 for the purchase of 75 million cubic feet of natural gas a day to be delivered by Northern Natural at a point on Michigan Wisconsin's system near Janesville, Wisconsin.

Michigan Consolidated alone added 41,000 heating customers, and about 70 per cent of all homes served now use gas for heating. Similar results have been attained by the Milwaukee Gas Light Company. The financial position of the concern, which enjoys a highly capable management headed by President Ralph T. McElvenny, is strong, and the debt ratio was 60.5 per cent in 1959. Through its subsidiary, American Louisiana Gas Pipeline Company, the American Natural system controls a large-diameter pipe line between its sales area and the prolific gas-producing area of southern Louisiana.

The system owns and operates extensive underground storage fields in west-central Michigan. These fields have a normal working storage capacity of about 110 billion cubic feet. They permit the system's pipe-line companies to operate at a very high load factor throughout the year and are vital in keeping the cost of gas comparable to that of other fuels. Underground storage reserves enable the system to handle the tremendous variations in daily and seasonal requirements caused by the severe winters, and additional facilities can be developed as needed.

The Columbia Gas System, Incorporated

One of the most famous utility corporations with a dramatic history is the gigantic Columbia Gas System. Columbia played a great role in the 1920's when holding companies were the fashion of the day. When the death knell—the death sentence clause of the Public Utility Holding Company Act of 1935—was sounded, the Columbia System was one which survived.[10] Under the expert management of Charles S. Young[11] and its late chairman, Stuart M. Crocker, Columbia worked hard and successfully to consolidate its operations and simplify its organization. The number of subsidiaries has been cut from sixteen in 1943 to eight in 1956, and further organizing steps are planned. *Forbes* points out that the stockholders of the system fared very well because of a generous dividend policy which gave them the highest pay out, 93.6 per cent.[12]

Serving a thickly populated area of high industrial activity such as

[10] Ralph K. Huitt, "Natural Gas Regulation Under the Holding Company Act," *Law and Contemporary Problems*, Vol. XVIIII, No. 3 (Summer, 1954), 455–73.

[11] In May, 1960, Mr. Young was named chairman and chief executive officer, and Cecil E. Loomis was appointed president.

[12] Columbia Gas publishes annually a report of financial and statistical operating data which is most interesting. Columbia Gas took its present name on April 30, 1948. Its original name was Columbia Gas and Electric Corporation, and it was founded under this name on September 30, 1926.

Ohio, Pennsylvania, Kentucky, New York, West Virginia, Virginia, and Maryland, Columbia Gas sold 735.9 billion cubic feet in 1959 through its well-known operating subsidiaries like United Gas Fuel, Atlantic Seaboard, Ohio Fuel Gas, Manufacturer's Light and Heat (Pittsburgh), and many others, despite the adverse effects of the steel strike. Residential and commercial sales increased 2.1 billion cubic feet; industrial and other retail sales, 23.4 billion cubic feet; and sales at wholesale rates to other distributors for resale by them, 11.1 billion cubic feet. The system's operations are located in an area which is particularly favorable to industrial development because of the availability of transportation, raw materials, and labor supply. Therefore, industrial sales, which are affected by industrial expansion and development, will increase at a somewhat faster rate than sales for residential purposes, which depend on population growth. Columbia now serves more than 2,500 industrial customers in a great variety of lines. Increasing amounts of gas are also sold for use in chemical plants both as a fuel and as a raw material.

At the close of 1959, Columbia Gas System had more than forty rate cases pending. Most of these were before the FPC for increases in wholesale rates. The others were before state commissions. A Columbia subsidiary, the Manufacturer's Light and Heat Company, was recently awarded a 6.5 per cent return on investment by the FPC.

On December 30, 1958, Columbia acquired a pipe line which runs from the gas-producing area in southern Louisiana to eastern Kentucky. This pipe line is now owned and operated by Columbia Gulf Transmission Company and constitutes an additional source of the system's gas supply from the Southwest. The system's proven reserves, including those held under leasehold or by fee title as well as those under contract, total 14.7 trillion cubic feet, and in 1961 Columbia entered into contracts covering the purchase of over six trillion cubic feet of gas to be produced from fields located on the King Ranch of Texas.

Columbia Gas has been a pioneer in underground storage. The Appalachian region which Columbia serves is richly endowed with geological formations that are able to hold vast quantities of natural gas. Many of these formations are producing fields. Others now act as huge warehouses in which gas, pumped from the Southwest, is stored in summer for winter use. Over 60 per cent of all underground storage gas in the country is in the Appalachian area. Columbia Gas System operates forty-two other gas storage fields, some of which have more than one reservoir. On November 1, 1957, Columbia had 368 billion cubic feet of gas—one-fourth of the nation's total gas in storage—stored in these fields. They are able to deliver 2.3 billion cubic feet of gas, or 51 per cent of the gas available, on the winter's peak day. Through underground storage, gas customers in this area enjoy both economy of operation and availability of supply with the result that families here use more gas than in any comparable section of the country. The Appalachian gas supply is particularly important because it is near system markets and affords a high degree of control, and the search for large gas reserves at deep horizons in the Appalachian area, below the known producing zones, continues to attract wide-spread interest.

Below are some figures showing the progress Columbia Gas System made between 1950 and 1959:

COLUMBIA GAS SYSTEM COMPARATIVE STATISTICS 1950–59

	1950	1959
Customers:		
Residential and Commercial	1,110,459	1,428,045
Industrial	2,102	2,567
Wholesale	87	115
All Others	5,816	8,208
TOTAL	1,118,464	1,438,935
Gross Plant Additions (Thousands of dollars)	35,833	94,345
Gas Revenues (Thousands of dollars)		
Residential and Commercial	78,813	212,396
Industrial	32,598	89,068
Wholesale	35,096	153,953
All Other	3,872	9,930
TOTAL	150,379	455,347
Net Income (Thousands of dollars)	17,427	40,377
Average Annual Revenue per Residential Customer (Dollars)	67.32	136.88

Cost of Gas Purchased (Cents per 1,000 cu. ft.)

Appalachian	19.46	25.39
Southwest*	21.67	35.39

Sales (Million cu. ft.)

Residential and Commercial	139,164	258,074
Industrial	88,818	157,454
Wholesale	111,245	308,894
All Other	4,486	11,503
TOTAL	343,713	735,925

Peak Day Sendout (Million cu. ft.)	2,231	4,772

Sources of Gas (Million cu. ft.)

Purchased—Appalachian	68,885	76,140
" —Southwest	250,201	653,279
" —Manufactured	3,637	——
Produced—Natural	67,159	64,957
" —Propane	239	65
" —Manufactured	6	——
TOTAL	390,127	794,441

Gas in Underground Storage (Million cu. ft.)†

Stored During Year	64,370	175,265
Withdrawn During Year	51,254	145,183
In Storage at Year's End	106,338	384,423

Average Annual Consumption per

Residential Customer (Thousand cu. ft.)	117.1	163.1

Gas Acreage‡

Operated	1,425,208	1,535,491
Reserve	2,177,555	2,579,326
TOTAL	3,602,763	4,114,817

Producing Gas Wells§	9,718	9,973
Producing Oil Wells	1,512	1,408

* Includes cost of transporting gas purchased in the Southwest.

† Does not include native cushion gas.

‡ Includes acreage in which both oil and gas rights are held.

§ Includes wells used for underground storage.

Consolidated Natural Gas Company

This is another large integrated system located in New York. Consolidated simplified its organization under the Public Utility Holding Company Act of 1935. Originally owned by Standard Oil of New Jersey, Consolidated, which is called "a paragon of conservatism" by *Forbes*, has five wholly-owned subsidiaries, which it acquired in 1943: Hope Natural Gas Company, founded in 1898 and well-known through the history-making Hope Natural Gas Case decided by the Unitel States Supreme Court; the East Ohio Gas Company, the system's largest distribution company serving Toledo, Youngstown, Akron, Canton, and other Ohio cities; the seventy-five-year-old Peoples Natural Gas Company; the River Gas Company, established in southeastern Ohio in 1894; and New York State Natural Gas Corporation, founded in 1913 and currently supplying New York and Pennsylvania gas companies. New York State has the largest underground gas storage operation of the concern. In 1957, Consolidated acquired a sixth company, the Lake Shore Pipe Line Company, which purchases gas from Tennessee Gas in Pennsylvania and transports it to Ohio for sale to the East Ohio Gas Company and to a large industrial customer. The distribution company subsidiaries have served the public more than sixty years.

The primary business of Consolidated is the retail distribution of natural gas, and it also sells large volumes of gas at wholesale prices to thirty-four nonaffiliated gas companies. The system engages in all phases of the natural gas business, including production, transmission, and storage of natural gas and the extraction and sale of by-products.

The Columbia Gas System serves residential, commercial, and industrial customers in 807 cities and towns in Ohio, Pennsylvania, and West Virginia. The retail service area is highly industrialized and includes Cleveland and Pittsburgh. Wholesale customers who buy some or all of their gas from the system serve 345 communities in New York, Pennsylvania, and West Virginia. The availability of large gas supplies from the Southwest and the extensive development of underground storage fields in the system's market area have made it possible to meet the new demands created by increasing use of gas for house-heating and industrial purposes.

Almost three-fourths of the total gas supply is purchased from pipe line companies that transport gas from the Southwest. Most of the remainder is produced from the system's own wells or purchased from independent producers in the Appalachian area.

Consolidated is active in all phases of operation—exploration, leasing, and test-drilling. Three years ago, the Columbia system began a program of gas exploration and development in the Louisiana Gulf Coast region. That Consolidated is using underground storage to a very large extent is understandable. In 1959 gas drawn from storage supplied 34 per cent of the total customer requirements throughout the heating season and 60 per cent on the peak winter day.

Consolidated and Columbia are very active in sales promotion to meet the competition from the electric industry. Household and commercial uses of gas are vigorously encouraged. In Columbia territory 99 per cent of all restaurants use gas for cooking. It is employed to heat water and dry clothes at almost all laundromats in Consolidated's territory. Great attention is being devoted to the introduction of new models of gas-operated air conditioning equipment. Here hotels, offices, stores, restaurants, and hospitals are particularly promising.

The growth of Consolidated Natural Gas Company is illustrated by the following comparative figures:

	1943	*1959*
Operating revenues	$ 62,400,000	$334,500,000
Gas sales in MCF		
Residential and commercial	58,100,000	259,200,000
Industrial	57,900,000	147,700,000
Wholesale and other	11,400,000	141,600,000
TOTAL	127,400,000	548,500,000
Retail customers	756,000	1,175,000
Gas plant investment	$211,000,000	$788,000,000
Employees	5,729	8,367

The Peoples Gas Light and Coke Company

The Peoples Gas Light and Coke Company, one of the great names in the gas industry for more than a hundred years, serves the Windy

City with natural gas. Since July 1, 1956, the heat capacity of Peoples' fuel has been increased from 900 to 1,000 Btu's per cubic foot to be sure its market—a population in excess of 7,000,000 in six Midwestern states—is adequately supplied. But its chief market is the Chicago area with more than 5,000,000 people. To render dependable, continuous service in such a changeable and severe climate is no easy task. There was a day in January, 1957, when the average temperature was zero, and the wholly-integrated corporation had a peak-day sendout of 543 million cubic feet to firm customers.[13]

The following data from the 1959 annual report illustrate the volume of Peoples' business:

PEOPLES GAS (CHICAGO) CONSOLIDATED SALES, 1959

Total Year-round Firm Gas Service	107,813,244,600 cu. ft.	$121,185,550
Total Valley Gas Service	49,437,137,200 cu. ft.	15,217,066
Other Gas Utilities	290,925,610,000 cu. ft.	80,049,181
TOTAL	448,176,342,800 cu. ft.	$216,451,797

The year 1959 was a memorable one for Peoples Gas because it was the first time since June, 1946, that the Company had been able to offer gas for space heating to all single- and two-family dwellings on the service waiting list. During the thirteen intervening years, there were sometimes more than 100,000 applicants in single-family dwelling units on the company's waiting list. Of the 4,400 new homes completed in Chicago in 1959, about 99.2 per cent are heated with gas, .5 per cent with oil, and .3 per cent with electricity. The number of space-heating customers was 335,000, ten times the number being served in 1946. Other figures from the 1959 annual report tell of considerable progress in supplying gas to the huge city.

Peoples' gas supply comes from three pipe lines, two of them owned by the company and the third one belonging to Midwestern Gas Transmission Company which completed a pipe line to the Chicago area in October, 1959. Midwestern delivers 20 million cubic feet a day. Peoples Gas now owns the Peoples Gulf Coast Natural Gas Pipeline Company, which absorbed the former Texas Illinois Natural Gas

[13] Expansion projects completed by the company in 1960 boosted the maximum-day natural gas delivery by 260,000,000 cubic feet to 2,890,000,000 cubic feet.

Pipeline Company. Within the greater Chicago area, the Chicago District Pipeline transports for Peoples Gas and for two other utilities. The supply area of Natural Gas Pipeline is the Texas Panhandle, and in 1956 an important extension of its system took place when gas reserves from three gas producers in Jack and Wise counties in Texas were acquired under long-term contracts. Estimated at 80 million cubic feet a day for twenty years, the reserves were obtained at an initial price in the field of 13¢/MCF. Another remarkable addition to its gas supply came to Natural Gas Pipeline in the form of a contract with well-known Lone Star Gas Company of Dallas, Texas, making available up to 100 million cubic feet a day.

A vital step taken by Peoples Gas to secure and to steadily increase the huge deliveries which are required on peak days was the development of a storage system. Underground storage has a twofold purpose: to store gas reserves from a steady flow from a pipe line in a slack season and to make gas readily available on peak days during the cold weather. Peoples Gas, through a subsidiary, Natural Gas Storage Company of Illinois, has constructed underground storage at Herscher, Illinois.[14] Herscher Dome lies only forty-four miles south of the northern terminals of the two pipe lines, Natural Gas and Peoples Gulf Coast Line. It makes available a peak day withdrawal capacity of 575 million cubic feet, which can be further increased to 605 million cubic feet through additional use of the Galesville and Mount Simon formations at Herscher and Coops Mills. At the end of 1959, inventories of gas in underground storage belonging to customer companies totaled 22.6 billion cubic feet, of which 8.9 billion were owned by Peoples Gas. Peoples Gas is actively seeking other suitable formations for underground storage development and is active in exploration and development along the Louisiana Gulf Coast.

The chairman of the board of Peoples Gas is Remick McDowell,

---

[14] Joseph A. Kornfeld, "Aquifers for Underground Natural Gas Storage," *American Gas Journal,* Vol. CLXXXVII, No. 4 (April, 1960),45ff. See also subsequent issues of the *American Gas Journal* where Herscher Dome, Redfield, Florissant, Doe Run, and Troy Grove storage fields are described. Herscher Dome and Redfield were developed by Northern Natural Gas Company. Florissant is owned by Laclede Gas Company of St. Louis, Missouri. Doe Run storage field belongs to Louisville Gas and Electric Company of Louisville, Kentucky, and the Troy Grove Field is a project of Northern Illinois Gas Company.

and the president is Leslie A. Brandt. The magnitude of Peoples Gas, which is located at 122 South Michigan Avenue, Chicago, can be seen from the total on the balance sheet which was, in 1959, $827,402,944 with a debt ratio of 52.4 per cent.

Northern Natural Gas Company

Northern Natural Gas Company is located in Omaha, Nebraska, and is under the expert guidance of John F. Merriam, chairman of the board. In 1960, it entered its thirtieth year of operation. Northern had made progress in 1959 in expanding its market and service area. Its service area is one of the coldest in the United States and includes the twin cities, St. Paul and Minneapolis, and the even colder area around Duluth. Northern extended its markets into Illinois, selling 50 million cubic feet of gas daily to Northern Illinois Gas Company. As mentioned in the comments above on American Natural Gas Company, Michigan Wisconsin Pipe Line Company will receive 75 million cubic feet daily from Northern Natural. Annual gas sales exceeded 400 million cubic feet for the first time in 1959, and gas reserves also reached a new high of 13.1 trillion cubic feet. At the same time the debt ratio was 55.3 per cent. The company now supplies gas to utilities which serve about a million customers in communities in Iowa, Illinois, Kansas, Minnesota, Nebraska, South Dakota, and Wisconsin and has a distribution division called Peoples Natural Gas which provides retail natural gas service in 119 communities in Iowa, Minnesota, Nebraska, and Kansas.

Northern Natural operates what may be the largest aquifer storage project in the natural gas industry at Redfield, near Des Moines, Iowa.[15] Redfield has an ultimate reservoir capacity of about 140 billion cubic feet and a working capacity of 40 billion cubic feet. This aquifer project is operating under a temporary certificate from the FPC covering 25 million cubic feet of gas a day.

Northern Natural Gas Producing Company is a wholly-owned gas and oil exploration and production subsidiary. It owns 368.2 gas wells and 71.81 oil wells, and had approximately two trillion cubic feet of gas reserves at the end of the year 1959. This company has one-third interest in the Savanna Creek Field in the foothills area of Alberta,

[15] Kornfeld, "Aquifers for Underground Natural Gas Storage," *American Gas Journal,* Vol. CLXXXVII, No. 4 (April, 1960), 46–47.

Canada, and has a contract to sell this gas to another pipe line which will transport it to the Pacific Northwest. Export and import permits were granted during 1960.

Northern Natural also owns 93 per cent of the common stock of Permian Basin Pipeline Company,[16] which operates a natural gas pipe-line system in western Texas and southeastern New Mexico. Its principal activity is to purchase, gather, process, transmit, and sell natural gas. Proved reserves of natural gas controlled by Permian are estimated at 3.8 trillion cubic feet.

The general location of reserves and volumes of gas purchased from various fields during the year are shown below:

Field	Billions of Cubic Feet	
	Gas Reserves	Gas Purchased
Puckett Field, Pecos Co., Tex.	1,485	49.3
Spraberry Trend Area, Tex.	109	23.5
Andrews County Fields, Tex.	390	27.4
Lea Co., N. M. (Wellhead)	1,223	44.2
Emperor Field, Winkler Co., Tex.	194	5.3
Other Fields in N. M. and Tex.	434	25.3
TOTAL	3,835	175.0

Pacific Gas and Electric Company

Pacific Gas and Electric Company (PG&E) is a fully integrated company with assets of $2,479,000,000. It supplies gas and electricity to the northern part of California, principally the San Francisco area, and operates 3,850 miles of gas transmission lines and 18,500 miles of gas distribution lines within the state of California. This system is augmented by the McDonald Island gas storage field outside San Francisco, which has a capacity of 30 billion cubic feet and will deliver 400,000 MFC of gas on a peak day when fully developed.

In 1960, PG&E sold 370 billion cubic feet of gas to 1,690,523 customers and delivered 140 billion cubic feet of gas as fuel to its electricity-generating plants. Peak-day sendout was about two billion cubic feet. The PG&E system has handled gas from California fields since 1929 and from fields in Texas and New Mexico since 1950 (PG&E buys gas from El Paso at the Arizona-California boundary).

[16] Permian merged into Northern Natural in December, 1960.

It expects to receive delivery of Canadian gas by the end of 1961 under the Alberta-California Project.

The Alberta-California Project[17] is described as follows in Pacific Gas and Electric's 1960 annual report:

A. PARTICIPATING COMPANIES

1. *Alberta and Southern Gas Company Limited*

This Alberta corporation is a wholly-owned subsidiary of PG&E. Its principal function will be to purchase gas from producers in Alberta and arrange for its transportation to the international boundary. It will not own any pipeline facilities and will have only nominal capitalization.

2. *The Alberta Gas Trunk Line Company Limited*

This company will construct, own and operate all pipeline facilities, estimated to cost about $92 million, required by the project within the Province of Alberta. It will gather gas, including the gas purchased by Alberta and Southern, from a number of fields in western Alberta and transport it as a contract carrier to the Alberta boundary. It has no corporate connection with PG&E or any other participants in the project.

3. *Alberta Natural Gas Company*

This company will transport gas as a contract carrier for Alberta and Southern and also for Westcoast Transmission Company Limited through the Province of British Columbia to the international boundary. It will construct, own and operate pipeline facilities estimated to cost $35 million.

4. *Pacific Gas Transmission Company*

This company will purchase gas from Alberta and Southern at the international boundary, transport it through Idaho, Washington, and Oregon to the California border, and sell it there to PG&E. It will also transport, as a contract carrier, gas purchased from Westcoast Transmission Company by El Paso Natural Gas Company. It will construct, own and operate pipeline facilities estimated to cost about $121 million.

5. *Pacific Gas and Electric Company*

PG&E will distribute the gas made available by the project to its customers in Northern and Central California. It will construct, own and

[17] The Alberta-California Project is described in "Bids for Big System Going Out Soon," *Oil and Gas Journal,* Vol. LVIII, No. 35 (August 29, 1960), 47. In regard to Pacific Gas and Electric Company, see Coleman, *P.G.& E. of California.*

operate pipeline facilities, estimated to cost $58 million, extending from the Oregon-California border to Antioch, California, the principal point of connection with the Company's existing distribution system.

B. THE PROJECT IN BRIEF

The Alberta-California Project was conceived more than four years ago to obtain an independently controlled supplemental source of natural gas for PG&E customers. Negotiations for gas purchase contracts and the design and engineering of the pipeline got under way. More than two years ago the applications for the necessary governmental approvals began to be processed through regulatory agencies in Canada and the United States. In August of 1960 the last required governmental approval was obtained, and shortly thereafter construction contracts were awarded.

The project is scheduled for completion by the end of 1961. The pipeline will extend 1,400 miles from Alberta to the San Francisco Bay area. Initial deliveries of 415 million cubic feet a day will increase PG&E's gas supply by about 20%. The line has been designed to handle twice the initial delivery by installing additional compressor facilities.

Financing arrangements completed for Pacific Gas Transmission Company included the sale of 2,210,000 shares of common stock producing net proceeds of slightly under $20 million; the sale of $13,260,-000 of Convertible Subordinated Debentures issued pursuant to rights allotted to common stockholders; and the private placement of $90 million 5¼% First Mortgage Pipe Line Bonds. PG&E owns 50% of the common stock and purchased for investment the debentures to which it was entitled to subscribe.

Financing arrangments for Alberta Natural Gas Company have also been completed by a private placement of $25 million (U.S.) of 5¾% First Mortgage Pipe Line Bonds, and by the sale of 852,016 shares of common stock, the proceeds from which approximated $8½ million (Can.). The common shares are owned in equal portions by Westcoast Transmission Company Limited, Pacific Gas Transmission Company, and the public. Westcoast Transmission Company and Pacific Gas Transmission Company have entered into a voting trust agreement under which each will nominate four of the eight directors of Alberta Natural Gas Company.

The California section of the line, estimated to cost $58 million, will be financed as a part of PG&E's overall construction program. In addition to its direct investment, it is estimated that PG&E will have an investment of approximately $19½ million in the securities of Alberta and Southern Gas Co. Ltd. and Pacific Gas Transmission Company at the commencement of operations.

Pacific Lighting Corporation

Pacific Lighting Corporation, with assets of $760,000,000, provides gas service to a population of 8,400,000 in southern California, including Los Angeles. Subsidiary companies are Southern California Gas Company, Southern Counties Gas Company of California, Pacific Lighting Gas Supply Company and Pacific Natural Gas Exploration Company. In 1960 about 20 per cent of the 567,000,000,000 cubic feet of gas purchased came from California sources. The remaining 80 per cent (457,000,000,000 cubic feet) was purchased at the Arizona-California border from El Paso (1,143,000,000 cubic feet a day) and from Transwestern (300,000,000 cubic feet a day). Deliveries by Transwestern may be increased to 640,000,000 cubic feet a day, and new deliveries by El Paso through its Rock Springs Project may amount to 620,000,000 cubic feet a day in 1965. The average cost of purchased gas to Pacific Lighting in 1960 from all sources was 31.3¢/MCF.

Pacific Lighting has opposed the Tennessee Gas Transmission project under which Texas and Mexican gas would be imported into California for the use of Southern California Edison in its electricity generating plants. The new supply would remove an important interruptible load from the Pacific Lighting system.

The history of the company is described as follows in the company's 1960 annual report:

> On August 24, 1886, a new name was added to the corporate roster of the State of California. Pacific Lighting was created to lease a new type of gas light to homes and business establishments.
>
> Organizers of the corporation were C. O. G. Miller and W. B. Cline, two young men who were employed by the Pacific Gas Improvement Company, a San Francisco distributing firm headed by Miller's father.
>
> Their Pacific Lighting sideline paid off well for Miller and Cline. In short order they had several hundred customers using their gas lights, primarily places of public gathering which were willing to pay the two dollar weekly rental charge for each unit. Had they been content with this, however, Pacific Lighting might have shortly expired with the advent of the electric light. When Miller and Cline learned that Pa-

146

cific Gas Improvement was planning to dispose of its controlling interest in a San Bernardino gas plant, they bought it and Pacific Lighting entered the gas distribution business.

During the next year they pursued the matter in earnest, purchasing plants in Eureka, Colton, Riverside and Santa Barbara. The most important move the men made was to buy the Los Angeles Gas Company in September of 1889 and the Los Angeles Electric Company the following year.

The two firms were merged and Cline went to Los Angeles to supervise their operations. The other companies were eventually sold, but this new firm was to form the nucleus of the Pacific Lighting System in southern California.

The problems of struggling local gas and electric companies in the early nineties were many and serious. Pioneer equipment was crude, and the rapid changes brought about by engineering developments created a need for capital to buy new equipment. This was difficult enough without the added burden of finding still more money with which to extend lines to new residences which were already beginning to spring up in southern California. Within two years after Pacific Lighting had established itself in Los Angeles the city's population had quadrupled. By 1900, 100,000 people were living there.

At the time, all of the gas distributed in the state was manufactured from coal or oil. In 1907, however, the Santa Maria Gas Company began distributing natural gas from local fields.

Within six years, natural gas was piped into Los Angeles from fields in Kern County, and the Los Angeles Gas and Electric Corporation introduced this new fuel into its distributing lines.

While there were numerous small companies serving various communities in southern California, the business was beginning to stabilize, with Los Angeles Gas and Electric, Santa Maria Gas, Southern California Gas and Southern Counties Gas being the major distributing firms.

The discovery of great natural gas fields in the midst of these companies' service areas aided their growth. The smaller companies which did not have the capital to bring this superior fuel into their systems were unable to compete. They closed down their operations or merged with their better equipped and more effectively managed competitors.

It became apparent that there were benefits to even the larger firms in merging their interests. In 1925 Southern Counties Gas Company came into the Pacific Lighting System, followed in 1928 by the Santa Maria Gas Company.

147

In 1929, the large Southern California Gas Company joined Pacific Lighting.

The considerable problems of territory boundaries were now eliminated and a better balancing of sources of supply, storage and disposal of off-peak surpluses became possible.

The four major gas companies of southern California, exclusive of San Diego County, now became one system, physically interconnected at all points of meeting. Gas could be obtained by each of the companies through existing facilities without construction of major new pipelines.

In 1937, after the electric properties were sold to the City of Los Angeles, the gas distributing properties of Los Angeles Gas and Electric were acquired by Southern California Gas Company through merger.

In 1941 Santa Maria Gas Company was merged with Southern Counties Gas Company. Pacific Lighting then had two distributing companies, Southern California and Southern Counties Gas.

Providing prodigious quantities of energy to an area where almost every home is heated by gas and where nine out of ten homemakers cook with it, where there are the heavy demands of industries that are almost solely dependent upon it, or on the electricity that is largely generated from it, is a task that staggers the imagination. Pacific Lighting, however, has always managed to keep ahead of needs.

Yet in the early 1930's, it was predicted that southern California would never have to reach outside its own natural gas fields for sufficient quantities of this fuel.

Less than 15 years later, in 1947, the first of the giant inter-state pipelines was completed to augment the supply of gas obtained from local fields. Now, more than 80 per cent of the gas consumed in southern California comes from out-of-state and a fifth major pipeline is planned for construction.

An important subsidiary of the Corporation is Pacific Lighting Gas Supply Company. Created in 1950 as an outgrowth of Industrial Fuel Supply Company, which had been in the Pacific Lighting System since 1925, its job is to procure, gather, store and supply gas for the distribution companies.

In 1960 the Pacific Natural Gas Exploration Company was formed. This new subsidiary is working to discover and acquire increased reserves of natural gas to feed the future needs of energy-hungry southern California.

A long way has been traveled since Miller and Cline leased their first gas lamp. Perhaps they could be called men of vision. More likely, however, they considered themselves merely good businessmen who recognized a need and went about filling it in the most competent way they knew. Even the most vigorous promoters of the climate, beauty and inherent wealth of southern California could not have known what was in store for this favored region.

While southern California enjoyed steady, even rapid growth by the standards of the rest of the country, it has been in the past two decades that the development of the area has mushroomed at an almost incredible rate. From 1940 to 1960 the population of the southern California area served by the system grew from approximately 3.5 million to 8.6 million. The numbers of meters served increased from approximately 970,000 to almost 2,500,000.

Consumption of natural gas grew from 106 billion cubic feet per year to more than half a trillion cubic feet annually. Since World War II nearly half a billion dollars have been invested to expand the system to keep pace with this growth.

TYPICAL PIPE-LINE COMPANIES

Tennessee Gas Transmission Company

"Every year since Tennessee Gas went into operation has been one of expansion." Nothing could more adequately describe the fifteen-year history of this non-integrated gas pipe line than this statement by Gardiner Symonds, its president. Under his aegis, "Tennessee Gas has rolled up one of the industry's highest and most consistent rates of growth and produced a good return on equity and new investment."[18]

Second only to El Paso Natural Gas Company, the largest non-integrated carrier of natural gas, Tennessee Gas was built during the war year 1943–1944 to relieve a desperate fuel shortage in the East and has operated since October 31, 1944.[19]

A few figures taken from a "Growth Record" in the 1959 annual report may show an amazing development.

Finance	*1945*	*1958*	*1959*
Operating Revenues	$14,310,639	$408,569,673	$463,063,753
Net Income before Federal Income Taxes	4,090,022	74,967,488	70,889,341

[18] *Forbes,* Vol. LXXXV, No. 1 (January 1, 1960), Annual Report Issue, 70.

[19] In 1957, Tennessee Gas joined the companies having a capitalization of $1,000,000,-000 or more. Tennessee Gas' total capitalization at that time was $1,047,198,275.

	1945	1958	1959
Net Income and Special Credit after Taxes	3,965,022	47,295,672	52,450.097
Earnings Available for Common Stock	3,448,776	38,870,985	44,909,111
Per Share	0.17	1.67	1.93
Gross Property, Plant and Equipment	64,168,721	1,378,744,995	1,565,391,859
Capitalization	65,175,436	1,142,626,157	1,315,613,475
Long-Term Debt	46,553,000	678,478,339	744,740,165
Equity Capital	18,622,436	432,314,317	514,069,991
Minority Interest in Consolidated Subsidiaries	—	4,618,501	422,319
Short Term Notes	—	27,215,000	56,381,000

Operations	1945	1958	1959
Volumes of Gas (MCF at 15.025 psia)		--	
Daily System Capacity (End of year)	200,000	1,980,000	2,505,000
Total Sold and Transported for Others	73,564,224	713,991,119	745,121,783
Purchased	79,427,357	680,461,449	726,366,925
Miles of Gas Pipe Line	1,284	10,195	12,160
Installed Compressor Horsepower	60,000	641,300	772,630
Oil Condensate and Plant Products (Net daily production in barrels)	—	26,658	35,011
Producing Wells (Net)	—	2,746	2,788
Producing Leases (Net acres)	—	241,464	326,698
Undeveloped Acreage (Net acres)	—	5,882,290	10,370,236
Refinery Crude Oil Runs (Barrels)	—	11,407,568	12,333,829

These figures, financially and operationally, tell the extraordinary growth story of Tennessee Gas. What they do not reveal, however, is the planning that marked the road to this achievement. A dual form of expansion was the goal of Mr. Symonds. He wanted to couple an expanding gas-carrying system with other enterprises including oil and gas production, refining, and marketing. Such activities combine the important advantages of integration, tax incentives, and non-regulated profit possibilities and may expand faster in the future than the regulated phase of Tennessee's business. Of this type are the investment in a wholly-owned insurance company and the 50 per cent company-owned Houston butadiene plant of Petro-Tex Chemical Corporation which, in 1958, was operating near capacity.

Tennessee's markets cover thirteen states from Louisiana to New Hampshire and bracket the country's most populous and industrialized area. Deliveries to New England (Massachusetts, Connecticut, Rhode Island, and New Hampshire) are the result of a struggle Tennessee had with Texas Eastern Transmission Corporation for the New England market. The contestants, both leaders in their field, were the late president of Texas Eastern, Reginald Hargrove, and Mr. Symonds.[20] The outcome was that Texas Eastern got most of Connecticut, all of Rhode Island, and eastern Massachusetts including Boston. The remainder went to Tennessee Gas, but the New England market is not large. "New England," says *Fortune*,[21] "is one area where pipelines have overbuilt. Competition there has fragmented the market while the long haul imposes prices too high to persuade the consumer to convert from other fuels—except on a luxury basis."[22]

Tennessee Gas fought and won another battle which may be more rewarding in the long run—the battle of Midwestern Gas Transmission Company—a wholly-owned subsidiary of Tennessee Gas. The significance of Midwestern is twofold: it supplies a large highly populated region which experiences severe winters, and it opens up the valve

[20] For a vivid description of this struggle and the rapid rise of the transmission industry after World War II, see John Osborne, "A Brawling, Bawling Industry," *Life*, Vol. XXXII, No. 10 (March 10, 1952), 101ff. This article also introduces Mr. Symond's Washington lawyer, Thomas G. Corcoran, whom readers will remember as Franklin Delano Roosevelt's "Tommy the Cork."

[21] Smith, "The Unnatural Problems of Natural Gas," *Fortune*, Vol. LX, No. 3 (September, 1959), 258.

[22] However, John F. Rich, president of New England Gas and Electric Association, Cambridge, Massachusetts, and director of Algonquin Gas Transmission Company, reports progress for his company, especially in house heating and sales of gas appliances. See John F. Rich, "The Unlimited Horizons of the Natural Gas Industry," *Public Utilities Fortnightly*, Vol. LXIV, No. 8 (October 8, 1959), 42, 44.

of huge Canadian gas reserves for the Middle West.[23] Midwestern has has two pipelines, one in operation and the other under construction. The line in operation was authorized by the FPC in May, 1959. It runs from Portland, Tennessee, to Joliet, Illinois, and is a 350-mile 30-inch pipe line drawing its gas from onshore and tidelands wells in the prolific Texas and Louisiana Gulf Coast area. It started deliveries on October 7, 1959, and supplies the highly industrialized Chicago-Gary, Indiana, area. Two hundred million feet go daily to Northern Indiana Public Service Company, 100 million cubic feet to Peoples Gas, Chicago, and 60 million cubic feet to North Illinois Gas Company, all three of which are distributors of natural gas.

The second pipe line for which the Canadian government gave the gas export permit on April 1, 1960, consists of a 504-mile 24-inch pipe line from Emerson, Manitoba, to Marshfield, Wisconsin. The largest customers of the line, which supplies North Dakota, South Dakota, Michigan, and Wisconsin, are Michigan Wisconsin Pipe Line Company with 158,000 thousand cubic feet daily and Northern States Power Company with 29 million cubic feet a day. This northern extension of Midwestern began service in 1960. Once in full operation, Midwestern will add a great many new customers to the gigantic Tennessee Gas system in one of the two outstanding gas-consuming growth areas of the country (the upper Midwest, including Chicago and environs being one, the West Coast with Los Angeles and the Bay area of San Francisco being the other), but it will also constantly require new supplies.

The supply situation of Tennessee Gas appears to be favorable. In both 1958 and 1959 the annual report mentioned additions to reserves. On December 31, 1960, gas reserves dedicated to the pipe-line system stood at an estimated 18.8 trillion cubic feet.[24] In an effort to add substantial new supplies to its already large reserves, Tennessee Gas is purchasing Pan American's producing leaseholds in Bastian Bay, Plaquemines Parish, Louisiana, for more than $150,000,000[25]

[23] In 1960, Midwestern Gas Transmission began construction on its 504-mile 24-inch line from Emerson, Manitoba, to Marshfield, Wisconsin. This line brought Canadian gas into the upper Midwest for the first time. The $52,000,000 project was under construction for five years, but here too the FPC cut the requested rate of return from 7 per cent to 6.5 per cent.

[24] Tennessee Gas Transmission Company, *Annual Report* (for 1960), 8.

[25] "Tennessee Gas Transmission Buys Pan Am's Bastian Bay Gas," *Oil and Gas Journal,* Vol. LIX, No. 6 (February 6, 1961), 86.

as Texas Eastern did before with its $134,000,000-purchase of Rayne Field, Louisiana. "Acquiring full ownership of reserves gives the buyer control over production and marketing of the gas."[26] Reserves are to be recalculated at the end of five to seven years, and the sale price will be adjusted at that time to cover any addition to reserves during the period. Thus, the huge pipe-line system will gain at least one trillion cubic feet of gas for interstate transmission and sale.

Formation of Tenneco Corporation to own the non-pipe-line properties of Tennessee Gas Transmission Company and Tenneco Oil Company to operate the parent firm's far-flung producing, refining, and marketing properties was announced on December 12, 1960, by Mr. Symonds. Tenneco Corporation is a subsidiary of Tennessee Gas, and Tenneco Oil Company is a subsidiary of Tenneco Corporation. Board members and officers of both subsidiaries were drawn from the present Tennessee Gas organization. Mr. Symonds is chairman of the board of both companies. This organizational pattern puts into operation a plan to establish a corporate realignment that will more clearly separate the government-regulated, gas pipe-line business of Tenneseee Gas from its oil and other non-utility operations. All of the company's non-regulated business interests in the petrochemical, life insurance, and real estate fields also became subsidiaries of Tenneco Corporation. Tenneco Oil Company will function as an integrated oil company and operate the facilities presently being operated in twenty-four states and six foreign countries by three Tennessee Gas divisions, Tennessee Gas and Oil Company, Tennessee Oil Refining Company, and Tennessee Overseas Company.

After the realignment, the Tennessee Gas pipe-line system of more than 12,000 miles, which is fully regulated by the Federal Power Commission, will be concentrated directly under the parent firm. Tennessee Gas Pipeline Company will continue as a major division operating the main Tennessee Gas natural gas transmission system from the Mexican border to New England. Midwestern Gas Transmission Company, which has two pipe lines in the Midwest, and East Tennessee Natural Gas Company, which has a pipe line within the state of Tennessee, will be direct subsidiaries of Tennessee Gas. W. C. McGee, Jr., is President of Tennessee Gas Pipeline Company and a director of the parent company.

[26] *Ibid.*

El Paso Natural Gas Company

Another striking example of a successful natural gas pipe-line company is El Paso Natural Gas Company which has grown rapidly under the direction of its founder and board chairman, Paul Kayser, a leading figure in the natural gas industry for more than thirty years. Until recently El Paso was the sole out-of-state supplier of California. The fastest growing region in the country from the standpoint of population, this great state was still self-sufficient in natural gas in 1945 but has now become dependent on other areas for supplies. California's own reserves (8.59 trillion cubic feet as of December 21, 1959) are dwindling. El Paso has therefore been compelled to expand greatly to "deliver the goods" as they are needed.

Crowning the development that made El Paso the biggest non-integrated carrier of natural gas was the acquisition of Pacific Northwest Pipeline Corporation through merging, one of the biggest transactions in the industry. It represented an outlay of about $151,-800,000 in El Paso common stock.[27] The merger of Pacific Northwest into El Paso was authorized by the FPC on December 23, 1959, and the facilities formerly owned and operated by Pacific Northwest are identified as the Northwest Division of El Paso Natural Gas and, together with El Paso's San Juan Division, form the Rocky Mountain Region with Vice-President R. W. Harris as Manager and with headquarters in Salt Lake City.

The California and Pacific Northwest distribution company customers of El Paso forecast a growing demand for natural gas over the next decade. Since service was first inaugurated to California by El Paso in 1947, this demand growth has been of major proportions. El Paso's immediate expansion plans, designed to meet a portion of these market projections, include the delivery of 100,000 MCF daily for use by the Pacific Lighting subsidiaries[28] through facilities estimated to cost about $55,000,000 and an additional 470,000 MCF daily to the distribution subsidiaries of Pacific Lighting Corporation. The latter program involves an estimated $58,000,000 construction job consisting largely of a new thirty-four-inch pipe line from the California-Nevada border to a connecting point with the present pipe-line sys-

[27] "El Paso Pushes New Frontier," *Business Week*, No. 1430 (January 26, 1957), 76ff. This article describes the marriage of El Paso and Pacific Northwest.

[28] In 1959, Pacific Lighting Corporation and its subsidiaries had 2,409,000 customers who consumed 392 MMCF of natural gas from out-of-state sources.

tem of Colorado Interstate Gas Company near Rock Springs, Wyoming. El Paso would purchase approximately one-half the proposed throughput from Colorado and would draw more heavily upon the capacity of its Northwest Division. The company also has an agreement to sell to Pacific Gas and Electric an additional 200,000 MCF daily through a two-part construction program estimated to cost around $85,000,000.[29]

It appears that El Paso has made headway in acquiring reserves for its California market and has access to considerable additional reserves, particularly in Wyoming and elsewhere in the Rocky Mountains and from the Dakota formation in the San Juan Basin. The California market should continue to expand with population growth, and the vigorous fight against smog in the Los Angeles Basin fortifies the outlook for an increased gas demand in this El Paso sales area.

El Paso has a long-term debt ratio of about 70 per cent and has engaged in considerable diversification. El Paso Natural Gas Products Company is a subsidiary which conducts the non-regulated activities of the huge concern and represents about 10 per cent of consolidated net plant. El Paso Products owns 95 per cent of Odessa Butadiene Company, its largest subsidiary. It owns wholly Odessa Styrene Company, another petrochemical subsidiary.

Texas Eastern Transmission Corporation

Texas Eastern Transmission Corporation entered the gas industry through the acquisition of the Big Inch and Little Big Inch pipe lines of World War II fame. Under the Big Inch name and government ownership, the line carried petroleum from the Southwest to the East during World War II, and it became a transporter of gas when it was purchased by a private firm in 1947 for $143,027,000.

Little Big Inch has returned to its old profession of transporting oil and oil products, and newly-built gas pipe lines have taken its place. Major companies such as Esso Standard Oil Company, Mobil Oil Company, Phillips Petroleum, and many other shippers of petroleum products are using Little Big Inch. In 1959, Little Big Inch carried 39.9 million barrels.[30] Of this volume, 50 per cent was gasoline, 40

---

[29] The Federal Power Commission approved this project in December, 1960. See "FPC Approves Rock Springs Project," *Oil and Gas Journal,* Vol. LIX, No. 1 (January 2, 1961), 52.

[30] See "Sharp Growth Seen for Products Lines as Over-all Demand Continues to

per cent fuel oils, and 10 per cent liquefied petroleum gas. According to Millard K. Neptune, senior vice-president of Texas Eastern and in charge of the Little Big Inch Division, jet fuels are expected to record the most future growth. Texas Eastern's 1,168-mile product pipe-line system extends from Houston to Moundsville, West Virginia, with a spur to Chicago. The present capacity is 185,000 barrels a day.[31]

The company has paid particular attention to the development of underground gas storage, and during 1959, Texas Eastern, through Little Big Inch, became one of the world's leading developers and operators of underground storage for LPG. Four underground storage caverns at Todhunter Terminal, north of Cincinnati, Ohio, were completed and put in service during 1959, and the fifth was put in service at the beginning of 1960. A salt-cavity storage well near Houston, Texas, received initial injections of propane in October, 1959, and a great expansion of this underground storage terminal (at Mont Belvieu) is being planned. Besides Oakford Storage near Pittsburgh, Pennsylvania, largest underground storage in the world, Texas Eastern was, during 1958, authorized by the FPC to acquire a one-fourth interest in the Leidy and Tamarack storage pools located in north-central Pennsylvania. Joint development of this new underground storage will be carried out with New York State Natural Gas Corporation and Transcontinental Gas Pipe Line Corporation. Development of Texas Eastern's portion of the area was completed by the 1960–61 heating season.

Since the purchase of the pipe lines from the government in 1947, the original business, the operation of gas transmission, is a record of continued expansion. Gas sales reached a total of 644.5 billion cubic feet in 1959. When one considers that property, plant, and equipment had, in that year, a net value of $746,634,196 compared with the original value of $143,027,000 in 1947, one realizes the rapid growth this company has experienced since its establishment. At the end of 1959, its reserves were estimated to be 12.7 trillion cubic feet, and it was tapping Mexican sources. The company made news on

Climb," *Petroleum Week,* Vol. X, No. 11 (March 18, 1960), 54ff. See also "Delayed Pay-off," *Forbes,* Vol. LXXXVI, No. 5 (September 1, 1960), 25. The latter article discusses the success of Little Big Inch's conversion.

[31] "Sharp Growth Seen for Products Lines as Over-all Demand Continues to Climb," *Petroleum Week,* Vol. X, No. 11 (March 18, 1960), 54.

August 22, 1957, when a valve was opened on the banks of the Rio Grande, and natural gas from Mexico began flowing through Texas Eastern's pipe-line system to markets in the East. For this purpose a 30-inch line from Beaumont to the Mexican border below McAllen, Texas, had been built. In 1959, fifty billion cubic feet were imported from Mexico. Another major event was the acquisition of one trillion cubic meet from the Rayne Field, Louisiana, with a total cost to Texas Eastern of $134,000,000.

The Gas Division is headed by senior Vice-President Baxter D. Goodrich. President is Orville S. Carpenter who was with the company from the beginning as was its chairman, George R. Brown and his brother Herman Brown. Of the other founders of the company, the late E. Holley Poe, the late E. L. DeGolyer, and Charles I. Francis, who is still a member of the board, played an important part in the founding and the history of Texas Eastern. Texas Eastern's first president was the late R. H. Hargrove, a gas man par excellence who helped lay a firm foundation for the company's present importance.

Another milestone in the twelve-year history of the company was the acquisition of La Gloria Oil & Gas Company in mid-1957 in exchange for one million shares of Texas Eastern common stock. As a result of the La Gloria acquisition, Texas Eastern has obtained an experienced management team highly regarded in the drilling and production field. The operations of the Oil Division, which includes activities of Texas Eastern Production Division and La Gloria Oil & Gas Company, the wholly owned subsidiary, are directed by Senior Vice-President John F. Lynch, an oil and gas industry veteran.[32]

[32] The long-term debt ratio of Texas Eastern was 65.2 per cent in 1959. It had been 66.2 per cent in 1958. *Petroleum Week's* report on product pipe lines also mentions that Texas Eastern is sounding out several utilities in the New York-Philadelphia area to see whether they could use coal slurry if a line were built to transport it. The company has been studying the possibility of building a 350-mile 24-inch line from Moundsville, West Virginia, to Philadelphia and New York to carry a mixture of powdered coal and water.

In a November 8, 1962, speech before the Los Angeles Society of Financial Analysts, Vice President J. W. Hargrove of Texas Eastern disclosed that the company was considering an eighty-million-dollar pipe-line project which would move liquid coal from Utah to the Los Angeles area. See "Texas Eastern Studying Coal Pipeline in West," *Houston Post,* No. 28,343 (November 9, 1962), page 2, Section 3.

Texas Eastern Transmission Corporation has received permission from the Federal Power Commission to undertake an eighty-three million dollar expansion which will increase its daily delivery capacity by 225 MCF and will increase its total capacity to about 2.5 MMCF a day, or close to one trillion cubic feet a year.

Transcontinental Gas Pipe Line Corporation

Another of the remarkable developments in the gas transmission industry is the non-integrated pipe line constructed by Transcontinental Gas Pipe Line Corporation, the first line to supply the New York metropolitan area with natural gas. Minor deliveries of gas were made in December, 1950, and increased each month until March, 1951, when substantial deliveries began. Over 17,000,000 people with almost 5,000,000 individual service connections, representing 5,500,000 families, received gas from the public utilities served by the company in the metropolitan New York, New Jersey, and Philadelphia areas. Gas received from this truly long-distance system (1,842 miles) is distributed in New York proper by Consolidated Edison Company of New York and in Brooklyn by Union Gas Company.

Transcontinental was the first pipe line making intensive use of 36-inch pipe, "the largest ever employed for long-distance transmission of gas."[33] This great pipe line traverses some of the largest present and potential gas markets in America—the rapidly industrializing Piedmont sections of North Georgia and the Carolinos and the metropolitan areas of New Jersey, New York, and Philadelphia. This development began under the pipe line's second president, the late Tom P. Walker, and continued under its present president E. Clyde McGraw. The pipe line commenced operations with a debt ratio of as much as 85.6 per cent in 1950 which decreased to 66.9 per cent in 1959. Transcontinental has not yet followed the trend of diversification but has exclusively concentrated on the transmission of gas and the strengthening of its reserves.[34] The total number of miles of pipe line with this system is 5,649 miles. Together with Texas Eastern Transmission the Company has been very active in developing underground storage. Transcontinental's total reserve of gas under acreage dedicated under contract to the company was estimated at 8.2 trillion cubic feet at the end of 1959.[35]

[33] Transcontinental undertook a one-million-dollar expansion of pipe-line facilities in 1961. This increased the pipe line's allocated capacity from 1.3 MMCF to 1.5 MMCF daily.

[34] In 1962 Transco decided to go ahead with the construction of the first liquefied natural gas plant on the East Coast of the United States. See "East Coast LNG Project Cleared," *Oil and Gas Journal*, Vol. LX, No. 45 (November 5, 1962), 61.

[35] On April 21, 1960, Transcontinental issued thirty-five million dollars' worth of bonds for 5.25 per cent interest at a price of 99 per cent and 800,000 common shares at

In 1960, the United States Supreme Court decided the so-called Con-Ed case. It denied permission to Con Edison New York to have 50 million cubic feet of natural gas transported daily through Transcontinental pipe line from two Texas fields. The gas was to be used for generating electricity in Manhattan and was preferred over coal or oil to avoid air pollution. The FPC had refused to grant the necessary certificate. The Supreme Court affirmed the commission's ruling, upholding the right of the commission to consider "end use" in deciding whether to issue a certificate of public convenience and necessity. Also, the price to be paid by Con Edison in the field, 19¼¢/MCF, was higher than the going rate in those Texas fields and could trigger a general increase in field prices.[36]

Panhandle Eastern Pipe Line Company

Panhandle Eastern Pipe Line Company, which remarked on the cover of its 1959 annual report, "1929–1959—30 Years in America's Fifth Largest Industry," occupies an important position among the great pipe lines. It is one of the oldest and has 6,400 miles of its own and controls the 2,300 miles of its subsidiary, Trunkline Gas Company. It also has a sound supply basis in the Hugoton and Panhandle fields and, through its subsidiary, in the Gulf Coast.[37]

Established in 1929 the company lived its early years through hectic times.[38] The construction of the company's first main pipe line was

$20.25 per share to finance the planned expansion. See "The Amazing Vigor of Transcontinental Gas," *Forbes*, Vol. LXXXVI, No. 2 (July 15, 1960), 15.

In celebration of the tenth anniversary of the arrival of gas in New York through the Transcontinental pipe line, the *New York Times* of Sunday, January 15, 1961, carried a very interesting interview with Mr. McGraw, the Transco president. Gene Smith, the interviewer, wrote, "Mr. McGraw looks to tremendous expansion in the house heating markets as providing the main growth for the company's New York future."

[36] *New York Times*, January 24, 1961, pp. 31, 58; "Cost Ruling Tightens Gas Controls," *Oil and Gas Journal*, Vol. LIX, No. 5 (January 30, 1961), 96; "Gas Sales Can Be Limited by End Use," *Petroleum Week*, Vol. XII, No. 4 (January 27, 1961), 9; President's Materials Policy Commission, *Resources for Freedom*, III, 19ff.; "Onward to Yesterday," *Wall Street Journal*, Vol. XXVII, No. 4 (January 6, 1961), 8; Joseph E. Moody, "Coal and Competition," *Wall Street Journal*, Vol. XXVII, No. 20 (January 30, 1961), 6.

[37] Panhandle Eastern plans a seventy-million dollar expansion of its own system and that of its subsidiary, Trunkline Gas Company. This will provide a 30 per cent increase in deliveries to gas customers in six states.

[38] *Investigation of Concentration of Economic Power*, Temporary Economic Committee, Monograph No. 36, *Reports* of the Federal Trade Commission on Natural Gas and Natural Gas Pipelines . . . , 89.

completed to the Illinois-Indiana border late in 1931 with an investment of $45,000,000 and an initial capacity of approximately 85,000 MCF of gas a day. Gas reserves available to the company at the times were approximately one and one-half trillion cubic feet. Despite adverse business conditions continuing during the period, additions were made to the system so that the company's pipe-line capacity was increased to approximately 225,000 MCF a day at the end of 1939, with a total investment of $62,000,000 New markets in Michigan were supplied with gas during this period.

Although the company's expansion was limited during World War II, the company nevertheless acquired, in 1942, the facilities of Michigan Gas Transmission Corporation (a subsidiary of the Columbia Gas System) in the states of Indiana and Ohio and commenced selling directly to customers in these states. By this acquisition the company's main pipe-line facilities were extended 400 miles. In 1943, with the construction of additional facilities, the Company's markets were extended in Ohio and made available to the Appalachian area gas that was critically needed for the war industries. The new markets acquired represent approximately 20 per cent of the company's present markets. Additional reserves of gas for such new markets were obtained from the company's own reserves and under long-term contracts with large producers of gas.

After the end of the war, a rise in the price of competing fuels created a tremendous demand for gas. In spite of steel shortages in the early postwar period, the company continued to expand its facilities so that at the end of 1949 its second parallel pipe line had been constructed and its capacity increased to 500,000 MCF a day, with a total investment of $162,000,000. Gas reserves available to the system at the time were estimated to be six trillion cubic feet. In addition, during the period the Company, together with Consumers Power Company, organized Michigan Gas Storage Company in order to develop greater flexibility of operation through the use of partially depleted Michigan gas fields for the underground storage of gas during the warm months for resale during the cold winter months.

The company entered into its greatest period of expansion in 1950 with the acquisition of Trunkline Gas Company and the construction of its facilities. This new line brought gas from the Gulf Coast areas of Texas and Louisiana into the Panhandle system for the first time.

The original Trunkline facilities consisted of a 1,300-mile, large-diameter pipe line with a capacity of 290,000 MCF a day, which was subsequently increased to 375,000 MCF a day in 1955. In 1959, Trunkline commenced the construction of its second parallel pipe line and the extension of its facilities to the Indiana-Michigan border to provide for sales directly to Consumers Power Company in Michigan. Trunkline's total investment in plant and equipment at the end of 1959 was $180,000,000.

A major step in the diversification of the company's business took place when the company joined with National Distillers and Chemical Corporation in the organization of National Petro-Chemicals Corporation to engage in the manufacture of petrochemicals such as polyethylene, industrial alcohol, ethylene, and liquid petroleum gas at Tuscola, Illinois. In 1957 the company exchanged its investment in National Petro for 1,500,000 shares of common stock in National Distillers. As the result of this transaction, the company became owner of 14.6 per cent of the common stock of National Distillers. Under the expert management of an outstanding chemist, Robert E. Hulse, this extensive plant produces polyethylene and markets it under the trade name, *Petrothene*. A new plant which went into production in 1959 is located in the Gulf Coast area at Houston, Texas. Operations are underway to increase the capacity of this plant and the Tuscola plant. Then National expects to produce 300,000,000 pounds of polyethylene on an annual basis and will be the second largest producer of this petrochemical.

The company also increased its own facilities, at a cost of $161,-000,000, by the addition of a third parallel pipe line, which brought the total sales capacity of the Panhandle-Trunkline system to 1,425,-000 MCF a day at the end of 1959. These additions and expansions brought the combined Panhandle-Trunkline investment in plant to approximately $480,000,000 at the end of 1959. The recoverable natural gas reserves owned or controlled through gas purchase contracts by Panhandle Eastern and Trunkline were estimated to be in excess of 13.2 trillion cubic feet at the close of 1959. Panhandle Eastern's own recoverable reserves were about one-fourth of that amount.

In 1959 the company organized a wholly-owned subsidiary, Anadarko Production Company, and transferred to this subsidiary production properties located in the Anadarko Basin in Kansas, Oklahoma, and Texas. In the same year, Panhandle Eastern had good drilling results, producing 109 billion cubic feet of gas from its own gas reserves and operating 656 gas wells and 117 oil wells.[39]

The principal marketing area of Panhandle Eastern covers central Illinois and Indiana, a large portion of Ohio, and nearly all of lower Michigan. This area is the industrial heartland of America, and its vigorous population growth reflects the expansion of established manufacturing operation and the introduction of new industries. This combination has resulted in a steadily increasing demand for additional gas supplies for both home and industry. In the area served by customers of Panhandle Eastern is the East Ohio Gas Company which has Cleveland as its principal market.

The company's pipe-line system, consisting of three parallel pipe lines, extends a total of 1,300 miles from the Panhandles of Texas and Oklahoma into Michigan. It supplies gas to over sixty utilities and municipalities along its system. Trunkline supplies gas to Panhandle in Central Illinois and Consumers Power Company in Michigan together with many small municipalities and utilities located along the pipe-line system. Its pipe-line facilities, which are partially looped, extend a distance of 1,500 miles from the Gulf Coast areas of Texas and Louisiana to a point on the Indiana-Michigan border near South Bend, Indiana. The combined facilities will constitute a total of approximately 8,700 miles of pipe line and 456,000 installed horsepower.

The head of this gigantic enterprise is its energetic president and chairman of the board, William G. Maguire.[40]

Panhandle Eastern has sizable direct industrial sales from which it obtains about 11 per cent of total revenues, or $14,000,000. These sales are not subject to direct control under the Natural Gas Act. "The preponderance of these (direct industrial) sales is for metallurgical, ceramic, and chemical uses." This shows the importance of

[39] Panhandle Eastern Pipe Line Company, *Annual Report* (for 1958).

[40] See Huitt, "Natural Gas Regulation Under the Holding Company Act," *Law and Contemporary Problems,* Vol. XVIIII, No 3 (Summer, 1954), 455–73, and Clemens, *Economics and Public Utilities,* 310ff., for further information concerning Mr. Maguire and Panhandle Eastern.

See page 279 for a discussion of the landmark decisions on which Panhandle Eastern was a party and in which the price of gas produced from company-owned leases was set on the basis of a cost-of-service formula, rather than at commodity value.

natural gas in "special-advantage" or "higher-end" uses for which it is well suited because it makes possible an easily controllable application of heat.

On October 2, 1959, Panhandle Eastern discontinued deliveries of gas to Michigan Consolidated Gas Company, the utility serving Detroit. The daily delivery had been 127,000 MCF, and an additional capacity of 30,000 MCF was obtained by modernizing the compressor engines. These deliveries were distributed among Panhandle Eastern's other customers, who had contracted to buy the gas when delivery to Michigan Consolidated was discontinued. The question of the right of Panhandle to discontinue such deliveries was, in 1960, before the Court of Appeals for the District of Columbia Circuit where Michigan Consolidated had filed an appeal. An agreement was reached between Michigan Consolidated Gas Company and Panhandle Eastern early in January of 1962. This agreement assures large, long-term gas supplies for Michigan Consolidated and provides the basis for an amicable relationship between the two companies. Upon completion of an expansion program, now in progress, Panhandle Eastern will deliver to Michigan Consolidated 46 billion cubic feet of gas each year during the months of April through October for a term of twenty years.

OTHER NATURAL GAS COMPANIES

Southern Natural Gas Company

Southern Natural Gas Company of Birmingham, Alabama, is a transmission company which has operated since 1936 with C. P. Rather at the helm. Its main territory includes Alabama, Georgia, Louisiana, Mississippi, and South Carolina, and it is a supplier to the Alabama steel industry. The company has grown with the development of the petrochemical industry in its service area. It sold 335.89 billion cubic feet in 1959, an increase of almost 25 billion cubic feet over the 1958 figure, despite the adverse effects of the steel strike. The major reason for the increase was an expansion in delivery capacity during 1959. The design delivery capacity is now 1,365 million cubic feet daily, an increase of about 38 per cent over the previous daily capacity of 990 million cubic feet. The company expects that the present delivery capacity will be sufficient to enable it to meet its winter peak requirements.

Texas Gas Transmission Corporation

Established in 1948, Texas Gas Transmission Corporation is located in Owensboro, Kentucky. The company serves an eight-state area including the Big River region. This region enjoyed continued industrial development during 1959 when 111 new industries moved into it. The company makes the greatest portion of its direct industrial sales in the Louisiana Gulf Coast area. This area is a center for the growing petro-chemical industry. Industrial expansion throughout southern Louisiana is progressing at a rapid rate, and the company expects its operation in this vital area to grow. A large extraction plant, operated on the Texas Gas Mainline at Eunice, Louisiana, is jointly owned by Texas Gas' subsidiary, Texas Gas Exploration Corporation, and Union Texas Natural Gas Company.

The year 1959 saw one of the most important market developments undertaken by Texas Gas, an estimated $40,000,000 expansion to provide transportation service to Hope Natural Gas Company, a subsidiary of Consolidated Natural Gas Company. The FPC authorized a daily delivery of 100 million cubic feet. The gas is gathered and transported to a point near Lebanon, Ohio, where it is delivered to Texas Eastern for the account of Hope Natural under the the terms of a twenty-year contract with a guaranteed minimum delivery of 75 per cent.

Texas Gas system has 4,136 miles of pipe line. The system begins in northern Louisiana around Shreveport and Monroe but draws its supplies through a large-diameter line from the prolific southern Louisiana area. It takes a north-northeasterly course to Ohio, traversing the states of Arkansas, Tennessee, Indiana, and Kentucky. Among the cities it serves are Memphis, Evansville, and Louisville. This gas transmission system operates under the direction of William M. Elmer, president, and Henry H. Hillman, chairman of the board. Mr. Hillman succeeded his late father who helped Texas Gas develop to its present importance.

Underground storage continues to be an important facet of Texas Gas supply and sales operation. Six storage fields are in operation now, and additional ones are being acquired and developed.

Arkansas Louisiana Gas Company

Once part of Henry Doherty's empire, Arkansas Louisiana Gas is now an independent company serving the Arkansas and northern Louisiana areas and some adjacent sections of Texas. Under the management of W. R. Stephens, chairman of the board and president of the company, Arkansas Louisiana Gas has experienced great expansion. The state of Arkansas has long been a sleeping beauty, a state whose recognized resources have been little developed. Best known was the famous spa of Hot Springs, but now industrial development of this region is growing at a rapid pace. The transmission company has taken a leading role in this development by "providing one of the principal attractions in the portfolios of industrial development workers—a plentiful supply of natural gas at a lower cost than virtually any other section of the country. No other type of fuel," says the company in its annual report, "can even approach a competitive position with supplies by Arkansas Louisiana Gas Company. The fuel bill of our largest industrial customer would double if it were to change to the next cheapest type of fuel."

While Arkansas Louisiana continued gathering, transmitting, and distributing natural gas and producing oil and gas, it adopted a diversification program which is quite unique in the whole industry. The list of subsidiaries tells this story. It includes Arkla Air Conditioning Corporation, which is engaged in the manufacture and sale of Arkla-Servel All-Year gas air conditioning for home and industry; Arkansas Cement Corporation, which manufactures and sells Portland cement of all types; Arkansas Louisiana Finance Corporation, engaged in promoting the sale of gas appliances and the use of gas; Reynolds Gas Regulator Company, which manufactures gas regulators and control devices in Anderson, Indiana; Pitts and Bryant Company, Incorporated, which constructs pipe lines and distribution systems; Arkansas Louisiana Chemical Corporation, which extracts and processes liquids from natural gas; Arkansas Industrial Pipeline Corporation, organized to construct and operate natural gas transmission lines in the state of Arkansas; Razorback Fiberglass Corporation, which constructs and markets a line of fiberglass sports and fishing boats.

Net income is about ten times the $2,000,000 figure of 1954. Gas sales have increased from 181 billion cubic feet to 230 billion cubic feet.[41]

41 Gene T. Kinney, "Aggressive Selling and Offbeat Ideas Spark Rebirth of Arkla Gas," *Oil and Gas Journal,* Vol. LVIII, No. 16 (April 18, 1960), 80ff.

Lone Star Gas Company

The Great Southwest has one large individual gas utility, the Lone Star Gas Company, one of the oldest natural gas distributing companies in the country. It was established on June 1, 1909, in Dallas, Texas, and serves that city and Fort Worth. In its fifty-three years of operation, Lone Star Gas has grown up with the cities it serves. By 1959, it was a utility with assets of about $460,000,000, twice the asset figure of ten years before. Dechard A. Hulcy, Sr., former president; Lester T. Potter,[42] now president; and Marshall Newcomb, long-term general counsel, guided and contributed to its growth.

Lone Star Gas Company is as widespread as the area which it supplies. It owns and operates interconnected natural gas transmission lines, gathering lines, compressor stations, gasoline plants, distribution systems, and related properties in Texas and Oklahoma. It serves 852,134 customers in an area with an estimated population of 3,400,-000. The company is continuing to add about 26,000 new customers to its distribution system annually for a 3 per cent growth rate. New home construction represents the principal impetus to its growth. A warm climate such as that of Lone Star's service area is particularly conducive to gas air conditioning. With many new skyscrapers and other large buildings, total industrial, residential, and commercial air conditioning now in use on the system exceeds 79,000 tons and provides a revenue of more than $1,000,000 a year.

Lone Star not only excels in vigorous promotion of air conditioning but also in other gas-appliance fields and thus has helped natural gas maintain its position as the most sought-after fuel. This company has a very successful dealer assistance program which includes demonstrations by home economists, and also offers a parallel program through an architect-builder assistance department.

The company owns one subsidiary, the Lone Star Producing Company, which is active in both exploration and production. It operates six underground storage reservoirs. Its transmission system traverses a total of 112 counties, 93 in Texas and 19 in Oklahoma. All but 24 of these counties have gas production.

The long-range planning policy and foresight of Lone Star in pro-

---

[42] Mr. Potter was elected president of the American Gas Association in October, 1960. See William T. Harper, "L. T. Potter—Ice Man Turned Gas Man," *Gas,* Vol. XXXVI, No. 1 (October, 1960), 85, for an excellent description of Mr. Potter's career.

viding for current and future gas needs has resulted in the stable gas supply position now enjoyed by the company. The conservation of available gas through better utilization was achieved in 1914 when the company built the first large compressor station in Texas at Petrolia. The company also built the Southwest's first gasoline plant. It has pioneered in the utilization of casinghead and residue gas, gas proration, gas cycling, pressure maintenance, repressuring, and underground storage.

Mississippi River Fuel Corporation

A smaller but financially very strong transmission company is Mississippi River Fuel Corporation with Glen W. Clark serving as president and William G. Marbury serving as chairman of the board. Mississippi River Fuel, which supplies the well-known LaClede Gas Company of St. Louis with natural gas, sold some 72 billion cubic feet of gas for industrial purposes and 104 billion cubic feet to utilities in 1959. The company has an unusually large non-regulated industrial business. About two-thirds of its gas supply is obtained from United Gas Pipe Line, with the balance coming from other suppliers (27 per cent) and from company-owned reserves (7 per cent).

Mississippi River Fuel, one of the oldest gas pipe lines, sold its chemical plant to one of the largest companies in the chemical fertilizer business in 1959. One of its most interesting transactions in that year was the acquisition of about 247,000 shares of Class A common stock in Missouri Pacific Railroad at a cost of $12,300,000. The Missouri Pacific, a billion-dollar operation, is one of the major railroads of the country. This transaction made Mississippi River Fuel, already an important underground carrier of natural gas, an important surface carrier also. The company owns the Milwhite Mud Sales Company, which manufactures drilling chemicals. It operates a very successful exploration-production division and is also active in the development of storage facilities in close proximity to the expanding St. Louis market.

Florida Gas Company

On June 1, 1959, natural gas came to the state of Florida. Prior to that date, only two small areas of the state, Pensacola and Tallahassee, were being supplied with natural gas. Peninsular Florida was

167

the last major population area in the United States to be supplied with natural gas. With the opening of the Houston Corporation pipe-line valve at Brooker, about forty-five miles southwest of Jacksonville, natural gas became available to substantially all of the state.[43]

Recently, the name of the Houston Corporation was changed to Florida Gas Company, and the Florida pipe-line system extends to most of the populous areas in the state and consists of 1,488 miles of main line, mostly 24-inch diameter steel pipe, and 1,169 miles of lateral lines. The project was conceived in 1954.[44] Coastal Transmission Corporation, the Texas Gas and Oil Corporation, the Jacksonville Gas Corporation, and the Clint Murchison interests took part in the project. Construction began in October, 1958, and was completed with the commencement of operations in June 1959. The pipe line transports gas for Florida Power and Light Company and Florida Power Corporation. The contracts with these two power companies provide for the transportation by the pipe line at rates of 17.5 cents and 13.5 cents, respectively, per million Btu's of gas purchased by these companies in Texas and Louisiana fields.

The initial throughput of the pipe line was 282 million cubic feet daily, and an expansion in the capacity is planned to 418 million cubic feet daily. The line was at first based primarily on an industrial load because Florida's semi-tropical climate did not offer the big space-heating market that exists in most of the United States. Some 100 million cubic feet will go to Florida Power and Light Company plants and 50 million cubic feet to the Florida Power Corporation plants daily. The FPC has approved an expansion project which will raise the capacity of the pipe line from 275 million cubic feet a day to 371 million cubic feet.

The gas supply comes from seventy-two fields located in the Gulf Coast area of Texas and Louisiana for an average price of 16.9 cents per MCF. A unique feature of the pipe line is the financial arrangement whereby the power companies purchase gas directly from producers in Texas and Louisiana and pay the pipe lines a transportation

[43] Paul Reed and Gene T. Kinney, "The Florida Pipeline—A New Concept in Gas Transmission," *Oil and Gas Journal,* Vol. LVII, No. 11 (March 9, 1959), 108ff.

[44] Subsequently, F. E. Stanley resigned as president of all three companies (Coastal Transmission Corporation; Houston, Texas Gas and Oil Corporation; and Jacksonville Gas Corporation). W. J. Bowen is president of Florida Gas Company and its subsidiaries.

charge. The pipe lines of the Houston Corporation are literally carriers and are hired for transmission. The delivery price is adjusted to the price of fuel oil.[45] (*Petroleum Week* graphically describes the competitive battle being waged in Florida between oil men and the new natural gas distributing companies.)

The Florida Gas Company is capitalized at $172,000,000 and owns and operates gas distribution properties at Miami, Orlando, Lakeland, Daytona Beach, Eustis, Mt. Dora, Umatilla, and Jacksonville, Florida. It owns two subsidiaries, the Coastal Transmission Corporation and the Houston, Texas Gas and Oil Corporation. Coastal operates a gathering and transmission system from near McAllen, Texas, to Baton Rouge, Louisiana, where gas is delivered to Houston, Texas Gas and Oil for transmission to Florida markets.

Florida should be a good market. In area, it is one of the largest states. Its population is increasing rapidly, and it readily attracts new industry. Florida's population gain of almost two million persons during the past ten years was the second largest, numerically, in the United States. During this period, its position among the states with regard to population changed from twentieth to tenth place, as over three thousand new residents moved to Florida each week. When gains from native birth were added, the state experienced a weekly gain of over four thousand persons.

The Houston Corporation elected J. French Robinson of Fort Pierce, Florida, and Cleveland, Ohio, to the board. He was formerly chairman of the board and president of Consolidated Natural Gas Company, the East Ohio Gas Company, and Peoples Natural Gas Company. In 1960, W. J. Bowen became president, and Mr. Bowen and Mr. Robinson were added to the executive committee. Also, Leon M. Payne, a director, was elected secretary and will serve as general counsel of the company and its subsidiaries.

Although the Houston Corporation operated at a loss in 1960, authorized rate increases and expansion of sales augur well for the future. A project planned for the future is the construction, with Sun Oil Company, of an extraction plant fifty miles southwest of Jacksonville. The $7,000,000 plant will operate under the name Florida Hydrocarbons Company. It will sell large amounts of propane and bu-

[45] See the discussion regarding direct sales in the field to ultimate consumers in Chapter 12 of the present work.

tane in the state and ship natural gasoline by tanker to a large East Coast refinery.

Transwestern Pipeline Company

The biggest single project of 1960, Transwestern Pipeline Company's 1,800-mile Texas-California system, was completed in the first half of that year. The project, costing $193,000,000, was started late in 1959, and more than 1,500 miles were installed in the first six months of 1960.[46] Transwestern, according to an FPC decision, had to file rates reflecting a 6.25 per cent rate of return rather than a 6.5 per cent rate. As a result the gas price is 42 cents per thousand cubic feet rather than 43 cents as originally projected by the pipe line which transports gas from Texas fields to the California border.[47] The Pacific Lighting Gas Supply Company distributed the fuel in Southern California, principally to Los Angeles.

This major gas transmission company has its headquarters in Houston, Texas, and was under the leadership of Mills Cox who served as president until 1962. Basil Kantzer, formerly a vice-president of the Union Oil Company of California, succeeded him in that year.

[46] "FPC Approves Piping of Canadian Gas to West Coast in $400 Million Deal," *Business Week,* No. 1615 (August 13, 1960); Norris Willatt, "Big Market for Gas," *Barron's,* Vol. XL, No. 33 (August 15, 1960), 5.

[47] "FPC Cuts Midwestern Rate," *Oil and Gas Journal,* Vol. LVIII, No. 35 (August 29, 1960), 52.

6

FROM PUBLIC UTILITIES
TO PRIVATE HOMES

by Alfred M. Leeston

LOCAL gas companies, which are public utilities, now channel natural gas into over 30,000,000 homes.[1] This fuel supply was made available through the vast network of pipe lines constructed and laid by transmission companies. While the transmission companies developed the pipe-line systems, the distributing companies worked to convert existing installations from coal gas and water gas to natural

[1] In 1960 the gas distribution industry was comprised of approximately 1,322 utilities of all sizes, ranging from small municipal gas systems of a few hundred customers to giant utilities like Southern California Gas Company with over 1,500,000 customers. To state that the makeup of the gas industry is complex would be an understatement. Basically, the industry has three major segments—production, transmission, and distribution. There are more than eight thousand independent producers. This term includes most major oil companies, many of whom produce both oil and gas. At the beginning of 1961 there were approximately 120 gas transmission companies taking gas at the wellhead and transporting it to the city gate where it was then sold at wholesale prices to gas distributors.

Of the 1,322 gas distribution utilities, approximately 300 are of major size. These serve 95 per cent of all customers in the United States. Seventy of the 1,322 operate transmission facilities and can be classified as integrated gas companies. In other instances some of the larger gas distribution companies have separate, wholly-owned subsidiaries in the fields of gas transmission and/or production. Peoples Gas Light and Coke Company, of Chicago, Illinois, is an example. Its subsidiaries include the vast Natural Gas Pipe Line Company, Natural Gas Storage Company of Illinois, which operates underground storage facilities, and the Chicago District Pipeline Company. All of the subsidiaries are separate entities.

For further information regarding industry operations, the reader is referred to: Federal Power Commission, "General Rules and Regulations Under the Natural Gas Act" (Sec. 154.91: Applicability, Independent Producers); Federal Power Commission, "Uniform System of Accounting for Natural Gas Companies" (Sec. 201.3–16: Regarding Transmission Systems and Distribution Systems); Federal Power Commission, *Direct Sales by Producers of Natural Gas to Interstate Natural Gas Pipeline Companies, 1960.*

gas, a fuel with almost twice the heat content of manufactured gas.[2]

A striking instance of successful conversion was that undertaken by Brooklyn Union Gas. This well-managed gas utility—one of the largest in the country—converted the appliances of the Brooklynites in 1952 at a cost of almost $21,000,000. This conversion was done with great skill and was certainly no mean accomplishment in such a crowded place as the Dodgers' former battleground.[3] Brooklyn Union was then serving 850,000 customers but now, after merging with two other gas utilities, it supplies over 1,000,000.

Not satisfied with the initial results, Brooklyn Union pursued a vigorous promotion campaign which was typical of the new aggressive spirit permeating both the transmission and distribution phases of the gas industry after 1945. A large advertisement in the *New York Times* of October 8, 1957, announced a "Big Fall Special":

> You can have gas heat installed for as little as $340.00 immediate delivery and installation. There's no need to suffer through another winter with costly, inferior heat when it's so easy and economical to enjoy worry-free GAS HEAT. *Imagine!* You can convert your present boiler to GAS in a few hours. Absolutely no fuss or inconvenience—even on the coldest day. *Remember!* GAS costs much less than other fuels. And there are no extra costs of any kind! No service contracts . . . no tank-failure insurance . . . no expensive repairs. GAS is so clean, you'll save money on painting and decorating—save many hours of housework too.
>
> YOU CAN'T LOSE! . . . Try cleaner, cheaper GAS HEAT for a year without risking a cent. If your heating costs should exceed our Certified Estimate, we'll remove the equipment and refund every cent you've paid on it—including installation costs! So before you order any more fuel, call us or ask your licensed plumber for complete details. But do it today!

Brooklyn Union wrote off $13,400,000 in plant investment made obsolete by the conversion. "The savings in operations made by the

[2] Natural gas has a heat content of 1,040 Btu's per cubic foot. One Btu or British thermal unit is the amount of heat required to raise the temperature of one pound of water one degree Fahrenheit.

[3] OEEC Technical Assistance Mission, *Long Distance Gas Transport in the United States,* 170. Another remarkable conversion was that accomplished by a neighbor of Brooklyn Union, the Long Island Lighting Company at Minneola, New York. This much smaller utility established an "extremely flexible and reliable" conversion plant. For further details of this conversion, see OEEC Technical Assistance Mission, *Long Distance Gas Transport in the United States,* 169–70.

conversion were sufficient to amortize this expenditure," said the president of the company, John E. Heyke,[4] "but we are in a tough competitive market. The thought has been expressed many times that gas distribution companies are monopolies. We are not monopolies. . . . the fuel market in New York City is about as tough a competitive market as you can find." Later in his testimony, Mr. Heyke added, "In the industrial field, except in cases where gas has a premium value for process use, natural gas must be at a strictly competitive price with coal and oil. This is particularly true of the price at which we sell interruptible industrial gas during our off-peak periods. Sale of off-peak or *summer valley gas* is important to us [Brooklyn Union] because it permits us to take gas from the pipe line at a higher load factor and thereby reduce our average cost of gas."

The load factor of Brooklyn Union and many other gas utilities is about 25 per cent, which means that the balance of the gas must be disposed of at something over the commodity price in order to make this cost. Thus, distributing gas in markets as competitive as that of Brooklyn Union and others found in the northeastern region of the country is a challenge. The local gas companies have great difficulties and little opportunity to overcome the price situation created by a highly competitive fuel market on the one hand and the constant increases in the cost of gas on the other. At the beginning of the construction of a vast transmission network, natural gas was extremely low-priced at the wellhead. The pipe lines opened up apparently insatiable markets and natural gas changed from a sellers' to a buyers' commodity. The average wellhead price rose 100 per cent—from 6¢/MCF in 1947 to 12.5¢/MCF in 1959 and still higher in 1960. Recent estimates from the ranks of the transmission industry foresee a virtual doubling of the city gate[5] prices that prevailed when gas was first delivered to the East.

Some of the problems that local gas utilities face are similar to those of the pipe lines but are far more intensified. The nature of their business is not an easy one. As public utilities, they are subject to

---

[4] On October 19, 1962, Mr. Heyke was elected president of the American Gas Association. See "Presidential Profile," *Gas,* Vol. 38, No. 10 (October, 1962), 75.

[5] The *city gate* is the point or measuring station at which a distributing gas utility receives gas from a natural gas pipe-line company.

regulation by state commissions and sometimes by local regulatory bodies. They distribute natural gas to industrial, commercial, and residential customers. The residential customers buy gas for space heating, cooking, water heating, and other purposes and are the main source of revenue. Yet, the industrial customers are no less important. The large quantities of gas they use help fill the gaps, *lows*, or *valleys* that exist between the peak demand by individual householders in the winter and the slack season in residential gas consumption that occurs in the summer. Commercial customers include offices, stores, clubs, hotels, and similar types of buildings. Hotels often purchase inexpensive valley gas for water heating, a big item of their operation.

Two types of service are rendered by the distribution companies, *firm* and *interruptible*. Firm service is the year-round delivery of gas without interruption. "Such sales come under public utility regulation, which requires that the need of the public be met on demand."[6] Interruptible sales are subject to interruption by the gas company at any time the gas is needed for delivery to household consumers. Interruptible customers, generally, are firm gas customers for a six-month warm weather period, then are subject to control by the gas company during cold weather periods when peak demands may occur. On the other hand, there are so-called off-peak customers whose gas usage is not subject to control by the gas company. These customers determine when they will stop using gas. The valley gas they purchase from the utility is available gas not required by the company in off-peak periods.

Interruptible and off-peak sales are made at low rates to attract industries that have seasonable demands or can afford to be interrupted when household demands take over. Firm industrial sales are also made a much lower rates than sales to residential customers. This is a common practice among service industries. They all are in need of filling slack seasons in order to keep operations and revenues as balanced as possible. To supply Philadelphia with natural gas, "a pipe line designed to meet the peak-day capacity of the space-heating load would be busy for the equivalent of only 75 days in the year. . . . The summer-time firm business is only about a quarter of the demand on a normal winter day, and only one-eighth of what we must plan

[6] Erich W. Zimmermann, *World Resources and Industries,* 563. See also the chapter on natural gas which begins on page 832 of the same work.

for a design day . . . that occurs once in 20 years but for which each gas company must be ready."[7] The pipe-line and distribution companies have gained experience in their struggle for existence in how to increase the number of residential consumers while adding industrial customers on both firm and interruptible bases. In this most interesting game of action and counteraction, the price of gas plays an all-important role.

In fixing the rate for house heating, public utilities such as Brooklyn Union Gas Company must solve a dual problem. They must both meet the high cost of service and compete effectively in the house-heating market. To do this, they establish rates for gas house heating competitive with the cost of oil heating even though the cost of distributing gas is high. The distributing company must bear the cost of the heavy capital investment in mains and services in the city streets. In any urban area, particularly a city such as New York, the costs of underground construction are very high in relation to the cost of running large pipe lines across the country through fields and unpopulated areas. There is also the cost of individual meters for each consumer. Even after the utility has made all the investment necessary to supply a customer, it has the costs of billing, meter reading, collecting, servicing, and sales promotion.

While it is true that the unsatisfactory load factor for space heating increases the cost of supplying this service, it has been only a minor factor in the establishment of rates for this service. Brooklyn Union is able to meet the difficult load-factor problem quite effectively with a combination of underground storage service provided by the pipe lines and the sale of any excess pipe-line gas over and above the firm and storage requirements in the summertime as interruptible service to large industrial customers.

Brooklyn Union has been very successful in the sale of interruptible gas in large volumes to commercial and industrial concerns, thus

[7] Charles H. Frazier, "Distribution Company Gas Purchasing Problems, or from Slide-Rule to Crystal Ball," paper presented to the Briefing Conference on Natural Gas and Oil Problems, Federal Bar Association and Bureau of National Affairs, Incorporated, Washington, D. C., March 6, 1959.

Two successive winters of unusual length and severity (1957–58 and 1958–59) proved more clearly and more conclusively than ever that it is necessary and profitable for local gas companies to be prepared to meet peak demand. Underground storage, as it is constantly being developed, may be one of the factors which will enable gas companies to stand ready to meet such peak demands.

175

leveling the deep valleys in sendout of natural gas during the warmer months of the year. In its 1957 annual report, Brooklyn Union mentions, as a striking example, the supplying of New York's gigantic International Airport. Brooklyn Union has an agreement with the company to provide gas on an interruptible basis as an alternate fuel for four 50,000,000-Btu boilers. These supply central heating and air conditioning to the International Arrivals Building. This sizable load will be increased with the addition of future buildings. In 1958, Brooklyn Union acquired another large summer load, this time as the result of a water heater rental program. Under this plan, 130 large-volume water-heating installations were made in apartment houses ranging in size from eight to sixty-five dwelling units.

In 1958 the number of Brooklyn Union space-heating accounts reached 100,000. This figure does not seem very large when it is compared with the 291,000 accounts listed in the same year by Peoples Gas Light and Coke Company of Chicago, but the Windy City is old gas-heating territory while Brooklyn needs to attract new loads either in the replacement market where natural gas replaces coal and oil, or in the highly promising field of residential heating in new buildings and residences. In all of these sales areas, the utility has been highly successful. A pattern of load growth in natural gas heating has definitely been established. For example, in 1958 replacement of oil installations accounted for 36 per cent of the sales in this field, and in the one- and two-family new home market this very aggressive utility is securing approximately 95 per cent of the heating business. The oil industry has expressed the hope that increases in the price of natural gas may halt the inroads being made by this fuel into the markets of other fuels, especially in the northeastern area of the country. The outstanding performance of Brooklyn Union proves convincingly that superb salesmanship will continue to increase the use of natural gas at least for residential heating, but the competitive struggle is serious.[8] In large commercial buildings, such as apartments or big

[8] W. B. Davis and J. H. Schweitzer, "Natural Gas—Partner and Competitor," *Journal of Petroleum Technology,* Vol. XI, No. 5 (May, 1959), 13; Thomas W. Phelps, "Petroleum's Place in the Future Energy Requirements of the United States," *Journal of Petroleum Technology,* Vol. XI, No. 7 (July, 1959), 22; Austin Cadle, "U. S. Petroleum Forecast and Dynamic World Growth in Petroleum Demands," *Proceedings,* American Petroleum Institute (Section IV, Interdivisional), Vol. XXXVIII (1958), 24; Cornelius J. Dwyer, *Nuclear Energy and World Fuel Prices* (Reports on the Productive Uses of

office buildings where No. 6 (heavy fuel) oil is used, Brooklyn Union's rates are not sufficiently competitive at this time to make much of a dent in this large boiler market. Energy competition is particularly keen in the densely populated metropolitan Chicago area. The margin between the cost and the selling price of gas used as boiler fuel is, in the case of a steam-generating consumer like Commonwealth Edison, very minute. Costs of supply are tending upward, and the lower cost now attributable to gas for space heating will probably rise until it equals or exceeds the cost of heating with oil and perhaps with propane. For the present, new buildings in the Chicago area are making use of gas for space heating to the extent that this service can be committed to them at the time of construction, but the future is uncertain. Increases in natural gas prices at the wellhead may be balanced by improved technological methods in pipe-line operation, by peak shaving through the use of liquefied natural gas,[9] and by importing natural gas from Canada, although such imports should not be allowed to slow down domestic explorations for natural gas as has been the effect of oil imports upon oil exploration.

Chicago's biggest gas utility faces a new kind of competition from electric heat which is moving into more homes as electric utilities reduce winter heating rates to offset their own wintertime valleys in demand.[10] It has not yet reached menacing proportions as competition for gas heat, but J. J. Hedrick, former president of Peoples Gas Light and Coke Company in Chicago, has warned that "the electric heating people mean business." Another well-known gas utility executive, Marvin Chandler, president of Northern Illinois Gas Company, calls electric heat a "novelty luxury." Executives of the electric utilities welcome this new device to increase the load of their companies. For instance, Philip Sporn, president of the American Electric Power Company, predicted an increase "from 14,200 electrically

Nuclear Energy, National Planning Association, Washington, D. C., 1958), 74; Perry D. Teitelbaum, *Nuclear Energy and the U.S. Fuel Economy, 1955–1980* (Reports on the Productive Uses of Nuclear Energy, National Planning Association, Washington, D. C., 1958), 17, 20, 187.

9 "In the Wake of the Methane Pioneer," *Petroleum Press Service,* Vol. XXVI, No. 5 (May, 1959), 172–74; William R. Connole, "The Role of Regulation in Developing the Transportation and Use of Liquid Methane," paper presented to the Briefing Conference on Natural Gas and Oil Problems, Federal Bar Association and Bureau of National Affairs, Incorporated, Washington, D. C., March 5, 1959.

10 William B. Colwell, "Electric Heat," *Wall Street Journal,* Vol. XXII, No. 118 (December 16, 1958), 1, 6.

heated homes at the end of 1958 to some 200,000 by 1963."[11] The chief drawback of electric heating is its high operating cost, and gas men maintain that electric heat is unable to cope with extreme cold. Many builders are firmly opposed to electric heating. A reporter for the *Wall Street Journal* quotes a builder who has installed gas heat in all fifty of his 1958 homes as saying, "Electric heat is too hard to sell to the public. People already are sold on gas heat."[12]

Many people saw in the electric heat pump what they believed was the answer to both heating and cooling problems, but their rejoicing was premature. Installation and operation costs for this device are extremely high, and it is far from perfect. "When the outside temperature stays much below the temperature at which the strip heaters cut in, the efficiency or performance factor of the heat pump can drop considerably and the cost of resistance heating can increase rapidly."[13] Adds the Zinder Report, "Design data for the majority of types of (heat pump) systems are inadequate, and it will be several years before proper development and design information will enable the widespread satisfactory application of the heat pump."[14] This stage has not yet arrived, and the gas industry still has a chance to make the most of the findings of the Zinder Report that culminate in such headlines as "Gas Is Cheaper" and "Costs Are Lower With Gas."

Much economic theory and government regulation surrounds the process of *rate making*. The economic theory of the prices which utilities, including gas companies, should charge for services has been well developed.[15] One of the problems involved in this development

[11] See the interesting booklet *Energy* which contains three addresses by Mr. Sporn. The author-president is a great natural gas promoter and was awarded the John Fritz medal, the highest award given by the A.I.M.E.

[12] Colwell, "Electric Heat," *Wall Street Journal,* Vol. XXII, No. 118 (December 16, 1958), 6.

[13] The heat pump needs a helping hand from resistance units when the mercury plunges under the zero mark. Then the same house that would need about $170 worth of electricity could be heated by oil at a cost of $160 and by gas for only $132, reports Mr. Colwell on page 6 of the *Wall Street Journal* article cited above in footnotes 10 and 12.

[14] Clifford A. Brandt and Fred E. Egan, "Gas and Electric Service in Multiple Housing," *Criteria for Determining Costs of Gas and Electric Service in Military and Public Housing Projects.* Report prepared by H. Zinder and Associates, Incorporated, Washington, D. C., 1957.

[15] See Ralph Kirby Davidson, *Price Discrimination in Selling Gas and Electricity,* 254ff.; Clemens, *Economics and Public Utilities,* 179–80; Troxel, *Economics of Public*

is whether a utility should charge all customers equally on the basis of marginal costs, or whether different rates should be charged for different types of service. Any utility with excess capacity is interested in increasing sales as a means of spreading the burden of overhead costs.[16] However, new business can be obtained only by offering the service at such lower price as competition from other fuels requires. If revenues are to be maintained, the lower price can be applied only to new classes of consumers or to increased volume of consumption by existing customers. Consequently, most gas companies classify the type of service available as residential, commercial, or industrial and set different rates[17] for each classification. Within any classification, rates decrease as the volume consumed increases.[18] So long as the rate set for the lower price customer covers all additional costs incurred to make the sale plus some contribution to the utilities' overhead expense, all customers benefit from the lower price sale.

Rates charged by gas companies are subject to local, state and federal regulation[19] under statutes which require that rates be fair and reasonable. The statutes give legal recognition to the principle of charging different rates for different services in that only undue discrimination is prohibited.

Figure 27, which shows the daily *sendout* (volume of gas sold) for

Utilities; Glaeser, *Public Utilities in American Capitalism,* 321–32; Bonbright, *Principles of Public Utility Rates;* Irston C. Barnes, *The Economics of Public Utility Regulation;* and American Gas Association Rate Committee, *Gas Rate Fundamentals.*

[16] Barnes, *The Economics of Public Utility Regulation,* 331.

[17] Such different rates are called *discriminatory rates* in economic theory. There is much theorizing about rate making by electricity and gas utilities, but Eli Winston Clemens, who seasons the extremely dull matter of utility economics with an occasional sprinkling of dry humor, says, "Scientific gas rates are made in much the same fashion as electric rates, but no matter how precise the cost allocation might be, a rate is not worth the hyperbolic paper it is drawn upon if no one will use the stuff anyway."
Concerning block rates adopted for promotional purposes and to compete successfully with oil and coal, see Clemens, *Economics and Public Utilities,* 297. About natural gas rates including city gate rates, see Davidson, *Price Discrimination in Selling Gas and Electricity,* 308.

[18] The change of rate with volume may be expressed in any of the several standard rate forms which include: flat rate, step meter rate, block meter rate, and demand and commodity rate. American Gas Association Rate Committee, *Gas Rate Fundamentals,* 174; Barnes, *The Economics of Public Utility Regulation,* 354.

[19] See Chapter 12 of the present work for a detailed discussion of gas industry regulation by local and federal authorities.

179

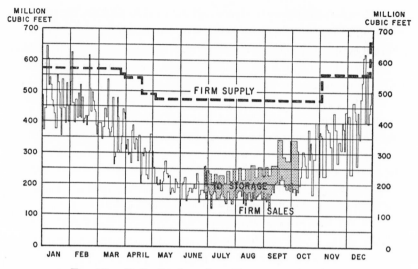

FIG. 27.—Daily Sendout for a Representative Area.

a typical year, illustrates the seasonal nature of gas sales. The sendout data are presented in more usable form from the standpoint of managing a gas distribution system in the typical load duration curve shown in Figure 28. The distributor of natural gas could insure gas availability to his peak-day customers by building facilities large enough to handle peak loads and by contracting for a firm supply of gas large enough for peak days. Under these conditions the peak-day consumer must pay for unused summertime pipe-line capacity and for unused summertime gas supply. Under the generic concept of *peak shaving* a number of procedures have been developed which either utilize excess line capacity, utilize excess supply, or make gas available at relatively low cost for short winter periods. The utilization of any of these peak shaving procedures results in a lower cost of gas to the peak-day consumer. At the sales end of the gas distribution business the interruptible industrial contract has been developed. The gas represented by the area between "Firm Supply" and "Firm Sales plus To Storage" in Figure 27 might be utilized for interruptible sales. At the supply end of the distributing business the contracts under which gas-distributing companies purchase gas from pipe-line transporters have been devised with the peak-shaving problem in mind.

180

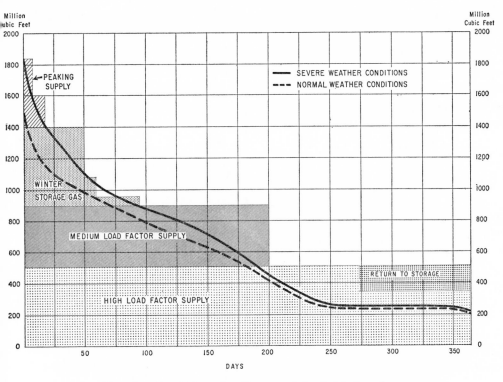

Fig. 28.—Load Duration Curve and Available Supply
for a Representative Area.

The term *load factor* as used in the natural gas industry means the ratio of the average deliveries over a given period to the maximum capacity of the pipe-line facilities under consideration. Thus, on an annual basis, gas supply which is contracted for over shorter periods represents a lower load factor supply than does gas which is to be taken over a longer period. For some purposes a 365-day firm supply would be considered a 100 per cent load factor supply. Generally speaking, the unit price of gas supplied to distributing companies increases as load factor decreases. Most distributing company gas-supply contracts set forth a two-part rate consisting of a *demand component* and a *commodity component*. The demand component represents a fixed monthly charge measured by the amount of gas which the seller must make available and is payable whether any particular quantity of gas is taken by the distributor or not. The com-

181

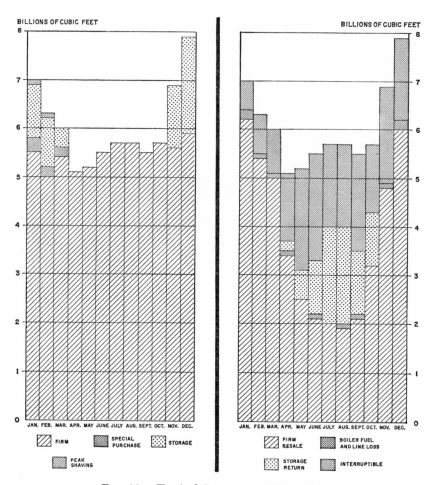

FIG. 29.—Typical Sources and Disposition
of Distributing Company Gas Supply.

modity charge is expressed in cents per thousand cubic feet delivered
and is directly proportionate to the quantity of gas actually taken
during the month by the distributor.

The gas supply of typical distributing companies is made up of a
mixture of purchases under four general types of contracts specified
by the load factor. The *high load factor supply contract* requires the

seller to have the stated quantity of gas available 365 days a year and requires the buyer to pay for some minimum annual quantity (usually 70 to 80 per cent of the available quantity) whether taken or not. Such gas is sometimes referred to as *firm supply*. Under a *medium load factor supply contract* gas is purchased for delivery over a 180- to 270-day period which is centered about the house-heating season. Frequently such supply is coupled with the right of the distributing company to require the seller to place some part of the purchased gas in storage ("return to storage") and redeliver the stored gas during the height of the heating season. Under a *low load factor supply contract,* winter storage gas is bought for delivery over a 60- to 90-day period. The selling pipe line uses underground storage to provide this type of service. The provisions of a *peaking supply contract* make gas available for very short periods of up to five or six days in the form of artificial gas from water gas manufacturing facilities or from propane-air plants which are usually owned by the distributing company. In the future peaking gas may be made available from liquefied methane plants located in or near the distribution area. The gas for such a plant might be supplied off a domestic pipe line.

Figure 28 has been marked to show the different parts of the load duration curve which may be satisfied with different types of gas supply. This figure illustrates the peak demand on a distribution system during the relatively few days when temperatures are extremely low. Figure 29 shows a typical year's experience of a representative distributing company regarding sources and disposition of gas.

Distribution company gas supply contracts involving the sale of natural gas in interstate commerce for resale are subject to control under the Natural Gas Act. Of particular interest are the Mobile and Memphis decisions of the United States Supreme Court to the effect that Natural Gas Act control does not entail the right to make unilateral changes in the contract price. However, many distributor gas-supply contracts contain a price provision of the type considered in the Memphis case which provides that the effective price under the contract shall be the stated initial price or such other price as may be put into effect from time to time under the Natural Gas Act.

7

NOTHING HEATS
LIKE A GAS FLAME

by Alfred M. Leeston

"NOTHING heats like a gas flame." The advantages of natural gas implicit in this slogan coupled with the energetic efforts of natural gas distributors constitute two of the more important actors responsible for the rapid growth of the natural gas industry. The distributors' efforts have been so successful in the highly competitive fuels market that they resulted in a sixfold increase in natural gas usage during the 1930–60 period, while total energy consumption increased only twice in that period. This growth has been encouraged by the advantages of natural gas[1] over other fuels: a reasonable price, which has usually been lower than that of competing fuels; dependability of supply, which is higher for underground pipe-line movement of gas than for surface transport of coal, oil, or electricity; cleanliness in burning without ash or smoke; convenience in the absence of user's storage facilities, in its continuous availability, and in its instantaneous heat-giving at the point desired; controllability—natural gas is more rapidly and accurately controllable than other fuels; and higher efficiency of utilization. Domestic heating tests show an efficiency of 80 per cent for gas, 57 per cent for oil, and 59 per cent for coal. Electricity is about 100 per cent efficient in home heating, but only 35 per cent of the fuel consumed at the generating station appears as electricity. Indeed gas is the immaculate fuel.

Although the growth of gas usage has been spectacular since 1930, the gas industry is one of the oldest of the public utilities. Only public water supply has a longer history. Gas distribution started in Baltimore in 1816, passenger railroad service commenced in 1830, tele-

[1] American Gas Association Rate Committee, *Gas Rate Fundamentals,* 53.

graphic service in 1844, telephone services in 1879, and the first commercial generation of electricity took place in 1882.[2]

The appliances which utilize gas are relatively simple, since they are based on a flame and have few moving parts. One of the first of these was the Bunsen burner, invented in 1855. Domestic gas ranges were introduced in 1851, and a whole panorama of gas appliances, including roasters, gas irons, space heaters, and gas engines, came into being after the Civil War. The invention of the incandescent electric lamp in 1879 heralded electricity's invasion of the lighting field. Nevertheless, the Welsbach mantle for incandescent gas lighting was introduced in 1885, and the sale of manufactured gas showed a loss in only two of the next thirty years. Gas refrigerators appeared in 1926, and gas air conditioning equipment was offered to the public in 1937. The list of appliances continues to grow and now includes clothes driers and refuse disposers. Another recent development has been the conversion from manufactured to natural gas. In 1930 two-thirds of gas utility customers received manufactured gas. In 1960 natural gas was served to 94 per cent of all gas customers in the United States.

The use of natural gas may be broken down into four end-use categories: residential, commercial, power generation, and industrial. Figure 30 shows past usage and predicted future usage of natural gas in the United States according to these general classifications. The following table shows the number of customers, therms consumed, and revenues produced for each category in 1960.

		Therms		Revenues	
	Thousand Customers	Millions Used	Per cent of Total	Thousand Dollars	Per cent of Total
Residential	30,417.5	31,881.2	34.4	3,177,430	56.5
Commercial	2,458.3	9,197.8	9.9	723,448	13.0
Industrial & Power Generation	140.6	47,093.6	50.7	1,563,285	27.8
Other	37.4	4,703.8	5.0	153,224	2.7
TOTAL	33,053.8	92,876.4	100.0	5,617,387	100.0

(Source: American Gas Association, *1961 Gas Facts,* section VI.)

[2] American Gas Association, "The Natural Gas Story," unpublished manuscript edited

The residential usage category covers all household uses of gas including space heating. Lighting, refrigeration, cooking, food processing, space heating and cooling, and other heat-consuming demands come under the commercial heading. Power generation includes that gas used in the generation of electricity. Fuel and feed-stock uses in such industries as petroleum refining, cement manufacture, metal manufacture and working, and chemical manufacture are classified as industrial.

RESIDENTIAL USES

In 1960 it was estimated that $18,000,000,000 was invested by some 31 million customers in domestic appliances, which represents an average of $600 per household served. The following table shows the use distribution of these appliances:

Type of Appliance	Number Used in Millions
Space Heating	39.9
Ranges	33.0
Water Heaters	23.1
Refrigerators	3.4
Driers	2.3
Incinerators and Gas Lights	0.7

(Source: American Gas Association.)

Demand seems to be far from the saturation point. In 1961 an American Gas Association study showed thirty-seven distributors who still exercise restrictions in the installation of new gas-fired equipment.

To sell gas appliances requires constant effort by the distributors to keep the American housewife convinced of the advantages that gas has over other fuels. United Gas has been outstanding in its promotional efforts.[3] Its aim is to teach housewives about the time-saving convenience, the comfort, the ease of operation, and the trouble-free

---

by Francis X. Welch. The latest step in the development of gas appliances is a gas-fired toilet exhibited at the American Gas Association Convention, Dallas, Texas, 1961.

[3] United Gas Corporation operates gas distribution systems in three southern states. The Texas Distribution Division serves cities and towns in the Lone Star state. The Louisiana-Mississippi Distribution Division supplies towns and cities in those two states. United's wholly-owned subsidiary, United Gas Pipe Line Company, operates extensive transmission facilities, supplies gas to United Gas Corporation's distribution operations and to other gas distribution companies, and also sells gas to other pipe-line (gas trans-

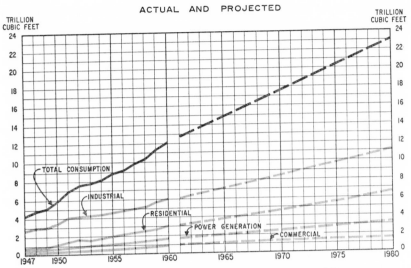

FIG. 30.—Consumption of Natural Gas in the United States.

maintenance characteristic of today's ultramodern, automatic natural gas appliances. ". . . sales personnel through the system bring this story to the woman of the Gulf South in many ways," according to United's annual report. "In addition to regular advertising in various media, which features the advantages, economy and smartness of modern gas appliances, sales personnel bring into play the sales techniques of demonstration and display of 'live' all-gas kitchens. Many company offices and major service centers are equipped with attractive, colorful 'live' all-gas kitchens. Cooking schools and other events are held for the public as well as organized groups. A feature of the cooking school program is Summer Cooking Schools for Teenagers who will become the housewives of the future.

"All of these demonstrations are so arranged that a large number of the women present become familiar with the pleasures of a gas kitchen by actually cooking in the oven and on top burners and by using gas driers, gas refrigerators, and other appliances in the kitchen.

"Major promotions of various kinds also are carried out with architects, builders and subdivision developers in home planning and in 'Parade of Homes' events which feature homes completely equipped

mission) companies at wholesale rates. Another subsidiary, Union Producing Company, engages in exploration, drilling, and producing activities.

with high-style all-gas appliances and other equipment. Special co-operation also is given to dealers and manufacturers in carrying out their programs of teaching women about the 'new era' of natural gas appliances.

"Another facet of the aggressive 'try-it-for-yourself' program is an exhibit building at Shreveport (headquarters of United Gas Corporation). Thousands of women spend countless hours in the four 'live' super modern, colorful kitchens and complete home laundry in the structure. Here, they learn of the advanced beauty and utility of gas appliances and secure ideas for decorating and planning their own kitchens.[4] Sales personnel conduct programs in connection with college and high school home economics teachers and classes in their home towns, and also bring class groups with their teachers to the exhibit building for a day of demonstration and instruction in the use of modern gas appliances."

The large company did not neglect the market for gas air conditioning units and gas lights, both being manufactured by subsidiaries of United Gas's neighbor, the very active Arkansas Louisiana Gas Company (Shreveport, Louisiana). The attractive "Gaslites" are being installed by the thousands in front yards, around patios and swimming pools, and at a great assortment of commercial establishments. "The distinctive charm of the soft unique light is apparent on sight," advertises Southern Union Gas Company in Dallas, Texas. These lights require only a minimum of service and consume more than a thousand cubic feet of gas per month. Even a seemingly small appliance can increase the consumption of gas.

How well the modern version of the romantic gas light has been accepted is revealed in recent American Gas Association figures which indicate that more than 300,000 gas lights of all types were in daily use in the United States at the end of 1960. The gas light renaissance will undoubtedly continue, and more than thirty different manufacturers, mostly small firms, are now producing them for domestic use.

Even more important is the sale of gas air conditioning units vigorously promoted by many gas utilities. The principal manufacturer is Arkansas Louisiana Gas Company which, through its subsidiary Arkla Air Conditioning Corporation, now turns out more than 20,-

[4] Armon Glenn, "Gas Appliances—They Are Making Steady Inroads on Competitive Equipment," *Barron's*, Vol. XXXVIII, No. 40 (October 6, 1958), pp. 11, 13.

000 units a year. This is more than a sixfold increase over production in 1957 when Arkansas Louisiana Gas bought Servel's gas air conditioning business. Arkla makes central units for year-round heating and cooling.[5]

Following the lead taken by Arkla, a number of other manufacturers have entered the gas air conditioning business. Bryant Manufacturing Company and its West Coast affiliate, Day and Night Manufacturing Company, are now marketing small units designed for residential application. Gas-engine-driven units are manufactured by several firms. The industry, under the auspices of the American Gas Association, is conducting numerous research programs to develop new types of gas-fueled air conditioning devices. One of the more promising of these devices, a free-piston engine powered compressor unit, developed at Battelle Memorial Institute, is now being studied and readied for commercial use by the Robertshaw Controls Company.

The gas utilities, in an effort to spur sales of gas air conditioning equipment, have turned to leasing plans in which the utility installs and services gas air conditioning equipment in homes, businesses, and industries for a stated monthly service charge. The customer pays only the cost of fuel plus the lease service charge and need not make any capital outlay. Most of the leasing plans now in effect cover equipment from small three-ton residential units up to large twenty-five-ton commercial units. Leasing of larger equipment—up to one thousand tons—is contemplated by a number of utilities. Early leasing plans were put into effect by Lone Star Gas Company, Dallas, Texas, and the Southern California and Southern Counties Gas companies, who serve nearly 2,500,000 southern California customers.

Another heir to Servel's mantle in gas refrigeration is Whirlpool Corporation, which bought Servel's patents and its plant in Evansville, Indiana, to make gas refrigerators. An aggressive newcomer to the field of gas refrigerators is the huge Norge Division of Borg-Warner. Arkla, when it started out in this new line of business, demanded and received a guarantee from major gas utilities and the

[5] *Ibid,* 13. This article points out that "with today's profit margins most producers [of gas appliances] will find it easier to translate this potential into higher sales than into significantly higher earnings." Consumer spending has considerably increased, but most of it is installment buying.

American Gas Association for the sale of a substantial part of its output for the first three years. Whirlpool and Norge, on the other hand, have received only the assurance of intensive promotion of their gas refrigerators from the gas distribution companies.

Because gas air conditioning and gas refrigeration have not entered the market in large quantities, gas ranges, water heaters, and clothes driers form the mainstay of the gas appliance business.[6] It is in this part of the appliance business that close co-operation between utility and dealer is required. Over a hundred companies share in the $1,000,000,000-a-year market for gas appliances and heating equipment. "In the appliance end," says Barron's "—mainly gas ranges, clothes driers and incinerators—are such firms as Tappan,[7] Norge Division of Borg-Warner, George D. Roper, Hamilton Mfg. Co., and Whirlpool."[8] There are also names like A. O. Smith, the large manufacturer in Milwaukee who is also prominent in production of steel pipe for pipe lines. "Among the major furnace producers are Holland Furnace, Iron Fireman, Worthington, Coleman, American Radiator, and Standard Sanitary Corp., Carrier, Trane, A. O. Smith and Rheem Mfg. Co. Several of the latter group also make water heaters. A. O. Smith and Rheem, in particular, have a big stake in this field."[9]

As to the structure of the appliance industry, it seems important to realize "that there are today more than 500 gas appliance concerns, some large companies, but the majority small, often family businesses, handed down from the founders."[10] This is one reason that the gas industry has difficulty competing with electric appliance industry giants through sales promotion. The small gas appliance concerns have fewer funds for advertising. Recently, the gas industry began

[6] Of course, this is in addition to the heating equipment for central heating, direct heating, and gas floor furnaces. Once the consumer has natural gas in his home for heating purposes, he usually chooses to install additional gas appliances.

[7] The sensational development of Tappan—a typical American success story—can be gathered from an advertisement for Reader's Digest in Time magazine, May 11, 1959, pp. 58–59. This spread illustrates what well-planned advertising can do to increase gas appliance sales.

[8] Glenn, "Gas Appliances—They Are Making Steady Inroads on Competitive Equipment," Barron's, Vol. XXXVIII, No. 40 (October 6, 1958), 13.

[9] Ibid., 11

[10] James H. Collins, "Gas Really Has a Hard Sell," Public Utilities Fortnightly, Vol. LXIII, No. 6 (March 12, 1959), 379–89. This contribution by a writer experienced in public utility matters deals with the marketing problems of the gas industry and deserves wide attention.

using the nation-wide facility of television, sharing with other sponsors the program "Playhouse 90." As to the advertising effect, the industry probably will study whether an outlay of $3,000,000 has the desired result or whether programs and commercials should be improved.[11]

In January 1960, the gas industry took a big step forward in promoting gas appliance sales and industry co-operation among its many manufacturers. The big step was the establishment of a Gas Appliance Center in the Dallas Trade Mart. The center is the only year-round, permanent display of its kind in the nation.[12] Strategically located in the heart of a burgeoning, busy, multi-million-dollar Master Market Center, the Gas Appliance Center is truly a "Show case for the Gas Industry's Products." In its twenty-five thousand square feet of display space, the center houses twenty-six exhibitors—all manufacturers of leading gas appliance lines. In addition there is an Industry of the Future Exhibit, displaying new developments and research projects in the gas industry, and a "general exhibits" area where small manufacturers who do not have offices and/or large exhibits may display their products.

The Gas Appliance Center provides a variety of services and has its own full-time staff, headed by a permanent manager. The broad-scale, year-round promotional program is designed to attract dealers, buyers, builders, designers, architects, developers, home economists, kitchen and remodeling specialists, and gas utility sales personnel. At the conclusion of its first full year of operation, the center has proven its ability to attract buyers, stimulate an uplifted attitude toward gas appliances in particular and the gas industry in general, and has helped develop a feeling of pride and excitement among those directly associated with the gas industry.

The Gas Appliance Center is seen as a forerunner of similar centers in other major metropolitan areas. Although not open to the public,

[11] Elizabeth M. Fowler, "Powerful Consumer—An Appraisal of the Need for Studies of Buying Habits at the Grass Roots," *New York Times,* February 13, 1959, business section. See also Stewart Britt, *The Spenders,* and George Katona, *The Power Consumer.*

[12] Complete details on the development and operation of the Gas Appliance Center appear in the *American Gas Journal,* Vol. CLXXXVI, No. 12 (December, 1959), 28; *American Gas Journal,* Vol. CLXXXVII, No. 2 (February, 1960), 26; and *American Gas Journal,* Vol. CLXXXVII, No. 11 (October, 1960), 42.

FOR SIX ROOM HOUSE, NORMAL WEATHER CONDITIONS

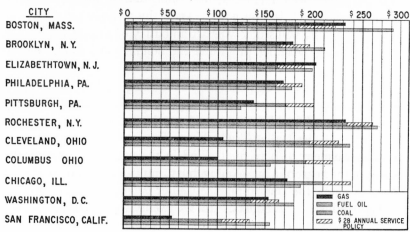

FIG. 31.—Comparison of Annual House-heating Cost.

its influence on other important appliance specifying and buying factors is great. Area gas utilities make good use of the center, sending
groups of employee personnel, home builders, and others to the center
on special tours. Its chief purpose is to train both housewives and the
nation's young folks to become aware of the advantages inherent in
the use of natural gas and gas appliances. A remarkable example is
the favorable development of gas clothes driers and built-in gas
ranges. After a rather slow start, these two appliances have scored a
great success, which shows that, though gas may have a "hard sell,"
as James H. Collins says, the utilities and appliance dealers are "dig-
ging in and selling."[13]

Figure 31 shows the relative cost of heating a house with gas, fuel
oil or coal in several large United States cities.

COMMERCIAL USES

Living in an age of comfort and luxury we see swank hotels and
motels built throughout the country. Here is a really great opportunity for utilities to increase their load through commercial selling
of natural gas in year-round large quantities. Indeed, such outstanding hotels as the Statler Hilton in Los Angeles, the elegant Beverly

[13] Collins, "Gas Really Has a Hard Sell," *Public Utilities Fortnightly,* Vol. LXIII,
No. 6 (March 12, 1959), 379–89.

Hilton nearby, the Statler Hilton in Dallas, and the brand new Sheraton-Dallas Hotel use natural gas in large volume. This adds a considerable amount to the gas utilities' load and also illustrates the fact that good cooking and perfect operation can be achieved with the aid of efficient, economical natural gas. Helen Corbitt, manager of the plush Zodiac Room of Neiman Marcus, Dallas, and author of an excellent cookbook, has found that gas is ideal for preparing broiled food and gives meat prepared in this way a more pleasing color.

Most gas utilities aggressively promote commercial sales of gas to hotels, restaurants, clubs, factory and other cafeterias, catering businesses, and hospitals. A remarkable job of kitchen engineering has been accomplished to serve the requirements of the huge, 1300-room Statler-Hilton in Los Angeles. The kitchens were planned and the hotel constructed around them. Gas-fired ranges, broilers, fryers and bake ovens were especially selected by the Statler planners for speediness, cleanliness, and flexibility of operation.[14] Engineers from Southern California Gas Company, the gas utility that supplies a vast area of this tremendous city, have been active in testing, adjusting, and advising in operation of equipment for the hotel since its inception. Such useful assistance is a boon to active promotion and co-operation in commercial projects like these. Besides five different kitchens, there are three gas-fired boilers of 350 rated horsepower each to serve the heating and hot water needs of the hotel. The boilers produce steam for the two dehydrators employed for garbage disposal. A gas-fired incinerator is also included.

About 1,500 miles southeast from the California metropolis lies Dallas, the home of the impressive twenty-story Statler-Hilton Hotel, completed in 1956. Here, again natural gas plays a major role. Three 380-horsepower gas-fired water tube boilers supply steam for the hotel's many uses: refrigeration, heating, cooking, baking, hot water, laundry.[15] Annual fuel requirements for all these services total about 212,0000,000 cubic feet of natural gas. Some 205,000,000 cubic feet are used annually to generate steam for air conditioning, heating, and hot water. Another 7,000,000 cubic feet are needed for the hotel's

[14] "Statler Hotel in Los Angeles Chooses Gas for Heating, Cooking, and Incineration," *Gas Age*, Vol. CX, No. 12 (December 4, 1952), 26.

[15] Bruce Cunningham, "Gas Does Everything Better in Dallas' New Statler-Hilton," *American Gas Journal*, Vol. CLXXXIII, No. 2 (February, 1956), 14ff.

elaborate cooking operations. A bake shop adjoins the main kitchen. Certain operations must be carried out at fast and accurate temperatures for which natural gas is outstanding: there is no burning and no spoiling.

In a sun-kissed place like Dallas, the air conditioning is of special importance. Air conditioning facilities with a capacity of 1,400 tons, which is equivalent to melting 2,800,000 pounds of ice every twenty-four hours, provides a cool, man-made climate throughout the new hotel. The total air conditioned area covers practically all of the hotel's six million cubic feet of space, including a huge meeting room that can accommodate 2,200 persons. The hotel is cooled by two 753-horsepower steam-turbine-driven centrifugal refrigeration machines. Two giant pumps circulate chilled water throughout the hotel to produce the necessary cooling results.

One of the largest commercial users of natural gas is Exchange Park in Dallas, Texas, a fully integrated $125,000,000 commercial development by William A. Blakeley, a cattleman and a United States Senator. The huge 120-acre park houses many other businesses in addition to Mr. Blakeley's Exchange Bank. This area includes an underground bowling alley, a cafe and restaurant, a savings bank, the home office of Braniff's International Airways, a 1,500-seat auditorium, a medical research center, and many other building and interesting features. A 1,000-room luxury hotel is to be added. The restaurant, La Tunisia, is one of the most atmospheric and exotic in the United States. Much of the tropical air is created by genuine palm trees imported from the African desert and maintained through the careful use of thermostatic heat control. Unique in Dallas, the Exchange Bank building that dominates the area is constructed so that no sun will reach its windows from March to November.

In Exchange Park, steam turbine equipment is employed to perform the tasks of complete heating and cooling by economical natural gas. An eventual cooling capacity of 13,000 tons makes the park the largest single gas-fueled air conditioning installation yet planned. This will require annual gas consumption of approximately one billion cubic feet to be furnished by Lone Star Gas Company. The utilities building now contains two gas-fired 5,000-pound boilers and three 1,000-ton compressors. As the project load warrants, four 2,5000-ton compressors will be added to achieve the required 13,000 tons, with a fifth 2,500-ton unit to be installed as stand-by equipment. At least two more boilers will also be required to provide the necessary steam. Electricity used in the project is also generated in the utilities building, fueled by gas equipment.

When this gigantic, unequaled all-gas project is completed, it will be possible to go from any part of one building to any part of another without ever leaving the comfort of gas air conditioning. Thus the entire layout and design is well adjusted to the demands for comfort and convenience in a warm climate.

An important new source of income for gas utilities is demonstrated in a project recently developed by the Hartford Gas Company of Hartford, Connecticut. This gas utility is building a $3,000,000 central gas-fired plant, plus over two miles of parallel steam and chilled-water lines, which supply heating and cooling to office buildings in downtown Hartford through utility lines. The plant went into operation in 1962.

Hartford Gas plans to sell its air conditioning service in a manner similar to its gas service, with meters used to determine the amount of steam and/or chilled water used by the air conditioning system of each building. Initially, the system will serve Constitution Plaza, a huge office-building-cluster development by the Travelers Insurance Company of Hartford. Included are three office buildings, a hotel, a broadcasting facility, and a shopping center.

The idea of a utility supplying heating and cooling has many merits. Customer buildings save space that would normally be devoted to individual heating and cooling equipment. They save on labor costs needed to operate individual equipment. A central plant, being a large-volume fuel user, has lower operating costs. In providing summertime air conditioning, it has found a way to ease a problem plaguing gas utilities for years—balancing the gas load to level out summer valleys and winter peaks. The gas utility's over-all load factor is also improved, giving the utility a better purchasing position with its suppliers, the gas transmission companies.

Culled from annual reports of the gas companies are many diverse commercial uses of natural gas, including gas air conditioning for hospitals, banks, office buildings, stores, schools, and other institutional or commercial buildings. Consolidated Natural Gas Company reports a remarkable, steady growth of its wide and substantial retail market that comprises such important cities as Cleveland, Akron, Canton and Youngstown in Ohio; Pittsburgh (in part), Johnstown, and Altoona in Pennsylvania; and Clarksburg, Parkersburg, Fairmont and Morgantown in West Virginia. "At year end, heating customers numbered 987,000 or 86 per cent of residential and commercial customers (out of a total of 1,145,000 gas users). . . . Natural gas enjoys a competitive advantage over other fuels in these markets (where coal and oil abound) because of its lower cost and its greater convenience and cleanliness."[16]

Laundries and bakers are frequent users of natural gas. Agricultural uses of gas are increasing in Southern Natural's market area, the states of the Deep South. A gas brooder acts as mother hen to small chicks. Students are taught dairy product processing in the gas equipped laboratory at Mississippi State University, and there is no end to the profitable and effective commercial application of natural gas.

Commercial consumption increased in 1960 by 13.5 per cent with an average increase of total consumption of natural gas of 6.1 per cent.[17]

INDUSTRIAL USES

Industrial uses constitute the largest single use category in the natural gas industry. As shown in the table on page 185, industrial and power generation sales in 1960 amounted to 47,093,600,000 therms, which is greater than the 41,079,000,000 therms of residential and commercial sales. At the same time industrial sales brought in 27.8 per cent of gas industry revenue, as compared with 69.5 per cent for residential and commercial sales. To understand the place of these large-volume, lower-priced sales in the gas industry, one must remember that gas is sold on both firm and interruptible bases. Interruptible sales are advantageous to higher priority users in that gas is made available on peak days and, since the interruptible sales pay part of the cost of operating the pipe line, rates to the higher priority users

[16] Consolidated Natural Gas Company, *Annual Report* (for 1958), 8.

[17] For 1960 the American Gas Association listed 2,490,300 gas industry commercial consumers and said that they consumed a total of 939,310 million cubic feet of natural gas. The comparable figures in 1959 show that 2,453,000 commercial customers consumed 827,450 million cubic feet.

are lower. A 1959 study showed that, of the $747,000,000 gross reve-
nues from interruptible sales, $392,000,000 was applied against the
fixed charges, thereby reducing residential rates.[18]

A considerable portion of industrial sales, especially sales for
power generation, are made on an interruptible basis. The Federal
Power Commission has approved such sales for boiler fuel where the
sales price is adequate to bear the pipe line expenses—both fixed and
commodity—properly associated with selling the industrial gas.

The magnitude of industrial gas sales has been described as follows:

> One of the most amazing developments in modern industry has been
> the industrial use of gas, in everything from the manufacture of carbon
> black, cement, fertilizer, and glass, to the tempering of pen points and
> watch springs. Altogether, more than 25,000 industrial processes make
> use of gas.
>
> Although the present era has often been called the age of electricity,
> many times as much energy is produced in the United States each year by
> gas as is produced by electric power. Consequently gas is one of the great-
> est of all American industries . . .[19]

Almost every production cycle involves heat. That means that
nearly every manufacturer's doorway provides the gas salesman with
an opportunity to sell his product. This wide range of natural gas
application in industry has been described as follows:

> Thus, natural gas is used to forge, cut, harden, galvanize, dry, purify,
> and perform countless other fabricating and processing chores. Thou-
> sands of products, ranging from food and clothing to home building
> materials and including weapons of defense, are made with or from gas
> and its related products. It has played an ever-increasing role in the
> manufacture of steel, textiles, plastics, paints, tile, cement, glass, salt,
> chemicals, clay, pipe, and paper—to name only a few.
>
> Out of a wider range of specific uses there is the gas tempering of mis-
> sile nose cones which must withstand intense friction heat. The body of
> a Polaris missile is hardened under three hours' exposure to 1,600-degree
> gas heat. Nine out of every ten of the 108 million meals served every day

[18] American Gas Association, "The Natural Gas Story," (ed. by Francis X. Welch).

[19] *Investigation of Concentration of Economic Power,* Temporary Economic Committee, Monograph No. 36, *"Reports* of the Federal Trade Commission on Natural Gas
and Natural Gas Pipelines . . . , 89.

by the nation's restaurants, hotels, schools, military mess halls, and other institutions are cooked by gas. And much of the food served has been previously prepared, packed, canned or otherwise processed with gas heat.

Not so well known are the industrial raw material uses of gas. In the petrochemical industry, which has mushroomed since World War II, natural gas and valuable liquid hydrocarbons extracted from it are combined with other substances to create plastics, synthetic rubber, miracle fibers, fertilizers, insecticides, medicines, explosives, detergents, solvents and many synthetic materials. Some of these new synthetic products have replaced natural products, including expensive imports formerly used, making the United States less dependent on foreign supply.[20]

The basically intrastate nature of industrial sales should be noted. Nearly 49 per cent of all industrial gas is consumed in the southwestern states of Texas, Oklahoma, Arkansas, and Louisiana although those states contain less than 10 per cent of the United States population. For example, it can be shown that industrial gas consumption at Lake Charles, Louisiana, is greater in volume than the total gas consumption of New York City.

The relative importance of several major markets for industrial and power-generation gas are illustrated in the table below showing consumption for the year 1959:

Type Use	Million Cu. Ft.	Per cent of Total
Field Use	1,737,402	21.9
Carbon Black Plants	214,612	2.7
Petroleum Refineries	752,239	9.5
Portland Cement Plants	188,000	2.4
Power Generation	1,627,097	20.5
Other	3,412,580	43.0
TOTAL	7,931,930	100.0

(Source: American Gas Association, *1961 Gas Facts*, 151.)

An important industrial use lies in the application of gas to brick and glass manufacture.[21] Panhandle Eastern reports that the highly industrialized area of its pipe-line system has substantial sales to a

[20] American Gas Association, "The Natural Gas Story," (ed. by Francis X. Welch).

[21] This statement was made by Marvin E. White of the Ohio Fuel Gas Company before a meeting of the American Gas Association Industrial Gas School, Pittsburgh, Pennsylvania, September 13, 1957.

number of large industrial consumers both directly and through local utilities. Of many large users of gas the report mentions the plants of A. P. Green Fire Brick Company, Harbison-Walker Refractories Company, and several other large brick plants in Missouri. Gas is essential to the fire brick and glass industries. It is used in burning brick and melting glass because the even temperatures required in such operations are most easily obtained with gas. Panhandle Eastern mentions such well-known glass plants as Libby-Owens-Ford Glass Company, Anchor Hocking Glass Corporation, Ball Brothers, Corning Glass Works, and the renowned Steuben Glass manufacturers. Libby-Owens-Ford became a large industrial gas customer in 1958 with a new glass plant at Shreveport, Louisiana, where Arkansas Louisiana Gas Company, the many-sided transmission system, is supplier of the precious fuel. Glass and ceramic plants also loom large in the gas sales of the Consolidated Natural Gas Company, which serves a highly industrialized area and sells large quantities of gas for industrial uses. Indeed, the glass and ceramics industry accounts for about a quarter of the system's industrial gas sales.

In the industrial heartland of the nation, other large gas users supplied by Panhandle Eastern include Ford, General Motors, Chrysler, and their suppliers located at various cities along that pipe-line system. Gas is used for heat treating in the manufacture of automotive parts. There are many other industrial operations for which gas is a most efficient fuel, and practically the only one applicable. For example, gas provides precisely controlled operating temperatures in a continuous annealing furnace at Jones and Laughlin Steel Corporation's new Stainless and Strip Division in Louisville, Ohio. This modern mill can produce three thousand tons of high quality stainless steel sheet and strip in a month.

Another interesting field of gas use is food processing.[22] The *1958 Statistical Abstract of the United States* lists food and kindred products as the largest major industry group in value added by manufacture ($15,374,000,000).[23] Among the major industry groups this food group is the fourth largest consumer of fuels. Because of its inherent

[22] This subject was discussed by Robert L. Davis of Baltimore Gas and Electric Company at a meeting of the American Gas Association Industrial Gas School, Pittsburgh, Pennsylvania, September 13, 1957.

[23] Pages 776–77.

cleanliness, gas is likewise important to the food-processing industry. Since production operations in this field are becoming highly automatic in nature, gas fuel is gaining in favor because of its adaptability to exacting process control requirements. The major applications for gas fuel in this industrial group are: baking, roasting (coffee, nuts, cocoa beans, some cereals), smoking (meats, fish, cheese), cooking (potato chips), and canning. The canning industry is particularly important because of its size and its season. There are more than 3,500 canneries in the United States practicing their 150-year-old food-preserving art. This is normally carried on in the summer during off-peak gas load periods.

NATURAL GAS ATTRACTS INDUSTRY

The gas industry is extremely active in promoting greater commercial and industrial sales. At a recent sales conference arranged by the American Gas Association,[24] Harold S. Walker, Jr., pointed out how much the 140,000 industrial and commercial gas customers mean to the gas industry generally. "Without industrial and commercial gas, residential rates would be in orbit. Just how important is this load to gas companies? This usage accounts for an awful lot of gas—64 per cent of the total sendout and it brings in 41 per cent of the revenue." Mr. Walker explained that "there is twice . . . as much revenue per dollar investment from industrial and commercial gas as from residential gas," and that "commercial gas accounts for only 9 per cent of the send-out but brings in 12 ½ per cent of the revenue. Commercial gas is one of the best and most profitable loads we have."

The conference discussed the method of group selling as one of the most effective media for bringing the gas industry closer to a major customer. It has been tried with great success by the group dealing with the textile industry, as pointed out by Charles B. Ziegler of the Public Service Company of North Carolina, a textile-producing state. "The greatest opportunity for profitable sales of gas in processing textiles is for drying purposes," he said. "Sales engineers spearhead a hard-hitting campaign to promote greater commercial and industrial use of gas. Industrial plants receive technical aid in new ways of adapting gas to their processes. Architects, design engineers, and con-

[24] *American Gas Association Monthly,* Vol. XLI, No. 5 (May, 1959), 32–36.

tractors are regularly encouraged to include gas appliances in their plans and specifications. Sales survey crews sell the use of gas in areas to which service is extended. Industrial development personnel seek to attract new industries to the system's service area."[25]

Through both its transmission and its distribution companies, the gas industry plays an important part in the regional economic development of service areas. The availability of natural gas is a great economic advantage and one of several determining factors for the location of industry. At the same time, the sale of gas for industrial and commercial use is, as we have seen, the assurance of an interruptible additional load factor compensating for the comparatively low load factor of residential space heating which is subject to heavy seasonal fluctuations. Out of this common interest pipe lines and local utilities have been undertaking a well-planned promotion program advertising the availability of low-cost, efficient, natural gas which can be used in countless technical and productive operations.

Many states in the country, aware of their untapped natural and human resources, have sought to call attention to the advantages their territory offers to industrial enterprises for settlement, relocation, or expansion. They have published special promotional sections in Sunday editions of newspapers such as the *New York Times,* discussing the economic, social, and cultural make-up of the respective state. Such a section in the February 2, 1958 issue of the *New York Times* sets forth a map showing Southern Natural Gas Company's pipe-line system which delivers millions of cubic feet of natural gas to Alabama's cities, towns and industries each day. The ad reads as follows:

> Within this fast growing area are hundreds of progressive communities with outstanding advantages for industries interested in serving the South. Here your company will find abundant natural resources . . . expanding markets . . . skilled and loyal workers . . . plentiful water . . . and equable year-round climate and sound and friendly local governments. Whether or not you ever expect to use a single foot of gas from our pipelines, our company will gladly help you find in Alabama the best location for your plant. We cordially invite you to write us for specific, confidential information. Or better still, come South and let us take you on a personally guided tour of this land of growing opportunity.

[25] Consolidated Natural Gas Company, *Annual Report* (for 1958), 10.

Alabama is the well-chosen site of Chemstrand's Decatur plant where *Acrilan,* the synthetic acrylic fiber made from natural gas, is manufactured. But there are many more important chemical and other plants that considered this area as a preferable economic location because of the abundant supply of natural gas from pipe lines of Southern Natural Gas and United Gas Corporation.

Similar promotion programs have been instituted by such companies as Northern Natural Gas Company, Cities Service Gas Company, Natural Gas Pipeline Company of America, North Central Gas Company (Nebraska), Transcontinental Gas Pipe Line Corporation, Piedmont Natural Gas Company, Public Service Company of North Carolina, Kansas-Nebraska Natural Gas Company, Central Electric and Gas Company, and Nebraska Natural Gas Company.

It is common knowledge that Oklahoma is one of the leading natural gas states, ranking fifth in possession of gas reserves in the United States. This state wants to use its precious resource to encourage the establishment of a diversified industry making use of tremendous, low-cost supplies. It is the advantages inherent in the properties of gas that attract industry. This may be seen in an ad of the Oklahoma Natural Gas Company in the *New York Times* of March 10, 1957.

Oregon, a "new" gas state that only recently joined the gas-receiving areas, is a good example of gas industry promotional advertising. A mild climate conducive to the supply of interruptible gas without interruption offers inexpensive industrial fuel as was advertised by the supplement "Oregon Welcomes Tourists and Industry" which appeared in the *New York Times* April 5, 1958:

> Natural gas in large volumes has been available in northwestern and northeastern Oregon since late 1956. Big new pipelines from the vast Peace River gas fields in British Columbia and Alberta, and from the San Juan Basin in New Mexico have a combined capacity of nearly a billion cubic feet daily.
>
> Natural gas has been a key factor in bringing several *new industries* to the Northwest, including an Owens-Illinois glass container factory in Portland and a $15,000,000 chemicals plant on the Columbia River.
>
> Large additional amounts of natural gas are on tap for both industrial and domestic use. Largest supplier in Oregon is Northwest Natural Gas Company, which serves an area with a population equal to half that of

Oregon, and has supplied interruptible gas to industries for two winters without interruption.

Expansion of the industrial load can be continued for several years, with the likelihood that interruptions during cold weather when space heating customers need their maximum of fuel, will be few and of short duration.

Canada uses the same pattern of industrial promotion as that applied in the United States. The Canadian province of Alberta, which is so rich in oil and gas, sees in this abundance a growth potential for its economy and the establishment of a diversified industry. In a supplement to the *New York Times* entitled "Alberta Canada's Oil Province"[26] numerous references were made to the varied uses of gas in industry. A $25,000,000 nickel refinery near Edmonton, Alberta's capital, is mentioned as using natural gas to refine ore from Manitoba.

PLANT LOCATION SERVICES

A method different from collective advertising is individual, active participation of the gas utility in area industrial development. The industrial sales manager or industrial engineer plays an important role on a local industrial development committee, a group trying to bring industry to the town served by the local gas company. There are many firms looking for a new place in which to expand or relocate their activities. How to play successfully the role of a matchmaker in bringing the parties together is described by J. R. Walton, a highly experienced industrial sales engineer, in an address about the gas utility's place in area development.[27] Using a Houston, Texas, team as a model, he points out the do's and don't's which such committee should follow to lure the new industrial citizen to the community and how to give advice to the scouter sent by the prospect to find out conditions and requirements needed for the final decision.

Houston, having not only a perfect industrial development team, but many natural aspects such as nearness to raw materials, water transportation, and markets, that qualify for relocation or expansion plans may not be the only place to exemplify Mr. Walton's points.

26 *New York Times,* June 1, 1958.

27 J. R. Walton, "Area Industrial Development," paper presented before the American Gas Association Sales Conference on Industrial and Commercial Gas, Milwaukee, Wisconsin, April 8, 1958.

Indeed, location-of-industry experts most recently found that "94 per cent of all new plants in the postwar period have been built in areas with less than 50,000 population."[28]

The composition of the committee and the men really active on it are of the utmost significance. "In a community where there is an Industrial Team or Development Group consisting of the working members of the railroad industrial or freight traffic departments, gas and electrical industrial sales, traffic and statistical departments of the Chamber of Commerce, bank industrial representatives, industrial realtors, oil, chemical, steel or what-have-you sales engineers and the like, the scout or scouts can get practically all of the information they want accurately and completely in a few hours and in confidence. . . . Under no conditions can competitive interests appear on the same panel—experience says this can be nasty."[29] A meeting between "Mr. Scouter" and the team will take place, and the scout will by all means withhold his identity.

To illustrate his address Mr. Walton mentioned the firms represented on Houston's basic team: water—Layne-Texas Company; finance—Prudential Insurance Company; labor—Hughes Tool Company, American Rolling Mills, Stauffer Chemical, and Humble Oil and Refining Company; electricity—Houston Lighting and Power Company; natural gas—Houston Natural Gas Corporation and United Gas Corporation; climate—the chamber of commerce; foundations, construction, costs, zoning, etc.—Lockwood K. Andrews and Freeze, Nicholls and Turner; and taxes—Texas Tax Association, Shell Oil Company, and Southern Pacific Railroad. If the scout is interested in petrochemicals or other chemicals or metal products, a representative of these groups is called in. "In this team or group, the Industrial Sales Manager or Industrial Engineer of the Gas Company" says Mr. Walton, "is the key figure."

Mr. Walton mentions other arrangements Houston has made to attract industry but the main thing he tries to show is that the gas utility through proper organization and skilled members of its staff can materially contribute to industrial sales of this type which benefit

---

[28] A. H. Raskin, "Big Factory Cities Losing Top Place as U. S. Jobs Rise," *New York Times,* Sunday, July 26, 1959, pp. 1, 35. Mr. Raskin quotes the findings of a study on the subject of plant location made by Leonard C. Yaseen, an expert in that field.

[29] Walton, "Area Industrial Development," 39.

its load. Mr. Walton gives an interesting example of how a hypothetical small plant moving to a new location, using gas for heat treating, and employing one hundred people may cause over-all gas sales of about 40,000 MCF per year, "half of which is high-priced gas. The plant is assumed to have a process gas requirement of 5,000 cubic feet per hour for a 16 hour, 22 day month, or 21,000 MCF per year. The gas requirements generated by this small industry are estimated as follows:

	MCF per Year
Process gas	21,000
Office heating and cooling (commercial account)	500
75 families at 150 MCF per year	11,250
School	1,000
Barber and beauty shop	300
Laundry	500
Tailor shop	500
Stores	200
Bakery	500
Entertainment	200
Cafes	3,000
Radio and TV Shops	50
Garages and filling stations	50
Churches	300
Out of towners—1,000 man days	400
TOTAL	39,750"

In many cases, the newly located industry may be much larger than the plant supposed in this instance and the load accruing to the gas utility correspondingly more substantial, but no increase to the load factor should be neglected.

INCREASED USAGE THROUGH RESEARCH

Individually and collectively through such organizations as the American Gas Association and the Institute of Gas Technology, leading gas companies support research projects aimed at increasing the market for gas. In 1960 the gasification of coal was receiving attention. At the burner end of the industry hopeful new uses lay in the fuel cell, the gas turbine, and the *energy package* whereby all heating, lighting, and air conditioning are provided for a building through the installation of one gas turbine-generator set.[30] Energy packages are being installed by Northern Illinois Gas Company in its new office building and at the McAllen, Texas, High School. These energy packages will supply all heating, air conditioning, and electricity necessary for the buildings involved and will be fueled only with gas. No outside electrical connections are involved.[31]

[30] See the discussion of new uses for natural gas which appears in Chapter 15 below. Also see J. Fred Ebdon, "Energy Packages—Natural Gas Fired," *Gas,* Vol. XXXVIII, No. 4 (April, 1962), 59.

[31] Dean Hale, "Modular Gas Turbine Energy Packages," *American Gas Journal,* Vol. CLXXXIX, No. 3 (March, 1962), 39; Dean Hale, "First All-Gas Compact School Underway," *American Gas Journal,* Vol. CLXXXIX, No. 5 (May, 1962), 44; Richard Martin, "Now, an All-Gas City," *American Gas Journal,* Vol. CLXXXIX, No. 4 (April, 1962), 60. Mr. Hale describes the Northern Illinois installation. Mr. Martin describes the Rochdale Village to be constructed in New York City. This village will use only gas to provide heating, air conditioning, and electricity and will consume 1.3 billion cubic feet of gas per year.

8

NATURAL GAS AND
THE PETROCHEMICAL INDUSTRY

by Alfred M. Leeston

SHORTLY after natural gas became the nation's favorite fuel, it scored another triumph in its recognition as a valuable and useful source for the petrochemical industry. It was discovered that rich hydrocarbon compounds such as ethane, butane, propane, and methane could be converted into building blocks for hundreds of synthetics. The petrochemical industry realized that methane, the main constituent of natural gas, was the ultimate simplest hydrocarbon raw material,[1] much simpler than coal. Thus natural gas provided a mighty stimulus for the nation's petrochemical industry.

The industrial chemist rose to meet opportunity, and methane became the basis for a very large, co-ordinated industry. This development began around 1930 when the Shell Chemical Company (now Shell Chemical corporation) began making ammonia, which once was synthetically produced by means of the Haber process, from natural gas. The Standard Oil Company of New Jersey also pioneered in this field. "The pace of development of the use of natural gas in making synthesis gas became greater than any other we have seen in the chemical industry. In 1941 the production of ammonia from natural gas was 42,000 short tons; in 1944 it was about 479,000 short tons, an eleven-fold increase in three years."[2]

[1] G. A. Purdy, *Petroleum,* 444; Kendall Beaton, *Enterprise in Oil,* 519.

[2] W. d'Leny, "Oil's Future as a Source of Chemicals," in *Essential Factors in the Future Development of the Oil Industry, q.v.* 176ff.

Natural gas is the base material for the preparation of hydrogen from which, by combining it with nitrogen from the air, ammonia is made. Three and one-fourth million tons of ammonia were produced in 1956 when the production capacity was over four million tons. The United States ammonia supply and demand were in balance for the first time in 1961. See Jack Melnick, "Ammonia Supply and Demand . . . In Balance by 1961?" *Oil and Gas Journal,* Vol. LVI, No. 50 (December 15, 1958), 109–12.

METHANE—TYPICAL HYDROCARBON COMPOUND

Methane (CH_4) is typical of a variety of hydrocarbon compounds obtained from natural gas and converted into petrochemical building blocks. One molecule of methane contains four particles of hydrogen (H) joined to a single particle of carbon (C). Processing these molecules results in the production of several valuable chemicals—carbon monoxide, methyl chloride, hydrogen cyanide, and acetylene. These are known as *intermediate chemicals* because each of them is vital to the manufacture of more profitable products. It is this process of *upgrading*—increasing the original value by converting or processing —that distinguishes the utilization of natural gas as a chemical raw material from its use as a fuel.[3]

TABLE 10
CHEMICALS FROM METHANE

Chemical	Major End Use
Ammonia	Fertilizers
Methyl Alcohol	Antifreeze and Raw Materials for Formaldehyde (Used in plastics)
Hydrogen Cyanide	Plastics and Synthetic Fibers
Acetylene	Welding, Vinyl Plastics, and Neoprene Rubber
Methyl Chloride, Methylene Dichloride, Chloroform, and Carbon Tetrachloride	Solvents and Refrigerants
Carbon Black	Rubber Compounding

This impressive list of chemicals derived from methane (see Table 10) should be supplemented with numerous products made from the other natural gas hydrocarbons such as ethane, propane, and butane from which ethylene, propylene, butadiene, and oxygenated chemicals can be made.

CARBON BLACK

There is an item in this table of methane-derived products that

[3] For instance, a chemical company starts with propane worth one cent, makes it into glycerine worth twenty-eight cents, and sells it to the cosmetic manufacturers who end up with five dollars worth of cold cream. See J. R. Walton, "Area Industrial Development," a paper presented before the American Gas Association Sales Conference on Industrial and Commercial Gas, Milwaukee, Wisconsin, April 8, 1958.

merits special attention. It is carbon black. The manufacture of this petrochemical product consumes between 200,000 and 400,000 million cubic feet of natural gas a year. An ardent conservationist would not say "used" but "wasted." While it is true that methods of producing this unique material are far from being economical in gas use, carbon black is a most desirable end product. It is an indispensable ingredient of synthetic and natural rubber tires, and its extremely fine state of subdivision, high purity, uniformity, availability in large quantities, and relatively low price make it an extraordinary product.[4]

Carbon black is obtained through the imperfect combustion of natural gas, and there are two general processes for its manufacture, the channel process and the furnace process. The Chinese followed a similar practice of imperfect combustion about 2,300 years ago when they produced their highly durable lampblack from vegetable oil. They used it as a black pigment for inks as did Western civilization until a plant in New Cumberland, West Virginia, began making carbon black from natural gas in 1872. Lampblack continued to be used for all types of inks, paints, varnishes, and lacquers until B. F. Goodrich Tire and Rubber purchased, in 1912, the first carload of carbon black used for the reinforcement of rubber. In 1910, the India Rubber Gutta Percha and Telegraph Works Company, Limited, had purchased a smaller amount for a similar use. The rapid development in the use of carbon black which followed is illustrated by the fact that forty-one plants produced 1,644,605,000 pounds of carbon black in 1958.[5]

Carbon black is used in a number of ways. In 1958, rubber companies took 1,192,162,000 pounds; ink companies 40,645,000 pounds; paint companies 10,997,000 pounds; and miscellaneous purposes required 7,133,000 pounds. This shows the overwhelming importance of carbon black for the rubber industry.

Of the Texas carbon black production, 474,564 pounds—more than 50 per cent of the total—were made in the Panhandle. The lack of market outlets for natural gas made this area an ideal stamping ground for carbon black manufacturers. They contracted millions of

[4] Leonhard H. Cohan, "Carbon Black," *The Science of Petroleum* (ed. by Benjamin T. Brooks and A. E. Dunstan), V, Part II, pp. 78–88. This is an excellent article on the manufacture of carbon black, a subject on which Mr. Cohan is an expert.

[5] U. S. Department of the Interior, Bureau of Mines, *1958 Minerals Yearbook* (II: Fuels), 296ff.

cubic feet of natural gas for prices so low that the average value of gas used for carbon black manufacture in Texas was less than one cent per thousand cubic feet in 1938 and 1939. Not all of this manufacture made use of sweet gas; large amounts of sour gas that could not be allowed to enter into transmission lines were also used. The Texas Railroad Commission in its struggle to conserve the gas and prevent its waste in carbon black manufacture eventually prohibited entirely the use of sweet gas for carbon black manufacture and permitted only the use of sour gas for this purpose "provided that at least one pound of carbon black is recovered by the plant for each 1,000 cubic feet of gas used, and also on the condition that the natural gasoline is shipped out before the gas is burned to make carbon black."[6] In 1958, the channel black method yielded 1.99 pounds per thousand cubic feet of gas used while the furnace black process yielded 7.81 pounds per thousand cubic feet.

It is predicted that there will be further decline in the use of natural gas for carbon black production. With the price of natural gas steadily rising, manufacturers are turning more to residual products of petroleum as a source material. "Yields from the gas are much lower than those from oil, and the use of oil is gaining ground. The yield from one gallon of oil . . . may be expected to reach at least 3.4 pounds by 1975. The furnace black process utilizing oil will undoubtedly supersede processes using natural gas. Oil blacks are superior for many uses. The price is higher but will drop as the process is developed further."[7]

TABLE 11

RUBBER AND CARBON BLACK CONSUMPTION[8]

Year	Rubber Long Tons	Rubber 1,000 Pounds	Carbon Black Requirements 1,000 Pounds
1955	1,500,000	3,300,000	1,227,000
1960	1,800,000	3,960,000	1,472,000
1975	2,500,000	5,500,000	2,045,000

[6] John R. Stockton, Richard C. Henshaw, Jr., and Richard W. Graves, *"Economics of the Natural Gas Industry in Texas,* 299.

[7] President's Materials Policy Commission, *Resources for Freedom,* IV, 197–98.

[8] *Ibid.*

FOUR METHANE-DERIVED INTERMEDIATES

The four outstanding intermediate chemicals produced from methane—carbon monoxide, methyl chloride, hydrogen cyanide, and acetylene—yield, in turn, a variety of products. Carbon monoxide is used in manufacturing methanol, an ingredient of antifreeze products that is also used to produce formaldehyde.[9] The latter is essential to the manufacture of such well-known plastics as Bakelite (Union Carbide), Resinox, Plaskon, and Beetleware. The second methane derivative, methyl chloride, is used in producing chloroform, carbon tetrachloride, and various industrial solvents. Hydrogen cyanide, the third intermediate obtained from methane, is used to produce acrylonitrile, acetone cyanhydrin, and ethylene cyanhydrin. These chemicals are vital to the manufacture of many products. From acrylonitrile both Orlon fiber and GR-A rubber are made. Acetone cyanhydrin is developed into sparkling lucite plastics and similar products, and ethylene cyanhydrin can be used to produce Orlon fibers by a secondary petrochemical process. Acetylene is a pace-setter among petrochemicals and can be used as a starting material for many chemicals now made from ethylene. This is of great importance because there is more methane available from which acetylene can be derived than there is ethane from which ethylene is usually manufactured. Acetylene, however, can be manufactured from calcium carbide (coke) sources. Union Carbide, for instance, produces acetylene from sixty base materials. American Cyanamid, Monsanto, Union Carbide, and Rohm and Haas have commercial scale plants for making acetylene by partial oxidation of natural gas.[10] Literally thousands of products including solvents, certain weed-killing agents, plasticizers for such plastics as lucite and polyethylene, DDT and other insecticides, antifreezes, detergents (such as Glim, Joy, Tide, and Fab), and fibers (like Dacron, Nylon, and Acrilan) can be based on natural gas and its constituents.

"THE FIBER STORY"

The sensational growth of the petrochemical industry, representing an investment of well over three billion dollars, should not conceal the costly difficulties involved in perfecting a synthetic fiber, plastic poly-

[9] First made from natural gas and shipped by tank cars in 1927.

[10] Rohm and Haas Company, *Chemicals for the Industry*. From 15 to 25 per cent of all acetylene is made from natural gas.

mer, or any other petrochemical product until it is ready to withstand the wear and tear of daily use, until it is not merely a substitute for natural products but is superior to them.[11] Acrilan, an acrylic fiber, went through some hectic times of trial and error before its present pleasing appearance was achieved and it became permanently dye-able. Manufactured by Chemstrand, a joint venture of Monsanto Chemical Company and American Viscose Corporation, Acrilan is made of natural gas and air. Monsanto furnishes the fiber's basic in-gredient, acrylonitrile, from its big plant at Texas City, Texas, not far from Galveston. In the fall of 1952, recounts Chemstrand in its booklet *Chemstrand—The Fiber Story,* Acrilan was introduced to the public, but all was not well. The new fiber developed color trouble. It "seemed to lose its color when it was subjected to abrasion." With-drawing an otherwise fine product from the market, Chemstrand be-gan what it calls "one of the sleuthing operations for which industry's research is most noted" on its 700-acre tract near Decatur, Alabama. The result was a vastly improved product applauded by the textile world. "A long process requiring infinite patience and the extremes in salesmanship" brought Acrilan back on the market to join the fam-ily of synthetic fibers which also includes Nylon, Orlon, Dacron, and many others.

Experience has shown that blending natural and man-made fibers is particularly successful because it makes some of the shortcomings of synthetic fibers disappear while it tends to accentuate their many advantages.[12] The following figures illustrate the relative popularity of various fibers in the United States:

[11] Dana L. Thomas, "Creslan, Darvan and Kodel," *Barron's,* Vol. XXXVIII, No. 41 (October 13, 1958), 3, 6, 18. This is a good survey on the development of synthetic fibers.

[12] See "What's New in Synthetic Fibers—New Processing Methods and New Raw Materials May Give a Boost to the Burgeoning Synthetic Fiber Industry," *Chemical and Engineering News,* Vol. XXXV, No. 30 (July 29, 1957), 12ff. This is a staff report of a symposium on the textile industry held by the Division of Chemical Marketing and Economics at the 131st National Meeting of the American Chemical Society, Miami, Florida, April 7–12, 1957. Commented panel members, "No single fiber can satisfy all textile requirements. . . . no fiber is best . . . . Although fully conscious of certain short-comings of the synthetic fibers in use at the present, the industry continues research for improvement and perfection . . . . Research and development costs may be from 10 million dollars to double that amount . . . . Initial plant costs from 30 to 50 million dollars with another 20 million needed as working capital . . . . Five hundred million pounds valued at about 700 million dollars was synthetic fiber consumption in 1956. While the older generation is more critical of the new fibers, the younger set is enthusiastic about

TABLE 12

DISTRIBUTION OF FIBERS IN THE UNITED STATES
1950–56
(*Millions of Pounds*)

Year	Cotton	Wool	Rayon & Acetate	Non-cellulosic	Silk
1950	4,680.1	647.0	1,351.6	140.5	8.4
1951	4,846.8	495.0	1,276.6	195.5	5.6
1952	4,437.1	477.5	1,215.5	249.1	6.9
1953	4,521.0	503.8	1,223.0	279.6	5.4
1954	4,125.2	389.9	1,154.8	328.7	6.4
1955	4,384.2	428.2	1,419.2	432.1	7.2
1956	4,339.1	454.9	1,201.1	482.9	7.7

(Source: *Textile World* [New York])

While cotton is still holding its own quite well, consumption of wool, rayon, and acetate is declining; but the consumption of synthetic fibers is increasing. The spectacular rise in the consumption of non-cellulosic fibers from 140.5 million pounds in 1950 to almost 500 million pounds in 1956 would not have been possible without continuous improvement in the quality of these fibers and their widespread acceptance by the American people. Note that the consumption of silk also shows some increase since even men now wear "silken clothes" in the summer.

THE SPECTER OF EXCHANGEABILITY

There is little doubt that natural gas is a top petrochemical source, as *Chemical and Engineering News* pointed out in its June 4, 1956, issue, but things change quickly in the petrochemical world where the creative spirit of the petrochemist meets the sharp pencil of the wholly unromantic cost accountant who insists on the use of the cheapest and most economical raw material, which may not always be gas. A flexibility and versatility which permits shifting from one base material to another is typical of the petrochemical industry, and the shift may be either toward or away from natural gas. The final decision depends upon many factors which are all part of the much-studied field of marketing. With some alternative raw materials, gas may hold its own as in the manufacture of ammonia, the "many splendored

the products of the petrochemical industry and this seems most important for certain, future, growth."

thing that makes the grass greener and the trees more fruitful."[13] Although some plants use refinery gas as a raw material, the development of methanol and many new processes will considerably add to the use of natural gas in the petrochemical industry. A process for making acetylene by partial oxidation of methane, discovered by a German chemical factory that was once part of the former I. G. Farben Trust, is providing new outlets for natural gas. In addition, the steadily increasing demand for acrylonitrile, a natural gas product and the basic ingredient of the attractive Acrilan fibers, contributes to increased industrial consumption of natural gas.

The specter of exchangeability is always present in the petrochemical industry. This was well illustrated in an address delivered by the renowned chemical engineer, T. G. Hughes, president of Oronite Chemicals Company, an affiliate of Standard Oil of California. At the annual meeting of the American Petroleum Institute in November, 1954, Mr. Hughes gave some striking examples of alternate sources for chemical compounds. One was duPont Nylon for which the same intermediate chemicals are being produced from six different sources (see Table 13). Here, because of favorable price, oil and natural gas are the preferred raw materials for Nylon and other fibers. The increasing popularity of acrylic fibers with natural gas as the base material and acetylene as the intermediate one will also increase the use of natural gas in the petrochemical industry.

Table 14 shows other large-volume chemicals and the percentages of these chemicals manufactured from petroleum and the alternate sources and illustrates the remarkable progress the chemical industry has made within fifty years. There has been the establishment of a major industry—the synthesis of ammonia—based first on coal, then oil, and now natural gas and methane. Now products from all of these raw materials compete with each other. A 1956 survey of petrochemical plants shows that, of two hundred individual factories making

[13] Lewis F. Hatch, "These Petrochemicals Use Ammonia," *Petroleum Refiner,* Vol. XXXV, No. 12 (December, 1956), 145ff. Eighty per cent of all ammonia is made from natural gas. See also "Features of the U. S. Petrochemical Scene," *Petroleum Press Service,* Vol. XXVII, No. 7 (July, 1960), 254. This is a report about an excellent address made by D. A. Shepard, executive vice-president of Jersey Standard. Said Mr. Shepard, "Natural gas provides the base for 100 per cent of formaldehyde, at least 90% of methanol, 80% of ammonia, and 15–20% of acetylene. But petrochemicals absorb only one to two per cent of marketed natural gas."

214

TABLE 13
NYLON RAW MATERIALS

Raw Material Source	Raw Materials
Natural Gas	Butane
Gasoline Fraction	Cyclohexane
Coal Tar	Benzene
Oat Hulls	
Corncobs	Furfural
Sugar Cane Bagasse	

TABLE 14
ALTERNATE SOURCES OF CHEMICALS

Chemical	Amount Produced From Petroleum Per cent	Alternate Raw Materials
Ammonia	85	Coal
Methyl Alcohol (Formerly called wood alcohol)	80	Coal and Wood
Ethyl Alcohol	57	Molasses and Other Agricultural Products
Toluene	60	Coal
Xylene	86	Coal

organic chemicals, only about thirty list natural gas as their source material. On the other hand, practically all plants make ammonia from natural gas. This nitrogen chemical manufacture requires natural gas in large amounts.[14] A single ammonia plant may consume eight million cubic feet daily for the production of two hundred tons of ammonia.

The United States consumption of methane expressed in billions of cubic feet is not very large compared with total new production of natural gas. To countries that are behind the United States in petrochemical industrial development, the amount of natural gas used here is impressive. Many countries manage to get along without natural gas. In fact, both Germany and England lack commercial quantities

[14] Of the 4,836,000 tons of ammonia produced in 1959, 4,099,000 tons were produced from natural gas and 737,000 tons from other sources. See E. von Allmen, "Economics Are Basic for Plant Location," *Chemical Engineering Progress*. Vol. LVI, No. 11 (November, 1960), 37.

of this most prolific source of chemically simple hydrocarbons. A remarkable exception is Italy. Having no coal deposits, she is very poor in natural resources, but there are considerable reserves of natural gas in northern Italy's Po Valley. There the Montecatini chemical concern has established a petrochemical plant at Ferrara which produces from natural gas everything that plants in other countries make from oil and coal. For instance, acetylene is obtained from methane at this Italian plant as are urea and ammonia.[15]

RICH STORES GIVE BIRTH TO AN INDUSTRY

In the United States, stores of incredible richness in hydrocarbons were found in oil and particularly natural gas and were developed and applied through the creative genius of the chemical engineer. Thus "a new chemical industry was born in the United States between the World Wars with the effect upon chemical science applied to the benefit of mankind more revolutionary than the establishment of its coal-tar division as the result of the First World War effort."[16] Thus "two great American industries—the petroleum and the chemical—have been transformed from good customers into potent allies."[17] The 1955 estimate of the consumption of natural gas hydrocarbons for chemical manufacture made by Robert L. Bateman of Union Carbide Chemicals Company indicated the consumption of 382 billion cubic feet of methane for use in the following ways:

To Make	Consumption Billion Cu. Ft.
Carbon Black	245
Ammonia, Methanol	99
Acetylene, Hydrogen Cyanide, Methyl Chloride, etc.	18
	362

"To arrive at the estimate, methane consumption for individual chem-

[15] Giulio Ballabio, "The Petrochemical Industry in Italy," *Proceedings,* Fourth World Petroleum Congress, Section IV, pp. 253–59; "What's New in Synthetic Fibers—New Processing Methods and New Raw Materials May Give a Boost to the Burgeoning Synthetic Fibers Industry," *Chemical and Engineering News,* Vol. XXXV, No. 30 (July 29, 1957), 12ff.

[16] William Haynes, *American Chemical Industry—A History,* V (1930–39). This is a monumental and tremendously fascinating work.

[17] *Ibid.*

icals was obtained from that portion of the United States production that was methane-derived . . . the carbon black figure is reported directly by the Bureau of Mines."[18] In addition to this quantity of methane, 45 billion cubic feet of natural gas hydrocarbons—ethane, propane, and butane—were consumed in 1955 in the production of ethylene, propylene, butadiene, and oxygenated chemicals. The 407 billion cubic feet of natural gas components utilized in 1955 to make industrial chemicals comes to only 4 per cent of the net production of natural gas. Even if this figure should increase to 500 billion cubic feet, is still is a comparatively small percentage of total net production.[19]

There are limitations in the use of natural gas in petrochemical manufacture, particularly if it is no longer "cheap" natural gas. The authors of the Olds-Draper Report and their witnesses based their conclusions on the assumption that the Great Southwest should keep its gas at home to supply the petrochemical industry until far into the future. Probably it will be there although a great deal of it is exported north, west, and east. The authors of the report were concerned that big gas producers would make billions of dollars selling their gas to the pipe lines for high prices. The question of local versus distant consumption is a controversial one, and the opposite opinion is convincing. "Any attempt on the part of one state or a group of states to reserve for local or regional use a national asset is bound to bring down upon it a storm of protest and lead to retaliation which will play havoc with the very roots of this nation's strength."[20]

CHOOSING LOCATIONS FOR PETROCHEMICAL PLANTS

Much of the petrochemical industry is located in the Great Southwest. Texas claims that 85 per cent of this industry is located within her borders, especially along the Gulf Coast. Other southwestern states are satisfied to claim 75 per cent, more or less, but the predominance of the Golden Crescent, which extends 250 miles along the Gulf

[18] Melnick, "Ammonia Supply and Demand . . . In Balance by 1961?" *Oil and Gas Journal,* Vol. LVI, No. 50 (December 15, 1958), 109.

[19] "Features of the U. S. Petrochemical Scene," *Petroleum Press Service,* Vol. XXVII, No. 7 (July, 1960). Approximately 1 to 2 per cent of all marketed natural gas production goes into petrochemicals.

[20] Zimmermann, *World Resources and Industries,* 564. This book is a classic in the field and deserves wide reading.

Coast from Louisiana to Brownsville, in the petrochemical industry is an indisputable fact. While there are important petrochemical plants inland—such as Texas Eastman's (Eastman Kodak, Rochester) establishments at Longview—the bulk of the petrochemical enterprises is found along the Golden Crescent.

The selection of an industrial location depends on many factors. A very thorough and useful study undertaken by Walter Isard and Eugene W. Schooler, experts in industrial planning, enumerates these factors. Entitled "Location Factors in the Petrochemical Industry," their study is highly revealing in several aspects, particularly in its discussion of the effect natural gas has on industrial location. Although the authors had the future development of the Arkansas-White-Red River basins under consideration, they reached conclusions which can be applied to the petrochemical industry in other parts of the Southwest and the nation.[21]

Particularly interesting is the motivation behind the petrochemical industry's selection of a certain location. In at least one instance the intermediate acrylonitrile became an important criterion in such a selection. Acrylonitrile is derived from acetylene which is made by the partial oxidation of natural gas as developed by Badische-Anilin and Soda-Fabrik. It is used in the manufacture of synthetic fabrics and a synthetic rubber (Bunan) which is particularly resistant to attack by hydrocarbon solvents.[22] The American Cyanamid Company manufactures acetylene and hydrocyanic acid from natural gas and produces acrylonitrile from these compounds. In a paper presented to the Fourth World Petroleum Congress, J. T. Thurston, E. L. Carpenter, and F. Derbenwick, three chemists employed by American Cyanamid, stated the reasons for locating their plant at Fortier, a suburb of New Orleans, Louisiana. "The site was selected because of the availability of relatively cheap natural gas and an unlimited supply of water." The labor market in that area is also very good, and the area

[21] Of the 300 petrochemical construction projects throughout the Free World, 118 are being built or are scheduled to be built in the United States of America. More than half of these will be concentrated on the Gulf Coast, close to the source of raw materials—petroleum and natural gas. More than 100 major petrochemical plants are already operating in the Gulf area. See American Petroleum Institute, *Oil Facts,* Vol. II, No. 5 (October–November, 1960), 3.

[22] Melvin J. Astle, *The Chemistry of Petrochemicals,* 267. This work is a fine introduction to a great modern industry, but the reader must know quite a bit of chemistry to use it effectively.

is an agricultural section which provides a nearby market for ammonia and ammonium sulfate, two of the products that are made in the plant. The Fortier plant also manufactures acrylonitrile, which is spun into a new synthetic fiber, Creslan (R), at a plant near Pensacola, Florida, and woven by textile mills in Georgia and the Carolinas. Thus, from its chosen location in Louisiana and Florida, Cyanamid has easy access to the water and natural gas from which its hydrocarbon products are made and to the markets in which they are sold.

While Cyanamid's location appears to be ideal with regard to both raw materials and markets, the location problem for petrochemical plants is seldom so simple. At a symposium on petrochemicals held by the Houston Chamber of Commerce in October, 1955, some of the complexities of this problem were revealed. From this panel discussion, there emerged some very significant facts concerning industrial location in the Gulf South. Representatives of Dow Chemical Company, which makes magnesium from salt water, explained that they were attracted by an adequate fuel supply and an abundance of organic raw materials. Phillips is now producing a new low-pressure polyethylene called Marlex in its huge plant at the Houston Ship Channel. There on a vast acreage they have developed a petrochemical center which processes raw materials such as natural gas, acetylene, ethylene, propane, propylene, butane, butylene, and others. Ethylene, the starting material for Marlex, is obtained by processing light hydrocarbons, such as propane and butane, extracted along with other liquids from raw natural gas. The dry residue gas that remains is not a raw material in polyethylene manufacture except as a source of heat. The chemical industry uses much more natural gas as fuel than it does as raw material, and Phillips chooses plant locations near this source of fuel and raw material.

Some interesting points were made by members of the panel regarding the selection of plants and plant locations. Many of these would serve as general guides to the location of industry anywhere: industrial-business climate, community morality, labor relations, community attitude, and taxation policy. Taxes are, as one panel member pointed out, one of the four main location factors. The others are raw material supply, market, and labor supply. Oddly enough, fuel and power usually rank about seventeenth or eighteenth on a list of thirty factors. Thus, the price and availability of natural gas as a

219

fuel is not always as important a factor in the location of a petrochemical plant as one might think, though its availability as a raw material is vital.

Transportation facilities are of great significance in the selection of a location for basic chemical industries. For instance, recently McGuire Chemical Company of Oakland, California, opened a new contract tanker terminal at San Pedro in Los Angeles Harbor. There deliveries of petrochemicals by tanker are made with savings up to 80 per cent of the cost of shipping by rail. Union Carbide Chemicals and Commercial Solvents are among the tenants of this new terminal. "The chemical industry is its own best customer. Our strongest competitor can sometimes be our best customer," declared a member of the symposium. The plants buy from each other. For instance Gulf Oil Corporation sells ethylene from its establishments at Port Arthur, Texas, to Allied Chemical, Dow, Monsanto, and Koppers.[23] Much of the huge quantity of petrochemicals absorbed by the West Coats plastics markets comes from natural gas produced in Texas and Louisiana, but West Coast refineries are increasing their output of chemicals from refinery gases. In order to remain competitive, Gulf Coast suppliers must employ the cheapest method of transportation available, and that has proved to be ocean shipment.

The Gulf Coast petrochemical industry depends largely on the markets of the West Coast and the Eastern Seaboard. The Houston symposium showed clearly that the huge, new petrochemical industry is not yet harnessed to an adequate market in the immediate Gulf Coast area. True, there is a slowly increasing consumption of petrochemical products in the Southwest, but the bulk of these goes elsewhere. This is especially true of plastics. Dow, for instance, makes styrene in Freeport, Texas, right on the Gulf, and ships it north to Connecticut for processing. Then it is shipped back to Fort Worth,

[23] See the Texas issue of the *New York Herald Tribune*, July 1, 1956, for a highly readable description of the fantastic industrial development that has taken place in the Lone Star state. Monsanto Chemical Company is building a seventy-five-million-dollar petrochemical plant at Chocolate Bayou, Texas. Natural gas for fuel and feedstocks will be supplied from the nearby reserves of Monsanto's own Lion Oil Division. The first unit of the huge complex, a 500,000,000-pound-per-year ethylene plant, went into operation in 1962. See "Monsanto to Build Ethylene Plant as First Unit in Petrochemical Complex," *Business Week*, No. 1636 (January 7, 1961), 30, and "Monsanto Planning a Big Chemical Complex," *Chemical and Engineering News*, Vol. XXXIX, No. 2 (January 9, 1961), 31–32.

Texas, for additional processing and then north again to Philadelphia. Many of the panelists believed that intermediate operations plants were needed in the Gulf Coast area. Once these plants were installed, they reasoned, processors and final fabricators would follow. Thus it would be possible to stimulate a growth in the petrochemicals market at their doorstep through intermediate operations.

A limited number of plastic goods manufacturers have set up shop in the Southwest, but most of the petrochemicals made on the Gulf Coast are still being shipped to distant points where they are processed into various plastic goods. These plastic products are durable items that compete with other products in both quality and price. Since this is so, petrochemicals, so important in the manufacture of plastics and no longer the product of "cheap" natural gas, must either be shipped inexpensively or produced close to the plastics market.[24] Facts like these led the authors of the Isard-Schooler report to conclude that "greater freedom in locating plants in or nearer consuming market areas" will prevail in the future. This goal can be obtained by the separation and use of C_{2-4} (ethane, propane, butane) and higher hydrocarbons at points along gas transmission lines, thus placing chemical operations closer to consuming areas. "Limiting factors to the use of natural gas are the rising costs which increase the price of gas at the wellhead and increasing transmission costs."[25]

Continued the Isard-Schooler report, "The major portion of expan-

[24] "Unless he operates in the Southern United States, where the Houston district or nearby is an obvious choice, the plastics manufacturer is likely to have a marked preference for a particular site—based not on sentiment but hard economic considerations—which may be convenient for distribution to his customers, or already developed as an industrial site and euipped with services, offices and plant for making auxiliary materials, or which can utilize by-products. While he may also consider locating his plant close to a major supplier of raw materials, he has to consider, in terms of cash, what the additional cost to him may be in severing a particular operation from his main factory." See J. W. Woolcock, "Some Problems of Raw Material Supply for the Plastics Industry," *Petroleum Times,* Vol. LXIII, No. 1624 (November 6, 1959), 693.

This area in Texas has been very aptly described in "Houston Complex," *Fortune,* Vol. LVIII, No. 2 (February, 1958), 127, as "Houston's Spaghetti Bowl" because of the crisscrossing maze of pipelines transferring hydrogen, acetylene, ethylene, ethane, propane, butadiene, butylene, butane, brine chlorine, hydrogen chloride, and minor products between some two dozen producers and users.

[25] W. E. Kuhn and J. W. Hutcheson, "The Petroleum Industry—Source of Chemical Raw Materials," *Petroleum Engineer,* Vol. XXIX, No. 6 (June, 1957), E–3ff. Both Mr. Kuhn and Mr. Hutcheson are well-known as authors of petrochemicals features, and both are connected with the Texas Company.

sion in natural gas-based petrochemicals capacity will be erected in natural gas areas. However, some expansion will occur at or near major metropolitan market areas and gateway points, particularly the Ohio Valley because of its general advantage in chlorine production. The future pattern of petrochemicals expansion is, therefore, likely to be somewhat less oriented to the Arkansas-White-Red River basins and other natural gas producing areas than is current production."[26]

Three striking instances offer ample proof of the resourcefulness exercised by members of the petrochemical industry in their search for ideal plant locations. One instance involves Phillips' ammonia plant at Kennewick in Washington State, a new industrial frontier with ample water supplies and a pleasant climate. The gas for the two-hundred-ton daily production comes from the former Pacific Northwest Pipeline, now Northwest Division of El Paso Natural Gas Company. There is a surrounding agricultural market for the chemical fertilizer it produces. This same consideration, a nearby market, motivated Shell to establish a plant at Ventura, California, where ammonia and urea[27] are produced. Here, too, a rich farming area is close at hand. Finally, Union Carbide Chemicals has planned a fifty-million-dollar factory in West Virginia where ethylene and other products will be made from locally produced natural gas. West Virginia is, of course, a strategic location with regard to vast consumer markets that include processors, fabricators, wholesalers, and retailers and their customers. Because these outlets are near at hand, transportation costs will not be high.

TRANSMISSION SYSTEMS AMONG PETROCHEMICAL RANKS

Many transmission systems are joining the ranks of petrochemical industrialists in an effort to improve their earning power beyond the public utility limitations set by the Federal Power Commission and to utilize their facilities such as pipe lines and hydrogenation and other plants. For instance, El Paso Natural Gas formed the Odessa Butadiene Company with Odessa Natural Gas, Union Carbon Company, and General Tire and Rubber, and achieved the production goal

[26] A case in point is Columbia Gas System's new natural gas plant in the Ohio Valley.

[27] From methane, through ammonia, urea is obtained for combining with formaldehyde to produce urea-formaldehyde, so important for the synthetic resins used in the manufacture of plastics.

of fifty thousand tons per year at a cost of $20,000,000. Tennessee Gas, as a partner with the huge Food Machinery and Chemical Corporation, produces 200,000 short tons of butadiene each year. Panhandle Eastern Pipe Line Corporation has a considerable interest in the highly successful operations of National Distillers and Chemical Corporation.[28] United Gas Corporation owns 50 per cent of the Escambia Bay Chemical Corporation at Pensacola, Florida, a $24,000,-000 investment by the end of 1956. Natural gas is the raw material for its ammonia and other products.[29] The Olin-Mathieson Chemical Corporation-Tennessee Gas combination is a many-sided chemical and petrochemical concern that utilizes ethane from Tennessee's low-temperature liquids extraction plant at Greensburg, Kentucky, in its Brandenburg, Kentucky, operations. All of these undertakings are based on the assumption that a continuous supply of oil and natural gas is available. Though there is some question about how long this supply will be available, there is evidence that it will last long enough to make these diversifications, frequently financed from internal sources, profitable.[30]

A PETROCHEMICAL LOOK AHEAD

The future of the petrochemical industry appears to be one of increase. The President's Material Policy Commission presented the following comparison of the 1950 statistics and predicted 1975 figures:[31]

---

[28] See the following three articles about this remarkable undertaking in the petrochemicals issue of the *Oil and Gas Journal,* Vol. LIV, No. 70 (September 3, 1956): John C. Reidel, "Expanding Facilities at National Petrochemical," p. 105; "More Ethylene at Tuscola," p. 108; and "New Wrinkles in Ammonia Manufacture at Tuscola," p. 111.

[29] United Gas, *Annual Report* (for 1958), 4, 21; United Gas, *Annual Report* (for 1959), 16, 17. The other 50 per cent is owned by Electric Bond and Share.

[30] The over-capacity in the plastics industry is considerable, and therefore the need for the development of new markets is great. In 1958 the polyethylene sales totaled 750 million pounds while the industry's output capacity was estimated to be around 1.3 billion pounds. In the same year, vinyl resin sales amounted to about 730 million pounds, about 200 million pounds less than capacity. Styrene sales were estimated to be around 625 million pounds, about 225 million pounds away from capacity. This over-capacity and accompanying lack of sales was pointed out by G. L. Pitzer, the vice-president for production of Bakelite Company, an affiliate of Union Carbide.

[31] *The Promise of Technology* (Volume IV of President's Materials Policy Commission, *Resources for Freedom*), 207.

	1950	1975
Primary Products (Million pounds per year)	9,900	54,000
Raw Materials Needed (Thousand pounds per year)	6,900	38,000
Requirements of the Petrochemical Industry (Weight per cent of crude oil and natural gas)		
For Raw Materials	0.7	1.9
For Raw Materials and Fuel	2.0	5.5

This forecast is based on three major assumptions: that an armed peacetime economy exists, that there is continued growth of the industry commensurate with an expanding population and uninterrupted by a serious economic recession, and that the manufacture of synthetic fuels with accompanying chemical by-products does not become a major factor during this period. Writes C. O. Tongberg, executive vice president of Esso Research and Engineering Company, "The most significant observation is that the magnitude of the petrochemical business in 1975, based on finished products, may be five-fold what is was in 1950. This will be accompanied by an increase in the percentage of crude oil and natural gas going to chemical raw materials. Even so, the petrochemical industry as a whole, including the fuel used in processing, may represent an outlet for only about 6 percent of the petroleum and natural gas production twenty years from now. In 1975, and because of their value as structural materials, plastics will probably be the outstanding consumer of petrochemical raw materials, and might represent as much as 45 per cent of the total tonnage. Synthetic rubber, fibers, surface coatings, detergents, and nitrogenous fertilizers will also show at least a two-four fold increase and will make up the lion's share of the future."[32]

The manufacturers of synthetic fibers—especially the acrylic fibers—are confident of a great future. The potential range of fiber uses appears to be very broad. Fundamental research and engineering are constantly striving toward further improvement and adaptation to provide even broader fields of application. In 1956 almost 500 million pounds of chemical fibers were produced. By 1965 annual production of chemical fibers will pass the billion mark, and a demand

[32] C. O. Tongberg, "Chemicals from Fuels," *Oil and Gas Compact Bulletin,* Vol. XIV, No. 1 (June, 1955), 30.

of four billion pounds per year is predicted for 1975.[33] This confidence in future development is typical of the petrochemical industry and its management as new frontiers are created by the development of synthetic products through skillful research and economical utilization of hydrocarbons. Considering the supply of hydrocarbons on which the industry is based in this country, it is justified. Our recoverable reserves of bituminous coal alone have been estimated at 524,-729 million short tons.[34]

[33] From a pamphlet published by Chemstrand in 1956 and entitled *1956—A Year of Progress.* The publication carried a concluding article written by Eward A. O'Neal, Jr., president of Chemstrand, under the heading "Our Future."

[34] Paul Avritt, Louise R. Berryhill, and Dorothy A. Taylor. *Coal Resources of the United States* (a progress report, October, 1953), U.S.G.S. *Circular 293.*

In addition to the works cited in the footnotes, the following reference materials were employed in the writing of Chapter 8:

American Cyanamid Company, *The Chemistry of Acrylonitrile,* second edition, New York, 1959.

Ballabio, Giulio, "The Petrochemical Industry in Italy," a paper presented at the Fourth World Petroleum Congress, Rome, Italy, June, 1955, and published in *Proceedings* (Section IV), *q.v.,* pp. 253–59.

Bateman, Robert L., "U.S. Petrochemicals Reach New Peak," *Oil and Gas Journal,* Vol. LVII, No. 37 (September 7, 1959), 121–22.

Brooks, Benjamin T., and A. E. Dunstan, eds., 5 vols., Oxford and New York, 1953. "Synthetic Products and Refinery Processes," V, Part III.

Burk, Robert E., and Daniel E. Strain, "Polyethylene (U.S.A.)," a paper presented at the Fourth World Petroleum Congress, Rome, Italy, June, 1955, and published in *Proceedings* (Section IV), *q.v.,* p. 167.

"Burning Gas for Carbon Black," in President's Materials Policy Commission, *Resources for Freedom, q.v.,* IV.

Chinitz, Benjamin, and Raymond Vernon, "Changing Forces in Industrial Location," *Harvard Business Review,* Vol. XXXVIII, No. 1 (January-February, 1960).

Cunningham, J. P., "Chemicals from Petroleum in the U. S.," a paper presented at the Fourth World Petroleum Congress, Rome, Italy, June, 1955, and published in *Proceedings* (Section IV), *q.v.,* p. 209.

Eck, Theodore, "The Outlook for the Southwestern Petrochemical Industry," *Business Review,* Vol. XLV, No. 9 (September, 1960), 2.

Goldstein, R. F., *The Petrochemical Industry,* second edition, London, 1958.

Greenhut, Melvin L., *Plant Location in Theory and in Practice—The Economics of Space,* Chapel Hill, N.C., 1956.

Hoover, Edgar M., *Location of Economic Activity,* first edition, New York, 1948.

Hutchison, A. W., and R. G. Stevens, "The Canadian Petrochemical Industry," a paper presented at the Fourth World Petroleum Congress, Rome, Italy, June, 1955, and published in *Proceedings* (Section IV), *q.v.*. p. 167.

Isard, Walter, *Location and Space Economy: A General Theory Relating to Industrial Location, Market Area, Land Use, Trade and Urban Structure,* New York, 1956.

———, and Eugene W. Schooler, *Location Factors in the Petrochemical Industry,* Washington, D.C., 1955.

Kobe, Kenneth A., and John J. McKetta, Jr., eds., *Advances in Petroleum Industry Chemistry,* 3 vols., New York, 1958–59.

Latourette, William I., "Petrochemical Plenty," *Barron's,* Vol. XXXVI, No. 37 (September 10, 1956), 11, 13.

Lösch, August, *Die Räumliche Ordnung des Wirtschaft,* Jena, 1944. English edition, *Economics of Location,* New Haven, 1954.

Manufacturing Chemists' Association, Incorporated, *The Chemical Industry Facts Book,* fourth edition, Washington, D.C., 1960–61.

Oil and Gas Journal, Vol. LIV, No. 70 (September 3, 1956), Annual Petrochemicals Issue.

"The Outlook for Energy Sources," in President's Materials Policy Commission, *Resources for Freedom,* q.v., III, 22.

"Petrochemicals Face New Challenge," *Business Week,* No. 1618 (September 3, 1960), 50ff.

Ponder, Thomas C., and J. J. McKetta, "Petrochemicals in Synthetic Fibers," *Petroleum Refiner,* Vol. XXXV, No. 2 (February, 1956), 109.

Pylant, Hugh S., "Big Surge in U. S. Petrochemical Building Projects May Be Last Pre-Maturity Fling," *Oil and Gas Journal,* Vol. LVIII, No. 36 September 5, 1960), 112ff.

Reppe, W., "Modern Methods of the Chemistry of Acetylene and Olefins," a paper presented at the Fourth World Petroleum Congress, Rome, Italy, June, 1955, and published in *Proceedings* (Section IV), *q.v.,* 291.

Standard Oil Development Company, "Forecasts for Petroleum Chemicals," Chapter 14 of *The Promise of Technology* (Vol. IX of President's Materials Policy Commission, Resources for Freedom), 205.

Thomas, R. W., "Relationship Between Petrochemical Diversification and Natural Gas," in *Economics of the Gas Industry, q.v.,* 237–54.

Thurston, J. T., E. L. Carpenter, and F. Derbenwich, "The Manufacture of Acrylonitrile from Natural Gas," a paper presented at the Fourth World Petroleum Congress, Rome, Italy, June, 1955, and published in *Proceedings* (Section IV), *q.v.,* p. 177.

Yaseen, Leonard C., *Plant Location,* New York, 1956.

9

THE LPG INDUSTRY

by John A. Crichton
and Alfred M. Leeston

LPG means *liquefied petroleum gas*. Most people will recognize it as "bottled gas" and "tank gas." The term liquefied is applied to this gas because it can be converted from a gaseous into a liquid state for transportation and storage under moderate pressures and ordinary temperatures. The liquefied gas changes into a vapor at atmospheric pressure.

Actually there are many liquefied petroleum gases. These gases are hydrocarbons found in crude oil, natural gas, and refinery gas. In crude oil they are members of the paraffin series of hydrocarbons and may be propane, isobutane, and normal butane, as found in crude oil or natural gas. In refinery gases they are propylene, propane, iso-butane, butylene, and butane. They are chiefly the products of natural gasoline plants, cycling condensate plants, and refineries. Since natural gas is the raw material from the first two plants mentioned, it may be said that natural gas is the basis for at least three-fourths of all LPG.

Certainly no industry has grown more rapidly than the LPG industry. The portion of natural gas liquids used in LPG production has more than doubled since 1945. At that time it represented about 28 per cent of the total. By 1959 it represented 58 per cent. In that same year sales of LPG rose to more than 211,000,000 barrels, an increase of 19 per cent over the previous year. A breakdown of these sales shows that 60 per cent was consumed for domestic and motor fuel. Chemical manufacture and the synthetic rubber industry used almost 30 per cent. The remaining 10 per cent was consumed in gas manufacture and industrial and miscellaneous uses. The immense production of natural gas and natural gas liquids, a domestic market unique

228

in physical extent and purchasing power, brilliant salesmanship, and big new consumers like the huge petrochemical industry are factors that have contributed to this phenomenal growth.

The greatest demand for LPG at present is for domestic space and water heating. To this should be added: lighting, cooking, refrigeration, irrigation, pumping, tractor fuel (1,500,000 tractors use LPG for fuel), flame weeding, and chicken brooding. The household and agricultural applications, such as tobacco curing, crop dehydration, fruit ripening, milk pasteurization, and fueling air conditioning plants, point to the fact that LPG is chiefly used in rural areas and towns still not connected to gas mains or electricity supplies. A report issued by Phillips Petroleum Company in Bartlesville, Oklahoma, emphasizes that house heating by LPG is spreading rapidly northward as people become acquainted with the cleanliness and convenience of using it. In recent years LPG has come to be of increasing importance to utility gas companies. It is now extensively used as a standby fuel to supplement normal gas supplies at peak times and in emergencies.

The excellent properties of the liquefied petroleum gases, their high heat content, their purity, and certain other physical and chemical properties, have established them as a popular fuel. Their gross calorific values in the gaseous state are between 2,700 Btu's per cubic foot (propane) and 3,400 Btu's per cubic foot (butane). Liquid gases have two to three times the heat content of natural gas and about five to seven times that of a similar volume of manufactured coal gas. Because of these favorable characteristics, they lend themselves well to "bottling" in moderately pressurized containers.

The bottled gas is kept liquid under pressure in the cylinder. When it is released from the bottle, it comes out as a gas. Propane is preferred to butane because of its more favorable physical properties. It is delivered in millions of steel cylinders to the kitchen door of about nine million rural and suburban homes. Butane consumption is catching up because of its increasing use in the manufacture of synthetic rubber. Together with styrene, it provides the raw material for this rubber in the copolymer plants. Propane gas is so economical that a single cylinder lasts an average family three or four months. Butane is used for blending, especially with natural gasoline having a high vapor pressure, to confer volatility.

Tireless efforts of the industry itself in co-operation with national

229

organizations such as the National Fire Prevention Association, the American Gas Association, and the American Petroleum Institute, have developed standards for the design and construction of LPG facilities at natural gasoline plants, refineries, tank farms, pipe lines, and marine terminals. These steadily improving safety measures are going far to reduce to a minimum fire and other hazards caused by transportation and handling of a highly inflammable substance.

In addition, a safety ingredient is added to liquefied gas. Having only a faint smell of its own, it is given an odor to provide a warning to the absent-minded housewife who might leave an unlit burner turned on. One of the odorants used is ethyl mercaptan.

The oil industry's direct needs for liquefied petroleum gases are so diverse and substantial that they have considerable bearing on the volume available for general sale. Unfortunately, liquefied petroleum gases extracted in natural gasoline plants do not occupy such a position of inelastic demand. The oil industry, having been in the research forefront for the last fifteen years, has not only greatly improved its oil-finding and refining methods, but has also developed about two thousand new petrochemical products. From this sprang up the synthetic rubber, plastics, and synthetic fiber industries. This startling success of industrial research proved a great boon to the LPG industry, which now sells nearly 30 per cent of its entire market to the chemical and petrochemical factories. Petrochemicals are still on the upgrade, and tubeless tires require more and more butadiene, the chief material for synthetic rubber. Thus, the base material, normal butane, will continue to be in high demand. Other petrochemicals, such as ethylene and polyethylene are consumed in ever-growing quantities, so that here, too, liquefied petroleum gas has a big customer. During 1943, chemical manufacture took 55 million gallons of LPG. In 1944 this figure jumped by 175 per cent to about 152 million gallons, plus an additional 162 million gallons that were used in the manufacture of synthetic rubber components. In 1954 chemical manufacture used over one billion gallons and synthetic rubber, 300 million gallons. The prosperity year 1955 witnessed an increase in the use of LPG for chemicals to 1.26 billion gallons.

A petroleum scientist, Eugene E. Ayres, who is connected with Gulf Oil Corporation and co-author of the book *Energy Sources, The Wealth of the World,* has predicted that LPG will replace natural gas as the main building block for petrochemicals in the future. He estimated potential United States reserves of LPG to be eight billion barrels from gas processing and three billion barrels from oil refining.

One of the most important petrochemical base materials will be ethane, ranking, among the fractions of natural gas, second to methane, its chief component. From ethane, ethylene can be manufactured. Ethylene, one of those wonder chemicals in our time, is being used to produce polyethylene, the fastest growing of all petrochemicals. Polyethylene is fashioned into rubber-like plastics, the most familiar product being the so-called squeeze bottles for cosmetic sprays and for catsup.

An interesting example of an establishment extracting hydrocarbons is the fifty-million-dollar petrochemical plant at Tuscola, Illinois, 150 miles south of Chicago. Operated by the National Petro-Chemicals Corporation and owned jointly by National Distillers Products Corporation (60 per cent) and the Panhandle Eastern Pipeline Company (40 per cent), it extracts hydrocarbons from 400 million cubic feet of natural gas each day. Of the hydrocarbons extracted, propane and butane as well as natural gasoline are salable without additional processing. It also extracts ethane, which is converted to ethylene. From this the plant manufactures ethyl alcohol and ethyl chloride. The ethylene plant, the largest of its kind ever built, can turn out 200 million pounds a year. This huge enterprise, which added to a large LPG capacity, lies at the intersection of one natural gas pipe line stretching from the Hugoton Field in Kansas to Detroit, and another transmission line running from the natural gas deposits of the Texas-Louisiana-Gulf area. After the hydrocarbons have been extracted from the natural gas, it is returned from the plant to the pipe lines for distribution to consumers. The petrochemical plant is a profitable diversification for both a whisky-making concern and a gas transmission company.

Plants like these are impressive examples of efficient utilization of natural gasoline and LPG. Making such good use of these gases conserves the nation's energy resources. The natural gas is actually improved by removal of the light hydrocarbons; it is made fit for transportation in long distance pipe lines. Gas which otherwise would be flared at oil wells finds a productive outlet, and the products extracted (natural gasoline and LPG) stretch our fuel supply considerably.

In one of its annual review-forecast numbers, the *Oil and Gas Journal* predicted that a much more stable summer market was in prospect for LPG. "Colder-than-normal weather in the principal consuming areas has made this season the best in many years for LPG producers; pressure tank cars are in great demand and more would be used if available. The expected result: lower stocks underground when spring comes and a place to put what normally would be distress supplies next summer." This terse statement touches the core of the problem besetting the LPG industry. About 60 per cent of the huge nine billion gallon sale of liquefied gases in 1959 was for domestic uses and motor fuel. An industry which sells the bulk of its products for household purposes is subject to heavy seasonal fluctuations. There is no less dependable ally than the weather, and the cycles between summer and winter demand have their unsettling effects on LPG prices. Another drawback of the predominance of household usage is the need for bottling liquid gas for retailing in millions of small, pressurized cylinders. The original cost of this processing is high, and transportation is expensive, despite a widespread, well-planned distribution system. Suppliers would prefer a still brisker expansion of industrial consumption where liquid gas could be moved by bulk transport with less cost than when it is moved in thousands of individual steel containers.

To offset seasonal fluctuations and avoid dumping of surplus supplies in slack seasons, the LPG industry has aggressively tackled a technically difficult and financially expensive solution, storage. In the early 1950's producers began to build underground storage facilities in addition to increasing the conventional steel storage tanks above ground. They adapted subterranean caverns in depleted oil and gas reservoirs, salt domes, salt water sands, and shale deposits for the large-scale storage of LPG during periods of low demand. Salt beds and domes are the rule and comprise almost 90 per cent of total capacity. Mined caverns are the exception. So successful were these new warehouses provided by nature that the Phillips report, mentioned above, estimated an underground storage capacity of 15 million barrels in 1955. By 1959 this had increased to 60 million barrels. Despite this truly remarkable accomplishment, there remains the need for more adequate consumer storage, new and increased summer loads, and planned deliveries.

LPG is transported by train, truck, and tanker. The number of high pressure tank cars has increased to around 20,000. About 50 per cent of the LPG movement is by truck. A significant innovation in LPG transport is the LPG tanker. In December 1953 a large, ocean-going carrier of LPG was built by Kieler Howardtwerke of West Germany for a Norwegian owner. This was the motor ship *Gaspras Norte* with 5,250 tons dead weight and a capacity of 4,000 tons, or about 1,176,000 gallons, of liquefied butane or propane. In 1960 there were between thirty and forty LPG tankers of this pressurized type in service, and each one had a gas cargo capacity between 5,000 and 7,000 tons. The biggest gas-carrying ship now in commission is the *Esso Puerto Rico*, a combined LPG-Crude Oil carrier with 36,000 tons dead weight which can carry over 80,000 barrels of liquid gas in fifty-eight pressurized cylinders and 210,000 barrels of crude in conventional wing tanks.

Aramco is building a plant at Ras Tanura on the Persian Gulf designed to make LPG available in refrigerated form for bulk shipment by ocean tankers at atmospheric pressure. This method is estimated to save 30 per cent by weight as compared to pressurized liquid tanks and a larger percentage of space. One tanker is already equipped to carry refrigerated LPG, and several more are being built.

The possibility of significant reduction in the cost of ocean transport of LPG is of special importance to distant markets. Western European demand for LPG totals about two and one-fourth million tons annually, or some 60 per cent of the overall consumption outside North America. Other rapidly developing, distant markets are North Africa, South America, Canada, England, Mexico, and the Scandinavian countries.

The transportation problem in the United States is being eased by the construction of products pipe lines. Texas Eastern Transmission Corporation converted its Little Inch to a products line, and it delivers products from Texas to Ohio. Other such lines are Mid-America's 2,200-mile project from Eunice, New Mexico, to Minneapolis, Minnesota, built at an estimated cost of sixty-seven million dollars.

There are wide differentiations in the pricing of LPG in various countries. In addition to seasonal fluctuations owing to the supply-demand position, prices vary greatly between different producing and marketing areas. Producers' current contract prices at tank car in the Gulf area are around four cents per gallon for propane and compare with prices of up to eight and one-half cents a gallon at New York port. On the basis of equivalent heat content, which is very high, LPG is usually cheaper than coal or electricity in many parts of the United States although it may retail for as much as thirty cents a gallon in the North Atlantic area.

Natural gasoline is a liquid mixture of hydrocarbons extracted from natural gas consisting largely of the "pentanes plus." The name "natural gasoline" is used to distinguish it from gasoline produced from crude oil by distillation and cracking in refineries. Natural gasoline is prepared primarily for use as a high quality fuel in motors of automobiles and airplanes and as a *blending agent*. It has a high volatility and possesses a higher octane rating than straight-run gasoline. It is more susceptible to the beneficial anti-knock effects of tetraethyl lead. For these reasons it is often blended with refinery gasoline stocks. Certain grades of lower vapor pressure can be used directly as motor fuel, but they usually are sent to refineries for blending.

Despite these valuable and useful properties, natural gasoline is subject to quick changes in markets. Sales of only a small percentage of the total product may cause heavy fluctuations in buyer demand and consequently in price. The efforts of the Natural Gasoline Association of America to increase consumption have aided greatly in market stabilization.

The history of natural gasoline plants is essentially a record of discovery, improvement, and refinement in extracting methods. Until the early 1930's, natural gasoline was virtually the only product of the natural gasoline industry. In 1941 it still represented 65 per cent of the industry's products, but from then on production of LP gases increased with rapid strides.

The process of extracting hydrocarbon liquids from natural gas has developed through three stages. In the early history of the industry, this extraction was accomplished chiefly in *compression plants* by compression and cooling. Early pioneers in natural gasoline like the Sutton Brothers and Edwards near Sisterville, West Virginia, compressed the gas and cooled it through lines laid in the Ohio River. The first commercial plants based on this method were built by William Fasenmeyer, Sutton Brothers and Edwards, and Reno Oil Company (1908), and were preceded only by a small unit operated by the Reverend William Mayberry (1905).

234

The industry grew at a brisk pace, and by 1912 there were 250 plants in the United States, all of the compressor type. Many simply designed compression plants began operations at a small cost. But because of the inefficiency of this method of extraction, their number has declined; and they have been replaced by larger and more efficient *absorption units,* in which the gasoline is extracted by placing the gas in contact with an oil and subsequently distilling it from the heavier oil. Great names in supplying the young industry with machinery are Bessemer (now Cooper-Bessemer), Ingersoll-Rand, and Clark.

It was the Hope Natural Gas Company, a subsidiary of Standard Oil (New Jersey), which built a large-scale absorption plant after seven years of exhaustive research conducted by George Saybolt. The plant became operative in 1913, almost forty years after the absorption process had become known in 1875. From the patent that was granted Mr. Saybolt in 1911, sprang a celebrated patent case. A lawsuit was filed by Hope Natural Gas Company against the Oklahoma Natural Gas Company for alleged infringement in 1918. Four years of litigation kept lawyers busy, but the Oklahoma company won.

The absorption process enjoyed increasing popularity. Considerably improved, complete plants were offered by the Koppers Company. Not only eastern and mid-continent fields, but California embraced the fledgling industry. Standard Oil Company of California completed a compression plant in 1916. By the middle of 1917 this state had thirty-one plants in operation.

In 1918 a competitor of the new absorption process appeared—the *charcoal adsorption method* introduced by G. A. Burrell and G. G. Oberfell. It consisted of passing the gas through adsorber towers containing activated charcoal to adsorb liquid hydrocarbons from the gas. Liquid hydrocarbons were then recovered by passing live steam through the charcoal. A number of plants in the Eastern fields and in the Texas Panhandle used the process which, although effective, was relatively expensive to operate. It has been replaced almost entirely by the *oil-absorption process*, which gives high extraction efficiency and is capable of close operational control.

A plant using a refrigeration process for extracting natural gas liquids from natural gas being transported through a high-pressure transmission line was placed in operation by the Tennessee Gas Transmission Company in 1951. The primary purpose of that plant is to recover light hydrocarbons for use in the manufacture of chemicals. It also makes the gas more suitable for pipe-line transmission after it has been stripped of about 15 per cent of the ethane and most of the heavier hydrocarbons.

The growth of this new industry has been marked with tragedy. On September 27, 1915, a tank car of casinghead gasoline exploded on a railroad siding in Ardmore, Oklahoma, taking forty-three lives and injuring more than five hundred people. This disaster aroused sharp criticism of natural gasoline by refiners, who were to become the largest users of this new product; but it greatly stimulated safety work, especially by the association of Natural Gasoline Manufacturers. Now the Natural Gasoline Association of America, this group has its headquarters at Tulsa, Oklahoma, and celebrated its silver anniversary in 1946. Today, the industry and its products have an excellent safety record.

One early advance in safe transport was the building of the first insulated tank car in 1913 by the General American Tank Car Company, now General American Transportation Corporation. Since that time these cars have become the standard of the industry. Wooden barrels and steel drums are no longer used. The tank car industry has progressed greatly and now builds aluminum cars for transporting petrochemicals.

The growth of the LPG industry, as we witness it in our time, was clearly foreseen by the famous engineer of the Bessemer Gas Engine Company, Frank Peterson, in these prophetic words in the *Oil and Gas Journal* of September 17, 1914: "But for domestic use for isolated conditions of lighting, heating and cooking service, for laboratory, technical and scientific requirements, for development of intensely high temperatures in small furnaces, for metal cutting and light welding, for marine light house and buoy lighting, the product commands the most ready and useful acceptance."

Liquefied petroleum gas has received increasing attention both inside and outside the natural gas industry from men who see in it both the answer to present problems and the threat of new ones. Listed below is a group of works that were helpful to the authors as they wrote this chapter and should prove helpful to the reader who is interested in LPG:

Benz, George R., Paul W. Tucker, and W. F. DeVoe, "LP-Gas Increase Largest in History," *Gas Age,* Vol. CXVII, No. 1 (January 12, 1956), 36.

Bizal, Robert B., "Growing Storage to Help LPG Pricing," *Oil and Gas Journal,* Vol. LVI, No. 39 (September 29, 1958), 40–43.

———, "LPG Storage Caverns to Grow 24%," *Oil and Gas Journal,* Vol. LVIII, No. 48 (November 28, 1960), 85.

Bureau of Mines, *1947 Yearbook,* 37.

Burrell, George A., "LP Gas and Its Use in Utility Service," *American Gas Journal,* Vol. CLXXVI, No. 5 (May, 1952), 27.

Carmical, J. H., "Modern Day Boom Is Boon in the Lab," *New York Times,* January 22, 1956, Sec. 2, pp. 1–2.

Institute of Gas Technology, *Natural Gas Production and Transmission,* Chicago, 1952.

"LPG—As Modern as the Missiles," a bulletin published by Sinclair Oil Company, 1961.

"LPG—The Gas that Flows from Bottles," *The Lamp,* Standard Oil of New Jersey's monthly magazine (June, 1947).

"New L.P.G. Barge Launched by Warren," *Oil and Gas Journal,* Vol. LIV, No. 25 (October 24, 1955).

Oil and Gas Journal, Review-forecast Issue (January 29, 1962).

Platt's Oil Price Handbook, annual editions.

"Refrigerating L.P.G. for Ocean Transport," *Petroleum Press Service,* Vol. XXVII, No. 7 (July, 1960), 241.

Stern, A. Richard, "More LPG—Bottled Gas Continues to Expand into New Markets," *Barron's,* Vol. XXXVIII (October 13, 1958), 5–6.

Thomas, Dana L., "Creslan, Darvan and Kodel," *Barron's,* Vol. XXXVIII (October 13, 1958), 3, 16, 18.

Vaughn, Harold E., "Gasoline and Cycling Plant Economics vs. Increasing Cost of Gas," *The Petroleum Engineer Reference Annual,* 1953, E–10.

10

UNDERGROUND STORAGE

by Alfred M. Leeston
and John A. Crichton

THE WINTER of 1957–58 was one of the severest and longest of late years over the eastern half of the United States. Gas sales soared on wings of ice as freezing weather brought an unparalleled demand to many utilities, according to the February 23, 1958 *New York Times*. Naturally, these icy blasts meant peak deliveries for pipe lines and gas utilities. Operating revenues of interstate natural gas pipe lines topped $2,500,000,000 in the twelve-month period ending February 28 of that year and were up 14.6 per cent over those of the previous year. The Consolidated Edison Company of New York sold more than 1.5 billion cubic feet of gas during the week ending February 16, and this figure can be compared with 1.207 billion cubic feet in the same week of 1957. Brooklyn Union Gas Company's record total of 266 million cubic feet in 1958 was 90 per cent above the figure for 1957.

The increased consumption can be attributed to the extremely cold weather and to a rapid increase in the use of natural gas in the New York area since Transcontinental Pipe Line Corporation brought the popular fuel to Brooklyn and New York City in March, 1951. "Virtually all utilities," wrote the *New York Times*, "that still have facilities for manufacturing gas were forced to turn out mixed gas—a combination of natural and manufactured gas—to meet peak demand that eclipsed all records." But these stand-by facilities for manufacturing gas provided only comparatively small quantities of fuel. The bulk of the gas came from the pipe lines and underground storage facilities.

Nothing could more forcibly illustrate the progress the construction of these underground reservoirs has brought in the use of natural gas for space heating than these experiences in a record heating season. Underground gas storage has many aspects of far-reaching significance for the producer of gas, the pipe lines, the distributor, and the consumer. Both transmission and distribution companies are fully aware of the usefulness of underground storage and are creating and enlarging a system of underground storage reservoirs. One can say without exaggeration that this impressive underground storage system with a total of 209 pools and a capacity of 2.6 trillion cubic feet at the beginning of 1960 was a decisive factor in the spectacular postwar development of the natural gas industry.

When a man in the natural gas industry talks of the weather, he talks in terms of *degree days*. To him the important question is whether the temperature outside has dropped to a point at which his customers need to heat their homes. The intensity of the heating season is expressed in terms of degree days. Adding the difference between 65 degrees Fahrenheit and the daily mean temperature for every day of the heating season gives the total degree days. These seasonal degree days are a fairly accurate measure of the amount of natural gas that will be consumed for heating purposes. Long-range weather forecasting is, therefore, of great importance to the gas man; it enables him to plan for the volume of natural gas needed for home heating. Both the American Gas Association and the American Petroleum Institute (for fuel oil) are promoting projects aimed at improving weather forecasting techniques.

In addition to peak seasons in gas demand, there are peak hours and peak days. For instance, millions of people prepare breakfast every day, putting a heavy strain on the gas distribution system early in the morning. Conventional wash days in many communities may create a water-heating and gas dryer peak.

The natural gas industry must provide the maximum requirement for gas deliveries during sustained cold weather and must make the large capital expenditures this necessitates. The various segments of the industry are affected differently by these requirements. The distributors' firm gas sales are made up of non-heating uses with a relatively good over-all annual load factor of 65 to 80 per cent, and space-heating sales with an annual load factor of 30 per cent or less. With the increase in space-heating requirements, the composite load factor of the distributor has tended to approach the space-heating load factor. Thus, composite load factors for distribution companies of 35 to

50 per cent are not uncommon. The producer sells his gas to the transmission company at a flat rate per MCF. Since transmission companies compete with each other in assuring themselves of gas supplies, one of the incentives offered the producer has been a gas purchase contract containing a "take or pay" clause. The transmission company obligates itself to pay for a certain volume of gas over an annual period, whether or not it takes this volume.

The pipe-line transmission company has a fixed daily throughput capacity with a high fixed plant investment. The fixed charges, including depreciation, ad valorem taxes, and income taxes, are high in relation to operating and maintenance costs, even after including compression costs. Hence, it is important to operate a long-distance, gas transmission pipe line at as high a load factor as possible to haul a maximum annual volume of gas through the line and keep the transportation cost per MCF at a minimum. Because of the high ratio of fixed charges to variable operating expenses, the transportation costs per MCF of gas delivered at a 50 per cent annual load factor is nearly double that of a 100 per cent load factor operation. Add to that the effect of "take or pay" contracts, and the cost at 50 per cent may well be three times that of a 100 per cent load factor operation.

The Federal Power Commission has acknowledged the requirement of a high annual load factor for the economic operation of natural gas pipe lines and has recognized a two-part tariff—demand and commodity—which gives gas distributing companies the principal incentive to maintain a high load factor. The gas distributing companies can do so by peak shaving, interruptible gas sales, and gas storage. *Peak shaving* is the use of manufactured oil gas, reformed propane gas, or propane-air gas to "shave only the extreme peaks of maximum sendout days." *Interruptible gas sales* are those to industry with the provision that the service can be interrupted when severe weather forces the gas company to supply domestic consumers first. Many gas companies cannot make satisfactory interruptible gas sales, and *storage* becomes the only answer to a satisfactory load factor. This, of course, means the storage of the gas not needed by residential customers in the summer so that it can be made available during the winter.

The transmission company also has an incentive to develop storage fields. The investment for pipe-line and compressor facilities is

241

about five hundred dollars per thousand cubic feet of maximum daily capacity; the investment per thousand cubic feet of peak-day capability is about one hundred dollars. It might be argued that the transmission companies are allowed a return on the original cost of the pipe-line and compressor facilities less accrued depreciation, and thus the pipe-line company would prefer the higher investment in pipe lines and a greater return. However, this argument neglects the fact that other fuels are competing with gas, and there is an incentive to keep the delivered cost low.

Each year the Committee on Underground Storage for the American Gas Association publishes a report on the underground storage of gas in the United States. The report of December 31, 1959, the ninth published by the Committee, shows the following figures:

GROWTH OF UNDERGROUND STORAGE IN
UNITED STATES, 1944–1959

Year	Number of Pools	Number of States	Ultimate Reservoir Capacity Billion Cu. Ft.
1944*	50	11	135
1947†	70	11	250
1949‡	80	11	497
1950	125	15	774
1951	142	15	916
1952	151	16	1,292
1953	167	17	1,735
1954	172	17	1,859
1955	178	18	2,096
1956	188	20	2,402
1957	199	20	2,603
1958	205	20	2,717
1959	209	20	2,820

*E. G. Dahlgren, A.P.I. Eastern District Meeting, Columbus, Ohio.
†E. G. Dahlgren, A.G.A. Natural Gas Department, Chicago, Illinois.
‡Max W. Ball, A.G.A. Natural Gas Department, French Lick, Indiana.

Total gas in storage reservoirs as of December 31, 1957, was 1,674,388,293 MCF, of which 673,212,171 MCF was working gas, 626,588,714 MCF was cushion gas, and 374,587,408 MCF was na-

TABLE 15

STATES WITH UNDERGROUND GAS STORAGE

State	Total Reservoir Capacity Thousand Cu. Ft.		Total Gas in Storage Reservoirs Thousand Cu. Ft.	
	Dec. 31, 1960	*Dec. 31, 1959*	*Dec. 31, 1960*	*Dec. 31, 1959*
Arkansas	5,204,421	5,204,421	5,042,026	4,831,380
California	270,920,132	99,038,182	121,893,310	64.875,494
Colorado	3,000,000	186,700	728,592	164,482
Illinois	104,992,153	45,915,003	52,600,820	46,133,579
Indiana	15,164,036	12,453,884	11,944,771	10,353,439
Iowa	65,534,074	49,893,534	65,534,074	46,071,983
Kansas	101,514,193	83,623,223	82,567,719	70,834,376
Kentucky	24,684,091	27,264,569	26,110,810	27,197,228
Michigan	464,876,424	397,498,020	341,315,633	281,454,218
Mississippi	6,701,795	7,056,540	5,465,174	6,008,696
Missouri	11,238,774	9,716,585	11,239,446	9,602,563
Montana	96,452,193	87,075,505	55,183,327	42,965,415
New Mexico	77,871,510	77,871,510	44,423,777	47,873,736
New York	65,519,261	65,231,688	59,222,409	57,559,840
Ohio	437,392,393	433,515,740	349,315,134	336,764,348
Oklahoma	175,533,723	179,977,245	118,899,739	117,780,031
Pennsylvania	476,927,507	496,848,519	454,598,685	407,290,892
Texas	59,975,056	50,686,975	61,051,332	49,862,121
W. Virginia	343,036,152	328,523,941	295,294,851	258,470,969
Wyoming	62,971,841	62,971,840	21,572,219	20,424,205
TOTAL	2,869,509,730	2,520,553,624	2,184,003,848	1,906,518,995

(Source: A.G.A.)

tive gas. Eight new storage pools with an estimated ultimate capacity of almost 35 billion cubic feet were under construction in 1957. During 1960, the total reservoir capacity for storage was increased to almost 3 trillion cubic feet. Table 17 shows the states with underground gas storage.

The storage idea is much older than most authors assume. They refer usually to the first project undertaken in Welland County, Ontario, Canada, in 1915, which was followed by the underground storage of gas in the Zoar Field, near Buffalo, New York, in Concord in 1916. Another early project was that in the Menefee County gas field near Rothwell in eastern Kentucky where, in the summer of 1920, the field was used for storage on a trial basis. But as early as 1885 storage of natural gas was discussed and "tentatively carried out" because "the waste of gas, especially in western Pennsylvania and in the Ohio fields . . . has been simply enormous, the amount reaching a total so marvelous that it is impossible to form any accurate conception of it," according to *Mineral Resources of the United States,* 1885. From 1930 on, the proceedings of the American Gas Association include papers of basic importance devoted to this vital subject, and the trade magazines of the oil and gas industry contain so many articles and reports on this subject that the American Gas Association and *Gas Age* periodically publish bibliographies of underground storage literature.

Natural gas is normally stored underground in depleted gas or oil fields, or in similar porous, water-bearing structures known as *aquifers.* All depleted gas or oil fields do not have the necessary characteristics for storage. The gas storage field is, with minor exceptions, not a large underground cavern, but a large volume of sandstone or other porous rock. One of the primary requirements is that the storage reservoir have sufficient permeability to permit high rates of gas injection and withdrawal. Good porosity, which means that a large percentage of the volume of the formation consists of open pore space, is desirable. Another requirement is the presence of an adequate impermeable rock, usually shale, overlying the porous reservoir. A third requirement is the presence of a trap, usually a closure caused by upwarping of the reservoir, which provides a dome-like condition in the rocks similar to an inverted soup bowl. This prohibits lateral escape of the gas. The storage field should be reasonably close to the ultimate markets. To find a structure that meets all these requirements is not easy. Hence, there are various reservoirs being used now for gas storage which are not depleted gas fields. The Herscher Dome, the huge reservoir of Peoples Gas (Chicago) contained only salt water. Other aquifers used for storage have been the East Hastings Field in Texas, and the Doe Run and Muldraugh fields outside of Louisville, Kentucky. The Playa del Rey project near Los Angeles, California, is a gas storage field in a partially depleted oil reservoir.

In planning for the reservoir pressure at which the gas will be stored, the engineers usually do not exceed the initial reservoir pressure since there would be danger of pushing gas out of the *spill point* around the anticline if this pressure were exceeded.

One-third to one-half of the gas in a storage field is always kept there and is known as *cushion gas*. The cushion helps to maintain the pressure in storage which is required to make large deliveries on cold winter days. This cushion gas may be ultimately recovered, but it represents a tie-up of capital during the active life of any storage project. The late Max Ball compared cushion gas very strikingly with "the spring behind the jack-in-the-box; the spring pushes the jack out fast enough for full effectiveness but it stays in the box. Cushion gas becomes part of the cost of the storage field . . ."

That there are considerable quantities and tied-up investments involved in cushion gas is apparent from the figures of the Columbia Gas System. This huge enterprise is most fortunate in that its service area, the Appalachian Oil and Gas region, has 60 per cent of the nation's underground storage fields. Columbia operates forty-three underground storage fields, some of which have more than one reservoir. The total storage capacity of Columbia Gas System's fields is more than 500 billion cubic feet. During 1958, Columbia had 368 billion cubic feet of gas stored in these fields—one-fourth of the nation's total. Of this volume 190 billion cubic feet was cushion gas. Consolidated Natural Gas Company, the other great system in the East, for 1958, had in its twenty-six underground storage fields, also in the Appalachian Area, an inventory of 317,467,000 MCF at a cost of $91,760,000. Twenty-three gas companies reported to the Federal Power Commission in 1958 that they had a combined investment in underground storage of $388,000,000. This was related to 918 billion cubic feet of gas in storage, of which 522 billion cubic feet was cushion gas. This gas was valued at $122,000,000, or at an average value of 23.3 cents per MCF.

Establishment of underground storage is a good business for lawyers and landmen. Before a field is converted into a storage field, the storage rights must be acquired through purchase or lease from the mineral owners and/or landowners. The acquisition of storage rights is sometimes not only difficult but costly because of the reluctance of some landowners to permit storage under their property. However, in a number of states, statutes authorize the condemnation of depleted formations for gas storage purposes. It is necessary to obtain the storage rights for the entire area under which gas is to be stored; otherwise, a single recalcitrant leaseowner could drill a well and produce a portion of the stored gas. Some landowners are reluctant to give storage rights because of the possible hazards of fire from gas leaking up through abandoned wells which were drilled years ago and forgotten. The gas companies have greatly reduced this hazard.

The cost of a storage project depends on the depth, the number of old wells that must be reconditioned or plugged, the number of new wells that must be drilled, the compression requirements, the total volume of storage required, and the maximum deliverability desired. Reports made to the Federal Power Commission for 1958 indicated that one dollar was the average investment cost for one thousand cubic feet of working storage cost. If fixed charges are calculated at 15 per cent on the dollar per MCF average investment in the storage facilities, and to this are added three cents per MCF for operating and maintenance, and twenty-eight cents per MCF for the cost of the inventory gas, we arrive at a total cost of forty-six cents per MCF of storage gas withdrawn. These are average figures, but the highest reported cost did not exceed one dollar per MCF. These are cost figures that make storage attractive to the transmission company, the distributor, and the consumer.

A few practical instances may illustrate the growing importance of underground storage and some of the problems associated with it. Herscher Dome, the giant project of Peoples Gas (Chicago), is located fifty-five miles southwest of the Chicago city limits and sixteen miles southwest of Kankakee, Illinois. It covers an area of 15,500 acres, overlying the Galesville stratum approximately 1,700 feet below the surface of the ground. About thirty million dollars have been spent to develop a deliverability of 575 million cubic feet a day; and, as of December 31, 1957, there were about 17 billion cubic feet of gas for the accounts of customer companies stored in the Herscher reservoir.

Gas injection was started at Herscher Dome on April 1, 1953. During the last week of July, after gas had been injected for four months, one of the shallow water wells in the town of Herscher began to bubble gas. During the following week, a total of thirty-three village water wells became active with gas. At the same time, the only oil well that was open to the surface became active. There was great excitement

246

about these mysterious incidents and a hectic search for the causes of them began. Gas injection into the reservoir was stopped one week after leakage had been detected. The old oil wells were located, cleaned out to their original bottom and allowed to vent. Several theories were advanced as possible explanations for leakage from the reservoir at 1,750 feet into the 150-foot level. Faulty well cementing was one of the assumed reasons, lack of adequate cap-rock another, faulting a third, and old wells a fourth.

The Natural Gas Storage Company of Illinois, operator of Herscher Dome, reported in a recently published folder a brief summary describing the many tests carried out to locate the cause of the leakage. There were about a dozen tests made with the most modern technical devices available in reservoir engineering. "Every known test —plus some newly developed ones," reports the operating company, "failed to reveal the leak. However, ingenuity has paid off in the form of a gathering system taking gas from about 200 feet below ground surface. It is gathered, taken to a central recycling plant and put back in the ground. As only a small percentage of the huge volume of gas is involved in this process, it is still an economically feasible service of tremendous value to the gas-hungry public."

Natural Gas Storage Company of Illinois established another underground gas storage project. During 1956 it acquired storage rights underlying six thousand acres and purchased 1.9 billion cubic feet of gas in place in the Cooks Mills area, about 150 miles south of Chicago near Sullivan, Illinois, and within 15 miles of the Texas Illinois main line. This additional storage reservoir was completed in December, 1957. Of the 1.9 billion cubic feet of natural gas in the Cooks Mills storage area, 900 million cubic feet are *top gas,* stored for the accounts of customer companies, and the balance will remain in the reservoir as *cushion gas.* Twenty-five million cubic feet daily can be withdrawn for about thirty-six days.

Tennessee Gas is developing five storage fields, three of which have been completed. The largest of these is Hebron Field near Coudersport in northern Pennsylvania—the gas state turned storage state with more than 500 billion cubic feet of natural gas stored beneath its soil. Hebron Field was discovered in 1931. After the initial supply had been depleted, its Oriskany sand reservoir made it highly suitable for storage. It began operating as a storage field in 1955. The total capacity of Hebron Field, in terms of top storage gas only, is 23 billion cubic feet. This field is certificated by the Federal Power Commission for a delivery capacity of 225 million cubic feet a day. With two newer fields—Harrison Field near Coudersport, and Colden Field near Hamburg, New York—and Hebron Field, Tennessee Gas is capable of holding 35 billion cubic feet of top storage. Participating with Tennessee Gas at Harrison is the New York State Natural Gas Corporation, a subsidiary of the Consolidated Natural Gas Company. New York State Natural is Consolidated Gas's second largest producer, and it has the largest underground gas storage operations. Organized in 1913, its principal office is in Pittsburgh. Tennessee's Colden storage field is jointly developed with Iroquois Gas Corporation, a subsidiary of National Fuel Gas.

This comprehensive storage development program will benefit some large utilities in the New York-New Jersey metropolitan area, such as Consolidated Edison Company of New York, Public Service Electric and Gas Company (Newark, New Jersey), and Brooklyn Union Gas Company. With no underground storage of their own, they are able to utilize some of Tennessee's storage capacity by injecting their gas into Tennessee's storage reservoir in the summer for winter withdrawal in certain specified daily quantities. Such exchange of service approaches an ideal concept of utility efficiency. This concept is equally well developed in Texas Eastern's tremendous underground storage program, which includes the largest storage field developed so far, the Oakford Field.

In 1950, Texas Eastern joined New York State Natural Gas Corporation as a co-equal partner in the development of underground storage facilities in an area of 19,000 acres not far from Pittsburgh, Pennsylvania, known as Oakford Storage. It is the largest operating underground natural gas area in the world.

Oakford was one of the depleted gas fields in Pennsylvania drilled in the 1870's. The Oakford Field is an anticlinical structure in which the Murrysville Sand at 1,500 feet and the Fifth Sand at 2,200 feet make conditions favorable for storage. From the fact that Oakford Storage has a capacity of 105 billion cubic feet, of which 45 billion cubic feet is used as cushion or base gas, it can be seen what tremendously difficult but most skillfully executed technical work went into the conditioning of Oakford Field as a storage reservoir. The maximum delivery capacity from Oakford is approximately 500,000 MCF of gas daily.

The cost of establishing Oakford Storage was about thirty-nine million dollars. This does not include the expense involved in the construction of a 30-inch, 791-mile pipe line by Texas Eastern from Kosciusko, Mississippi, to Connellsville, Pennsylvania. In the field proper, a compressor station costing eleven million dollars was installed, the largest single expenditure in the former gas field.

This storage field was an important factor in the growth of Texas Eastern as a supplier to New York, New Jersey, Massachusetts, and other northeastern markets. It not only served the interests of Texas Eastern and New York State Natural, but of other companies as well. Transcontinental, which serves the New York metropolitan area, was able to start storage service in 1954 in this field following an agreement with Texas Eastern. Under the terms of this agreement, Transco furnishes seven of its customers an aggregate of approximately 136,-000 MCF of gas per day during the heating season from the Oakford storage field. The Brooklyn Union Gas Company reports a storage gas supply of 22,487 MCF daily from Transcontinental. Transco made arrangements with Texas Eastern for the use of its storage facilities which reduced the cost of the project to Texas Eastern.

In December 1953, Texas Eastern founded the Texas Eastern Penn-Jersey Transmission Corporation. Its purpose was to allow Texas Eastern to supply additional natural gas to growing markets in the northeast and permit the company to provide a gas storage for another company. The subsidiary has shown a healthy growth.

Texas Eastern, New York State Natural, and Transcontinental went a step further. They entered, during 1957, into agreements for the joint development of the Leidy and Tamarack storage fields which are also located in Pennsylvania (in the northern part of the state). The storage capacity of these will be sufficient to provide an additional 200,000 MCF per day to eastern seaboard customers during the winter heating season.

The huge storage facilities in the East, particularly those of the Columbia Gas System and Consolidated Natural Gas Company, are being expanded. Remarked George S. Young, then president of Columbia:

Development of underground storage is expensive. It is true that we use

249

depleted, or nearly depleted, gas fields in the Appalachian Area for storage purposes. However, it is necessary to recondition existing wells and to drill new ones. New field lines must be laid. A compressing station must be built to pump gas into the storage fields. . . . At the end of 1956 we had invested in our underground storage facilities and "cushion" gas a total of $123,140,000. But it would have taken pipelines and related facilities at a cost of more than $600,000,000 to deliver the gas from the Southwest needed to fill the requirements on the last peak day.

On November 1, 1957, at the beginning of the heating season, the Columbia Gas System had 368.2 billion cubic feet in storage exclusive of native gas. During the current heating season, the peak day sendout on February 17, 1958, for Columbia amounted to 4,526 million cubic feet of which 2,295 million cubic feet or 51 per cent came from storage. Current estimates indicate requirements on the peak day for the next few years will continue to increase and that approximately 50 per cent of the gas requirements in those years will come from storage. In order to meet these increased requirements, the system will find it necessary to continue to expand its facilities.

Storage gas is also expensive for the distributing utility. In its excellent review of operations in 1957, the Brooklyn Union Gas Company presents the following table showing the average cost per MCF of natural gas purchased "by supplier and type of service." It gives a strikingly graphic illustration of the higher cost of storage gas as compared with that of high load factor firm gas.

AVERAGE COST OF NATURAL GAS PER MCF

	1957	1956	1955	1954	1953
Transcontinental					
Firm	$0.3478	$0.3484	$0.3358	$0.3177	$0.3220
Storage	0.6967	0.6351	0.6137	0.6444	——
Tennessee					
Firm	$0.4321	$0.3817	$0.3811	——	——
Storage	1.0779*	——	——	——	——
Extra Storage	0.7778	——	——	——	——
Texas Eastern					
Firm	$0.3729	$0.3938	$0.4419	$0.4749	$0.4984
Transco-Texas					
Eastern WPS†	$0.5340	$0.5165	$0.4892	——	——
Weighted					
Averages	$0.3794	$0.3678	$0.3580	$0.3293	$0.3290

*Does not reflect full year usage.   †Winter Peaking Service.

250

The American Natural Gas System, through its subsidiaries Michigan Consolidated Gas Company, Milwaukee Gas Light Company, and American Louisiana Pipe Line Company, supplying such important population and industrial centers as Milwaukee, Detroit, Ann Arbor, Grand Rapids and others, has large, underground storage fields in west-central Michigan. They are strategically located with respect to the major market areas and have a total capacity of about one hundred billion cubic feet of gas. The system also controls several depleted reservoirs, which can readily be converted to gas storage operations when required. Thus American Natural's distribution companies are in the position to meet winter peaks efficiently and to serve the heating load at a cost to the customer substantially below the cost of other fuels.

There are other gas companies and areas with large underground storage facilities. For instance, Cities Service Gas Company has about 75 billion cubic feet of storage capacity in Kansas. East Ohio Gas Company and Ohio Fuel Gas Company have tremendous facilities in Ohio. Oklahoma Natural Gas Company has a capacity of 160 billion cubic feet in this important natural gas state. Hope Natural Gas Company, Consolidated's famous subsidiary, has vast storage in West Virginia, as has United Fuel Gas Company. Lone Star Gas Company of Dallas has planned some 50 billion cubic feet of storage capacity in the nation's richest gas state. And finally, Pacific Gas and Electric Company's McDonald Island storage field, about fifty miles east of San Francisco, deserves mentioning. All this adds up to a total storage capacity of nearly 3 trillion cubic feet, which assures maximum efficiency of natural gas delivery for the consumer during the coldest days.

Underground storage of natural gas has become a fact of increasing importance to an industry faced every winter with the peak-day challenge. Listed below are the references used by the author in his discussion of this subject:

Abrams, Ernest R., "Another Peak Year Seen for Gas Home Heating," *Barron's,* Vol. XXXVIII, No. 11 (March 17, 1958), 27.

Ball, Douglas, "The Why of Underground Gas Storage," *The Mines Magazine,* Vol. XLVI, No. 6 (June, 1956), 55–58.

————, and Peter G. Burnett, "Storage of Gas in Water Sands," *The Mines Magazine,* Vol. XLIX, No. 11 (November, 1959).

"Charting Weather Years Ahead," *Business Week,* No. 1519 (October 11, 1958), 45.

Davis, N. Knowles, "Influence of Underground Storage Upon a Natural Gas Pipeline System," a paper presented at the 37th Annual Conference, Utility Commission Engineers, San Francisco, California, July, 1959.

Flanagan, Donald A., and Paul B. Crawford, "How Feasible Is Underground Storage of Liquefied Methane?" *American Gas Journal,* Vol. CLXXXVII, No. 11 (October, 1960), 34.

Fruechtenicht, H. L., "Benefits Are Universal in Underground Gas Storage in Michigan," *Gas Age,* Vol. CXXVI, No. 2 (July 21, 1960).

"Gas: On Call Near the Market," *Business Week,* No. 1357 (September 3, 1955), 102.

Griffith, Mortimer P., "What Does It Cost to Produce Peak Shaving and Substitute Gases?" *American Gas Journal,* Vol. CLXXXV, No. 5 (May, 1958), 47.

Kornfeld, Joseph A., "Aquifers for Underground Natural Gas Storage," *American Gas Journal,* Vol. CLXXXVII, Nos. 4, 5, 6, 8, and 10 (April, May, June, August, and September, 1960).

Lennon, Duncan E., "Income Tax Problems in Connection with Underground Storage," *Gas Age,* Vol. CXXIII, No. 3 (February 5, 1959), 32–36.

Nagler, K. B., "Transportation and Storage of Gaseous Fuels," a paper presented at the World Power Conference, Madrid, Spain, June 5–9, 1960, and later published in *Transactions, q.v.*

Roth, Ernest E., "Underground Storage of Natural Gas," *Petroleum Engineer,* Vol. XXV, No. 5 (May, 1953), D–86.

"Storage of Gas in Pools Gaining," *New York Times,* October 30, 1960.

Tennessee Gas Transmission Company, *Annual Reports* (for 1954–60).

Texas Eastern Gas Transmission Company, *Annual Reports* (for 1954–60).

Texas Illinois Natural Gas Pipeline Company, *Annual Reports* (for 1957–60).

Weeks, Joseph D., *Mineral Resources of the United States* (for 1886), Washington, D.C., 1887, 176ff.

II

OCEAN SHIPMENT OF NATURAL GAS

by Alfred M. Leeston

NOTHING seems more exciting than being witness to important technological advances. In our age of nuclear energy we are spoiled in this respect, but we have not yet lost enthusiasm for other demonstrations of creative genius such as the transportation of liquefied methane across the Atlantic. This feat was first performed by *Methane Pioneer* in January, 1959. The twenty-one-hundred-ton tanker transported *frozen gas* from Lake Charles, Louisiana, to an islet, Canvey Island, in the Thames Estuary, where the reconstituted gas was mixed with London's coal gas. The tanker has made six trips since its maiden voyage, a tremendous success that startled the world.

There still lingered in people's memory the disaster that befell the City of Cleveland, Ohio, in 1944. There, East Ohio Gas Company had stored liquefied methane in large quantities in steel tanks. The terrific cold of the frozen gas caused the tanks to become brittle, and they cracked. Leaking methane vaporized and caught fire. The blast rocked the city, killed more than one hundred persons, and shook up the entire gas industry. Thus, the world was amazed when *Methane Pioneer* made its first trip—and the subsequent crossings—safely and, as a severe testing has proved, without any damage to the ship and its equipment. In fact, "insurance rates on the Pioneer are no higher than those on ordinary gasoline tankers." The startling success was the result of innovations made by an outstanding expert on refrigeration techniques, Willard L. Morrison. The number one problem, "to provide ... maximum safety," seemed to have found a solution with Mr. Morrison's design of the equipment installed on *Methane Pioneer*. Other advantages of his innovations are that the equipment can be manufactured with minimum capital investment and operated at low cost.

Although the liquefaction of natural gas requires severe refrigeration down to about minus 260 degrees Fahrenheit, butane becomes liquid at 32 degrees Fahrenheit and propane does so at minus 40 degrees. The volume of butane is reduced to $\frac{1}{270}$ of its gaseous volume, and propane to $\frac{1}{230}$ at 60 degrees Fahrenheit. This can be done at atmospheric pressure, rather than through the application of pressures of 24 pounds per square inch to keep butane liquid and 110 pounds per square inch to keep propane liquid. Cylindrical or spherical pressure vessels of high grade steel with walls of appropriate thickness are required to maintain these pressures. When refrigeration is employed rather than increased pressure, the volume and weight of the containing vessels can be sharply reduced, which is of great economic consequence in ocean transport. It is estimated that the substitution of refrigerated for pressurized storage on a propane tanker would reduce the weight of the gas-containing tanks by 25 per cent, and would also save space. Thus, it seems that satisfactory solutions have been found for the technical problems of safety and economy.

There are numerous economic and financial factors involved in this new mode of transporting frozen gas, but an important factor should not be overlooked. The inherent advantages of natural gas as a fuel somewhat lessen cost consideration. Europe's source of frozen gas will not be the United States, where the field price is higher, but will be countries where the wellhead price is low, as it is in the Sahara, in Venezuela, and in the Middle East. Thus the price of gas, while a definite factor, should not be over-emphasized. It will not prevent successful penetration of gas-hungry countries by frozen gas.

Of the many studies on the economics of gas transportation by sea, the study of J. J. McMullen, a distinguished marine engineer and president of the shipbuilding firm of Hudson Engineering Company at Hoboken, New Jersey, is particularly interesting. In addition to the field price of the gas, both size and magnitude influence the planning of the liquefaction, storage, and regasification plants and associated facilities at the loading and unloading ports. The capital costs of the gas tankers are, according to Mr. McMullen, about twice those of oil tankers of comparable cargo capacity because the shipment of liquids in deep freeze introduces entirely novel features into the design of the heavily insulated cargo storage tanks. As with oil tankers, the unit

255

costs of building and operating methane carriers will decrease as the size of the ship increases. A methane tanker of 30,000 tons dead weight may cost only about 20 per cent more to build than one of 20,000 tons and 55 per cent more than a 10,000-ton ship. A methane carrier of 50,000 tons dead weight would cost only about 25 per cent more than a 30,000-tonner and would produce 21 per cent more ton-miles.

Tanker shipments of frozen gas are profitable only if very large quantities can be delivered. French estimates have shown that sea transportation of liquefied gas from the Sahara costs about 50 per cent more than transmission of natural gas through pipe lines, but the total costs of frozen gas from the prolific, remote wells are still low enough in comparison with city gas prices to attract European consumers. In addition, liquefied gas can be stored more easily because of its small volume and can be used for peak shaving. In the United States, frozen gas could play an important role as stand-by fuel in extremely cold weather, supplementing underground storage gas. Utilities such as Brooklyn Union Gas are studying these possibilities.

The company which is in the forefront of the efforts to make frozen gas an economically feasible commodity is Conch International Methane, Limited, with its headquarters in London. Conch is 40 per cent owned by the Royal Dutch Shell Group, 40 per cent by Continental oil, and 20 per cent by Union Stockyard Transit Company of Chicago. But Conch—Shell's trade symbol is a conch or marine shell —is only the end of a number of changing associations. Originally it was an American company that sponsored and encouraged continuation of Mr. Morrison's brilliant spadework. Called Constock Liquid Methane Corporation of America, it was chartered in Delaware in 1956 and consisted of the Continental Oil Company of Houston, Texas, and Union Stockyards Transit Company of Chicago, Illinois. Constock formed a jointly-owned firm, Constock International Methane, Limited (Bahamas) in which the British Gas Council participated. It controls British Methane, Limited (Bahamas) which owns the tanker that made the first, sensational, transatlantic run. It is now associated with Shell in the new firm, Conch. The driving forces in these events were Continental's dynamic president, L. F. McCollum, and the Chicago firm's chief executive, William Henry Wood Prince, who later became president of Armour and Company. Conch branched out in the huge Sahara gas field, Hassi R'Mel, through a French company, C.A.M.E.L. (Compagnia Algerienne du Methane Liquid), appropriately named for these desert adventures. C.A.M.E.L. is building a plant at Arzew, a small Mediterranean port near Oran, Algeria. There British Methane, Limited, and Gaz de France will pick up the natural gas to ship it as frozen gas to England and countries on the European continent. Among the many projects under consideration for bringing Hassi R'Mel gas to Europe is the possibility of pipe lines across the Mediterranean; but conveyance in liquid form by sea seems likely to remain a strong contender. Indeed, Methane Transport has been organized to build and operate at least one additional tanker. Commented Mr. McMullen, "It is possible that within the next ten years we may see in operation or under construction some 50 ocean going carriers."

A New England Gas Pooling Group, with R. J. Rutherford of the Worcester Gas Utility as chairman, is considering the construction of a liquid natural gas (LNG) plant with three billion cubic feet of storage at a cost of twenty-two million dollars, according to a Stone and Webster estimate. Venezuelan gas may be used to heat the Massachusetts, Rhode Island, New Hampshire, and Connecticut areas on their coldest days.

Liquid natural gas may soon be listed with underground storage as a possible solution to peak-day problems; however, some questions yet remain, and many of these are explored in the works listed below:

Balcomb, John D., *Liquefied Natural Gas and the International Energy Market*, New York, 1958.

Clark, L. J., "Sea Transport of Liquid Methane," a paper presented at the World Power Conference, Madrid, Spain, June 5–9, 1960, and published in *Transactions, q.v.*

Conch Methane Services, Limited, "Transportation of Liquefied Natural Gas," a paper presented before the Second Economic Conference on Asia and the Far East, Petroleum Symposium, Tehran, Iran, September 10, 1962.

Connole, William R., "The Role of Regulation in Developing the Transportation and Use of Liquefied Methane," a paper presented at the Briefing Conference on Natural Gas and Oil Problems, Federal Bar Association and Bureau of National Affairs, Incorporated, Washington, D.C., March 5, 1959, and summarized in the *Oil and Gas Journal*, Vol. LVII, No. 11 (March 9, 1959), 82.

"The Economics of Gas Transportation by Sea," *Petroleum Press Service*, Vol. XXVII, No. 3 (March, 1960).

Gehlhoff, Paul O., "Natural Gas Liquefaction as Means to Solve Transportation Problems," *Erdöl und Kohle*, Vol. XIII, No. 9 (September, 1960), 668–71.

Gilbert, Robert A., "Frozen Gas Expands," *Barron's*, Vol. XL, No. 34 (August 22, 1960).

Kinney, Gene T., "Liquid Methane May Warm East Coast on Coldest Days," *Oil and Gas Journal*, Vol. LIX, No. 5 (January 30, 1961), 90.

La Cova, Pérez de, "Liquefied Methane," an address before the Briefing

Conference on Natural Gas and Oil Problems, Federal Bar Association and Bureau of National Affairs, Incorporated, Washington, D. C., March 5, 1959, and summarized in the *Oil and Gas Journal,* Vol. LVII, No. 11 (March 9, 1959), 82, and in the *Foster Associates Report,* No. 155 (March 5, 1959), 18.

Lederman, Peter B., and Brymer Williams, "The Economics of Liquefaction, Storage and Transportation of Natural Gas," a paper presented at the 36th Annual Convention, Natural Gasoline Association of America, Houston, Texas, April 20–23, 1957, and published in *Proceedings, q.v.,* 42, and in *Gas Age,* Vol. CXX, No. 10 (November 14, 1957), 41.

Lippitt, Henry F., II, "Regulatory Problems in the Development and Use of Liquid Methane," *Texas Law Review,* Vol. XXXIX, No. 9 (May, 1961), 601.

"Liquefied Natural Gas," a series which appeared in the *Petroleum Times* (London), January 31, 1958–November, 1959.

Murphy, John A., and C. G. Filstead, "Ocean Transport of Liquid Methane," a paper presented at the Fifth World Petroleum Congress, New York, New York, June, 1959, and published in *Proceedings, q.v.,* VIII, 23.

"Natural Gas by Sea—The Limits Set by Economics," *Petroleum Press Service,* Vol. XXIX, No. 10 (October, 1962), 384.

Ritter, C. L., "Recent Development in Liquefaction and Transportation of Natural Gas," *Chemical Engineering Progress,* Vol. LVIII, No. 11 (November, 1962), 55.

"Storage of Liquid Methane in Britain," *Gas Age,* Vol. CXXIII, No. 11 (May 28, 1959).

Tanner, James C., "Frozen Heat," *Wall Street Journal,* Vol. XXVI, No. 67 (October 5, 1960).

Von Szeszich, L., "Ocean Transportation of Liquefied Natural and Petroleum Gases," *Oil and Gas Journal,* Vol. LVII, No. 2 (January 12, 1959), 76.

Young, A. Russell, "Liquid Methane—A Cheaper Means of Peak Shaving?" *Oil and Gas Journal,* Vol. LVII, No. 13 (March 23, 1959), 75.

12

PUBLIC CONTROL OF
THE NATURAL GAS INDUSTRY

by John C. Jacobs

THAT seeming paradox—the public control of business in a society proclaiming the free market as a basic tenant—has historical antecedents as hoary as the Egyptian pharaohs and the Roman emperors. In our Anglo-Saxon common law tradition, the propriety of the regulation of a business by the sovereign in the interest of the people was recognized as early as the seventeenth century. In the United States of America local control of utilities commenced in 1817, state control in Massachusetts in 1855, and the constitutional decisions necessary to the control of business through legislation were handed down by the Supreme Court in the 1870's and the 1880's.[1]

DEFINITION OF A PUBLIC UTILITY

Legally, public control of a business is proper if a business can be categorized either as a "public utility" or, under a more comprehensive term, as a business "affected with a public interest."[2] Persons engaged in transportation and distribution phases of the natural gas industry may be classified as public utilities. The production phase of the natural gas industry has been classified as a business affected with a public interest. The definition of a *public utility* lies in the following indicia which have been recognized in decisions:

1. Whether the business devotes property to a public use.
2. Whether the business has been regulated in the past.

[1] See discussion in the first chapter of this book regarding the history of the natural gas industry.

[2] See the excellent discussion of this subject in Clemens, *Economics and Public Utilities,* 12–37, which is closely followed here. See also Barnes, *The Economics of Public Utility Regulation,* 1–22.

3. Whether a franchise is necessary to enter the business.
4. Whether the service rendered is a necessity to the users.
5. Whether the business has the characteristics which create monopoly, viz., limitations of space, large capital investment, economies of decreasing costs, and technical limitations in the market.
6. Whether excessive competition will exist without public control.

A business may be regulated as one affected with a public interest where:

1. Regulation is necessary because of great or temporary emergency (e.g., war).
2. The business competes with a regulated industry.
3. Regulation is necessary to conserve national resources.
4. Regulation is in the national interest (e.g., promotes the national defense).
5. The legislature has solemnly and fairly exercised its discretion to regulate the business.

THE AVENUES OF CONTROL

Today the gas industry is regulated by local authorities and by both state and federal commissions. The powers of these commissions are limited by the wording of the legislative acts granting such powers, by judicial review of the acts of the commissions, and by the constitutional injunctions against taking property without due process of law, the confiscation of property, and discriminatory treatment.[3] All federal commissions are bound by the Administrative Procedure Act[4] which codifies court decisions and exerts a regulatory influence on state and local actions also. Basically each party to a commission proceeding is entitled to notice, fair hearing, just decision, and judicial review. Of particular importance as legal precedent establishing and limiting the public control of business through legislative act are the 1877 Supreme Court decision in *Munn* v. *Illi-*

---

[3] The Fifth Amendment of the United States Constitution sets forth these injunctions against federal agencies, and the Fourteenth Amendment outlines similar injunctions against state agencies.

[4] 60 Stat.237, 5 U.S.C. Sec. 1003 (1946).

nois[5] and the 1886 decision in *Stone* v. *Farmer's Loan and Trust Company.*[6] In *Munn* v. *Illinois* the Court upheld an Illinois statute which fixed maximum charges by elevators for grain storage on the grounds that such regulation of a business clothed with a public interest was proper under the police power of the state. In the Stone case the Court upheld a Mississippi statute which created a commission with power to control the railroads. In its decision the Court held that any rate regulation must be reasonable in that it may not involve the taking of property without just compensation or without due process of law.

There are no comprehensive official statements as to the over-all aim of the public control of public utilities. Instead the courts address themselves to the aim of the particular statute under consideration. One authority in the field has defined the aim of public control, insofar as rate regulation is concerned, in the following words: "In a broad sense, the objective of public utility rate regulation is to achieve through regulation the same results that would be achieved by competition."[7]

LOCAL CONTROL BY FRANCHISE

The *franchise* is a right granted by a municipality authorizing a private person to engage in the public utility business and to use public property for private profit.[8] It is commonplace in the distribution phase of the gas industry. Historically, franchise control was the first type of control exercised over public utilities. Scandals involving bribery and the resale of franchises between 1880 and 1910, plus the more effective control possible by the use of state and federal commissions, have led to a great reduction in the power and extent of franchise control. In many instances it now amounts to no more than a grant to the utility of the right to place utility property on the public street.

The right of a municipality to grant and to condition franchises is limited by the municipality's grant of power from the state and by the constitutional prohibition of the impairment of contractual obligations. The court decisions regarding the impairment of contractual

[5] 94 U.S. 113.

[6] 116 U.S. 307

[7] Clemens, *Economics and Public Utilities,* 153; Bonbright, *Principles of Public Utility Rates,* 109.

[8] See the discussion of regulation by franchise in Clemens, *Economics and Public Utilities,* 72–99, and in Barnes, *The Economics of Public Utility Regulation,* 194–196.

obligations generally hold that, under the police power, the municipality retains the right, after the granting of the franchise, to impose
reasonable conditions—which may require changes in the operating
methods in the franchised utility—as required by the public health,
safety, and welfare. The municipality has no such power of change
in regard to rates set forth in the franchise, however.

CONTROL BY STATE COMMISSIONS

Control by state commissions has replaced the more rigid and inadequate control of utilities by direct legislative action and by municipalities.[9] The commission, with its large experienced staff and its
ability to give constant attention to the problems of control, is better
able to cope with the intricate, technical nature of the utility industry
than were its forerunners. A typical commission today has groups of
experts organized to handle administration, public relations, legal
matters, hearings, research, rates, and all engineering phases of the
industry. State commission control applies to the distribution phase
of the gas industry since this is an intrastate operation, to transportation of gas in intrastate commerce but not interstate commerce, and to
the production of natural gas except when it is sold in interstate commerce for resale. Interstate transportation and sale of natural gas for
resale fall under the Federal Power Commission in its administration
of the Natural Gas Act.[10]

State commission control of gas production has grown out of the
following factual and historical background.[11] Oil and natural gas

[9] The organization and operation of state utility control commissions is discussed in
Clemens, *Economics and Public Utilities,* 400ff., in Barnes, *The Economics of Public
Utility Regulation,* 176ff., and in American Gas Association Rate Committee, *Gas Rate
Fundamentals,* 81–84. See also Everett C. McKeage, *Public Utility Regulatory Law.*

[10] Act of June 21, 1938, c. 556; 52 Stat. 821, as amended 56 Stat. 83, and 61 Stat. 459;
15 U.S.C.A. sec. 717ff.

[11] The most comprehensive treatment of state control of production is Erich W.
Zimmermann, *Conservation in the Production of Petroleum: A Study in Industrial
Control.* Other works of special importance from an engineering point of view are
Stuart E. Buckley (ed.), *Petroleum Conservation,* and Interstate Oil Compact Commis-
sion Engineering Committee, *Oil and Gas Production: An Introductory Guide to
Production Techniques and Conservation Methods.* Note also Rupert C. Craze and
James W. Glanville, "Well Spacing," *Fifth Annual Institute on Mineral Law* (1957), 68.

Of interest in the field of conservation are the three volumes published by the American Bar Association, Section of Mineral Law, *Legal History of Conservation of Oil and
Gas, Conservation of Oil and Gas: A Legal History, 1948,* and *Conservation of Oil and*

263

are fugacious materials which may be subterraneously drained off and produced through adjacent wells located on another's property. In deciding who owns such drained production, courts have established the rule of capture, which holds that the oil or gas belongs to the person through whose well it is produced. This doctrine encouraged the drilling of a maximum number of wells and the producing of every well at its maximum rate. Also, producing oil and gas under these conditions resulted in physical waste both at the surface (e.g., gas flaring) and in the underground reservoirs (e.g., low recovery of hydrocarbons in place), and in economic waste through distress marketing of oil and gas. The rule of capture did not provide a satisfactory solution to the problems raised by the fact that recoveries from one owner's property may be reduced by another owner's wasteful practices in the same reservoir. Judicial treatment of this *correlative rights issue* relegated the parties to self-help. Each was forced to protect himself by drilling more wells and producing at higher rates. An answer to these problems was worked out in the several state legislatures in the form of conservation statutes to be administered by public commissions. Today, most of the oil- and gas-producing states have statutes under which a commission is empowered to enforce petroleum conservation programs.[12] Although such programs vary greatly, provision is generally made for control of the number and location of wells to be drilled, the methods of drilling, completing, and producing the wells, and the quantity of production. Control

---

Gas: A Legal History, 1958. The reader should also see "A Survey of Texas Administrative Law: The Oil and Gas Division of the Texas Railroad Commission," *Texas Law Review,* Vol. XXXIII, No. 5 (May, 1955), 635ff., and William J. Murray, Jr., "Competition, Conservation, and Control," in *Economics of the Gas Industry, q.v.,* I, 153.

[12] Here notice should be taken of the Interstate Oil Compact Commission made up of representatives from most of the oil-producing states, operating under a compact between such states, and approved by the Congress in accordance with the Constitution (Art. I, sec. 10, clause 3). The Interstate Oil Compact Commission has no specific power under any state conservation statute; rather, it aids in co-ordinating and improving state conservation practices through the exchange of information at meetings and in publications. See Ernest O. Thompson, "An Administrator's Views on Conservation in the Production of Oil and Gas," *Sixth Annual Institute on Mineral Law* (1958), 88.

In an investigation according to Congressional mandate the Attorney-General has concluded that the Interstate Oil Compact is beneficial. See Department of Justice, *Third Annual Report of the Attorney General* Pursuant to Section 2 of the Joint Resolution of July 28, 1955, Consenting to an Interstate Compact to Serve Oil and Gas, 7 (1958).

of the quantity of production, better known as *proration,* involves regulation of the level of production (*allowables*) as well as the division of production among well owners (*ratability*). Proration level standards have been developed from the engineering viewpoint (MER, Maximum efficient rate of production without loss of ultimate recovery) and from the market standpoint (no production permitted in excess of market demand).[13]

[13] A great deal of current discussion in the conservation field is aimed at the question of whether market demand proration is in the public interest. The matter is discussed in Zimmermann, *Conservation in the Production of Petroleum: A Study in Industrial Control,* 268ff., 326ff.; in Robert E. Hardwicke, "Market Demand as a Factor in the Conservation of Oil," a paper delivered at the First Annual Institute on Oil and Gas Law and Taxation as It Affects the Oil and Gas Industry, Dallas, Texas, March 23–26, 1949, and published in *Proceedings, q.v.,* 149; and in Ernest O. Thompson, "The Texas Market Demand Statute on Oil and Gas and Its Application," *Texas Law Review,* Vol. XXXIX, No. 2 (December, 1960), 139.

See also Eugene V. Rostow, *A National Policy for the Oil Industry,* pp. 27ff., and 119ff., and Melvin G. de Chazeau and Alfred E. Kahn, *Integration and Competition in the Petroleum Industry,* 121ff. Rostow, de Chazeau, and Kahn see compulsory unitization of oil fields as a panacea for the higher crude oil prices they attribute to market demand proration. It is usual for a state conservation statute to grant authority to the state commission to require the unitization of gas-condensate fields. Some unitization statutes also contain a grant of authority for the compulsory unitization of any type of oil or gas field. See Robert E. Hardwicke, *Antitrust Laws, et al. v. Unit Operations of Oil or Gas Pools,* for a thorough discussion of the problems involved in unitizing oil or gas fields. Unitization is further considered in Raymond M. Myers, *The Law of Pooling and Unitization, Voluntary—Compulsory,* Leo T. Hoffman, *Voluntary Pooling and Unitization, Oil and Gas,* and in eight papers published in the *Proceedings* of the Third Annual Institute on Oil and Gas Law and Taxation as It Affects the Oil and Gas Industry, Dallas, Texas, January 17–19, 1952, *q.v.,* pp. 1–253.

The problems involved in state control of ratable taking were described by John C. Jacobs, Jr., in "Government Regulation of Gas Production—1956," *Fourth Annual Institute on Mineral Law* (1956), 58–61. "Developments in state regulation of gas production over the past few years have been principally in the direction of more perfectly achieving 'ratable take,' that is, an equitable allocation of field deliveries between wells," said Mr. Jacobs. See excerpts from Mr. Jacobs' article which are appended at the end of this book and note the list of articles and decisions regarding the ratable taking of gas appearing at the end of this chapter.

See Lee Cameron, "Effect of Gas Proration on Recent Special Orders," *Journal of Petroleum Technology,* Vol. XII, No. 3 (March, 1960), 22; Dee Kelly, "Gas Proration and Ratable Taking in Texas," *Texas Bar Journal,* Vol. XIX, No. 11 (December, 1956), 763; and Robert McGinnis, "The Texas Common Purchaser Statute as Related to Natural Gas," a paper presented before the Mineral Law Section of the State Bar of Texas, July 4, 1958, and later published in the *Texas Bar Journal,* Vol. XXI, No. 8 (September, 1958), 521.

Recent decisions regarding the setting of allowables and ratability include: *In Re:*

Commission control of oil and gas production based on a state statute has been upheld as a constitutional exercise of the police power because of the public interest in the conservation of natural resources.[14] Paragraph 1(b) of the Natural Gas Act exempts the production and gathering of natural gas from the jurisdiction of the act. Nevertheless, the act covers the sale of natural gas for resale in interstate commerce even though such sales are made during the production or gathering process.[15] Future litigation will decide the conflicts inevitably arising from state control of production and federal control of sales made during production.

Transportation and distribution are also controlled by commissions, operating under state statutes, through regulation of entry into and out of the utility business and by control of rates. Entry into business is represented by a permit called a "certificate of public convenience and necessity," which is usually issued after a hearing in which any interested party may appear. The certificate sets forth in detail the type of service to be rendered, the kind of facilities to be built, and the initial rate to be charged. Generally authorized services may not be terminated without commission approval. Rate regulation[16]

Conservation and Prevention of Waste of Crude Petroleum and Natural Gas in the Blue Basin Field, Wharton County, Texas, Railroad Commission of Texas, Oil and Gas Docket No. 128, No. 3–32,805, January 30, 1956, 5 O.& G.R. 1100; *In the Matter of Promulgation and Establishment of Field Rules to Govern Operations in the "J" Sands of the Adena Field, Morgan County, Colorado,* Colorado Oil and Gas Commission, Cause No. 26, Order No. 26–30, July 31, 1956, 6 O.& G.R. 511; *Railroad Commission of Texas and the Atlantic Refining Company v. Permian Basin Pipeline Company,* 302 S.W. 2(d) 238 (Tex. Civ. App., 1957); *Murray, et al. v. R&M Well Servicing and Drilling Company, et al.,* 297 S.W. 2(d) 225 (Tex. Civ. App., 1956, writ ref.); *Special Order Pertaining to the Matter of Requiring Purchase and Take of Gas in the Emperor (Devonian) and Emperor (Ellenburger) Field, Winkler County, Texas,* Railroad Commission of Texas, Oil and Gas Docket No. 126, No. 8–39,851, February 24, 1959, 10 O.& G.R. 239; and *Deep South Oil Company of Texas v. Texas Gas Corporation,* 328 S.W. 2(d) 987 (Tex. Civ. App., 1959, writ ref.) 12 O.& G.R. 597.

[14] *Ohio Oil Company v. Indiana,* 177 U.S. 190 (1900).

[15] *Phillips Petroleum Company v. State of Wisconsin,* 347 U.S. 672, 3 O.& G.R. 745 (1954). On the state-federal conflict see John F. Simms, "Recent Developments in the Law of Conservation and the Influence of the Interstate Oil Compact," a paper delivered at the Seventh Annual Institute on Oil and Gas Law and Taxation as It Affects the Oil and Gas Industry, Dallas, Texas, February 1–3, 1956, and published in *Proceedings, q.v.*

[16] Rate regulation is discussed in great detail in Clemens, *"Economics and Public Utilities,* Chap. 6ff., and in Barnes, *The Economics of Public Utility Regulation,* Chap. IXff.

has as its aim the establishment of a fair and reasonable amount of money to be received by the utility for its services. Rate making is dynamic in that rates are subject to the continuous review of the commission. Usually, the utility has the right to file rate increases, which may or may not be allowed after hearing. The commission, in turn, usually has the right to order an investigation of the utility's rates at any time which investigation may or may not result in a reducing of the existing rates.

THE RATE-MAKING FORMULA

The rate to be received may be represented by the following formula:

$$R = E + (V) r + d + T$$

where:

R = revenue to be received from the rates in question
E = annual operating expense of the utility
V = value of the physical property of the utility
r = rate of return, expressed as a fraction
d = current annual depreciation
T = taxes incurred by the utility

In the rate-making process all reasonable operating expenses are usually allowed to the utility. Only unreasonable expenses are disallowed, for example, excessive legal fees or excessive advertising expenses. In the case of operating expenses and other items in the rate formula, the figures used are those of a designated test period of actual experience, adjusted as may be reasonable to indicate future changes.

One of the most vexing problems in the public utility field has been establishing the *value of physical property*. Is the proper value the original cost, the depreciated original cost, or the present or reproduction value? In the landmark decision of *Smyth* v. *Ames*,[17] the

And see Warren J. Collins, "Problems Peculiar to State and Municipal Regulations of Gas Distributing Companies," a paper presented at the Eleventh Annual Institute on Oil and Gas Law and Taxation, Dallas, Texas, February 10–12, 1960, and published in *Proceedings, q.v.,* 51; Marshall Newcomb, "Federal and State Regulation of Gas Utilities," a paper presented at the First Annual Institute on Oil and Gas Law and Taxation as It Affects the Oil and Gas Industry, Dallas, Texas, March 23–26, 1949, and published in *Proceedings, q.v.,* 97.

[17] 169 U.S. 466. This lawsuit was instituted by a railroad to test the validity of a rate order issued under a Nebraska statute providing for the regulation of railroads. The

United States Supreme Court decided, in 1898, that utilities should have the right to earn on the "fair value" of the properties dedicated to the public service. However, the Court was ambiguous in stating what it meant by fair value, since the decision represented a compromise between the "original cost" and the "replacement cost" standards advocated by the parties to the litigation. At least three standards for evaluation were approved in the decision: the original cost, the amount and market value of bonds and stocks, and the present cost of construction. Over the years "fair value" came to mean "present fair value" or "cost of reproduction." Then the Court began to pay less attention to reproduction costs, and in 1923 in the case of *Southwestern Bell Telephone Company* v. *Public Service Commission of Missouri*,[18] the "prudent investment" concept of the value of utility property was promulgated in a dissenting opinion. In its 1933 decision in the case of the *Los Angeles Gas and Electric Company* v. *California Railroad Commission*,[19] the Court held that the procedure and method to be used in valuing utility property would remain in the jurisdiction of the commission where the utility had not proved confiscation. In this case, which involved a period of depressed prices, the Court pointed out that the cost of reproducing the property was a relevant fact in determining the value. In its 1942 Natural Gas Pipeline decision,[20] which upheld the constitutionality of the Natural Gas Act, and in its 1944 Hope Natural Gas decision,[21] the Court approved the use of a depreciated original cost method of valuation. In the Hope case the Court also pointed out that it was "end result" of

litigation occurred during a period of economic depression with the consequence that the railroad advocated an original-cost rate base, while the state authorities advocated a replacement-cost rate base. In the recent litigation which has taken place in the United States during a period of rising prices, these positions have been reversed with the utilities advocating replacement cost and the regulatory agencies advocating original cost. See the excellent discussion of the Supreme Court utility decisions in A. J. G. Priest, "Major Public Utility Decisions in Perspective," *Virginia Law Review*, Vol. XLVI, No. 7 (November, 1960), 1327.

[18] 262 U.S. 276. See Clemens, *Economics and Public Utilities*, 144ff.

[19] 289 U.S. 287. See Ralph K. Huitt, "National Regulation of the Natural-Gas Industry," on page 65 of *Public Administration and Policy Formation*, edited by Redford. The Huitt article discusses the development of utility evaluation standards in the Supreme Court decisions.

[20] *Natural Gas Pipeline Company* v. *Federal Power Commission*, 315 U.S. 575 (1942). See American Gas Association Rate Committee, *Gas Rate Fundamentals*, 97ff.

[21] *Federal Power Commission* v. *Hope Natural Gas Co.*, 320 U.S. 591 (1944).

the rate order and not the theory used in obtaining the new rates which was of importance. The "end result" formula from the Hope case means that commissions are no longer tied to the fair value interpretation of the rule of *Smyth* v. *Ames* and that the test of fairness of rates really lies in the effect of such rates upon the holders of utility securities.[22]

Depreciation is the expiration or consumption, in whole or in part, of the service life, capacity, or utility of property resulting from action of one or more of the forces operating to bring about the retirement of such properties from service. The forces so operating include wear and tear, decay, action of the elements, inadequacy, obsolescence, and public requirements. Depreciation results in a cost-of-service.[23] It is a proper operating charge by a utility and is not included in the rate of return. The depreciation charge is to be distinguished from maintenance expenses, which are included in the operating expense item. Under the doctrine of the "end result" in the Hope Natural Gas decision of the Supreme Court, commissions are free to adopt any reasonable methods for determining depreciation for use in rate making.

The *rate of return* is the payment made by the public as a fair compensation to capital committed to public use. The public does not guarantee this return to the utility investor; instead, the rate of return sets a ceiling upon utility earnings. Interest and dividends paid by utilities are not operating expenses; consequently such payments must be made out of the return. In theory, the rate of return should compensate for the interest expense of the utility, the risk undertaken by the utility, and financing costs of the utility. Also, in setting the rate of return, consideration may be given to the treatment of taxes, to whether a reward is to be included for management, and to whether a contribution to surplus is to be included. The outstanding United States Supreme Court decision on rate of return is the Bluefield Waterworks case which was decided in 1923.[24] In this case the court set forth the following principles governing the rate of return:

[22] The "end result" ruling of the Supreme Court was anticipated two years before by Irston C. Barnes in *The Economics of Public Utility Regulation*, 388.

[23] National Association of Railroad and Utilities Commissioners, *Report of the Committee on Depreciation*, xiv.

[24] *Bluefield Waterworks and Improvement Company* v. *Public Service Commission of West Virginia*, 262 U.S. 697 (1923).

(1) What annual rate will constitute just compensation depends upon many circumstances and must be determined by the exercise of a fair and enlightened judgment, having regards to all relevant facts.

(2) A public utility is entitled to such rates as will permit it to earn a return on the value of the property which it employs for the convenience of the public equal to that generally being made at the same time and in the same general part of the country on investments and in other business undertakings which are attended by corresponding risks and uncertainties . . .

(3) . . . it has no constitutional right to profits such as are realized or anticipated in highly profitable or speculative ventures.

(4) The return should be reasonably sufficient to assure confidence in the financial soundness of the utility, and should be adequate under efficient and economical management, to maintain and support its credit and enable it to raise the money necessary for the proper discharge of its public duties.

(5) A rate of return may be reasonable at one time or may become too high or too low by changes affecting opportunities for investments, the money market, and business conditions generally.

The final criteria for rate of return would seem to be the market cost of capital determined in competition with other capital-seeking industries.

The principal tax question in rate making is whether taxes shall be included on the basis of taxes actually paid by the utility or on the basis of a calculated tax assuming a normal corporate tax rate. In other words, are tax benefits to be retained for the utility investor or passed on to the consumer? It has been held[25] that benefits to utilities arising from liberalized depreciation treatment do not represent tax savings. but only represent tax deferrals, and that it is proper for the Federal Power Commission to order the dollars thus identified to be credited to a special restricted reserve account. On the other hand, the same case holds that income tax savings arising, under the Internal Revenue statutes, to an interstate pipe line out of its exploration and produc-

[25] *El Paso Natural Gas Company* v. *Federal Power Commission,* 281 F 2(d) 567 (5th Cir., 1960). This decision was concurred in by the Federal Power Commission in its Opinion No. 338 issued September 28, 1960, regarding the rate case *In the Matters of Phillips Petroleum Company,* 24 FPC 753.

tion activities are savings which are not different from savings in any other cost-of-service, with the consequence that such savings are to be passed on to the consuming public. The savings under consideration were those accruing to a pipe line in the operation of a gas-producing property as a result of the depletion allowance and the option to expense certain intangible drilling costs, all as provided under the Internal Revenue Code.[26]

LIMITATIONS ON STATE CONTROL

The commerce clause of the United States Constitution provides that the Congress shall regulate interstate commerce.[27] Conversely, a series of Supreme Court constitutional interpretations hold that the commerce clause prohibits the regulation by state government of interstate commerce, even though the Congress has not acted in regard to the particular commerce under consideration. Some of these decisions prohibit state governments from regulating the prices at which gas and electrical energy are sold in interstate commerce for resale. Two Supreme Court decisions deny to state governments the right to regulate the receipt of imported gas, characterizing the sales as bulk sales in interstate commerce for resale (i.e., sales to distributing companies, not to consumers) and as sales in which the national interest is paramount.[28] In another case the exporting state was denied control of the rates charged in electricity sales made at the state line to a utility of the importing state. The opinion of the Court stressed the constitutional prohibition of direct burdens on interstate commerce and declared that the type of sale involved, and

[26] The Federal Power Commission also concurred in the Fifth Circuit's ruling regarding depletion allowance and intangible drilling expenses in its Opinion No. 338, *In the Matters of Phillips Petroleum Company.*

[27] Constitution of the United States, Art. I, sec. 8, clause 3.

[28] *Missouri, et al.* v. *Kansas Natural Gas Co.,* 265 U.S. 298 (1924), interstate commerce ends at distributing mains; *State Corp. Commission of Kansas, et al.* v. *Wichita Gas Co., et al.,* 290 U.S. 561 (1934); *Peoples Natural Gas Co.* v. *Public Service Commission of Pa., et al.,* 270 U.S. 550 (1926). These decisions are based on the decision in *Gibbons* v. *Ogden,* 9 Wheaton 1, 6 U.S. 1 (1824) in which it was originally held that the Commerce Clause prohibits regulation of interstate commerce by state governments even though Congress has not acted. See John C. Jacobs, Jr., "Problems Incident to the Marketing of Gas," a paper presented at the Fifth Annual Institute on Oil and Gas Law and Taxation as It Affects the Oil and Gas Industry," Dallas, Texas, January 27–29, 1954, and published in *Proceedings,* q.v., 275.

not the business of the parties to the sale, was a controlling factor.[29] Although the decisions prohibit state regulation of bulk gas sales, they generally permit state control of burner-tip, natural gas sales even though the gas has been produced in another state and moved in interstate commerce to the burner tip.[30] Prior to 1938, the interstate natural gas business was designed to maximize the effects of the non-jurisdiction of the state commissions over bulk sales in interstate commerce. The consequence of such maximization was the Natural Gas Act.

FEDERAL CONTROL

The Natural Gas Act

In 1936 the Federal Trade Commission sent to Congress its report on utility corporations which stressed the plight of the consumer in the face of the control exerted by interstate pipe-line companies outside the jurisdiction of state commissions. In 1938 Congress passed the Natural Gas Act[31] without a dissenting vote in either house. The

[29] *Public Utility Commission of Rhode Island, et al.* v. *Attleboro Steam & Electric Co.*, 273 U.S. 83 (1927).

[30] *Pennsylvania Gas Co.* v. *Public Service Commission, et al.*, 252 U.S. 23 (1920); *Lone Star Gas Co.* v. *Texas, et al.*, 304 U.S. 224 (1938); *Western Distributing Co.* v. *Public Service Commission of Kansas, et al.*, 285 U.S. 119 (1932); *Public Utilities Commission* v. *Landon*, 249 U.S. 236 (1919). These decisions resulted from the Court's decision in *Cooley* v. *Board of Wardens of the Port of Philadelphia*, 12 How. 299, 19 U.S. 143 (1851), which first allowed state control of interstate commerce where Congress had not preempted in the field and where the subject matter was of paramount local, rather than national, interest.

[31] Act of June 21, 1938, c. 556; 52 Stat. 821, as amended 56 Stat. 83, and 61 Stat. 459; 15 U.S.C.A. sec. 717ff. For the legislative history of the Natural Gas Act see Jacobs, "Problems Incident to the Marketing of Gas," and note, "Legislative History of the Natural Gas Act," *Georgetown Law Journal*, Vol. XLVI, No. 4 (June, 1956), 695.

A list of some of the literature available regarding our national gas industry and its control under the Natural Gas Act follows: Federal Power Commission, *Natural Gas Investigation* (Docket No. G–580), 1948, outlines in two volumes the findings of Commissioners Nelson Lee Smith, Harrington Wimberley, Leland Olds, and Claude L. Draper regarding the natural gas industry. Frederick F. Blanchly and Miriam E. Oatman, *Natural Gas and the Public Interest*, describes the industry and considers the arguments for and against both state and federal regulation. Edward Falck and Francis X. Welch, *Federal Regulation of Natural Gas in the United States*, is concerned with the application of the Natural Gas Act to the gas industry. Huitt, "National Regulation of the Natural-Gas Industry," describes industry economics, rate regulation under the Natural Gas Act, the problem of end use control, and the independent producer controversy. Stockton, Henshaw and Graves, *Economics of Natural Gas in Texas*, describes economic aspects of the gas industry in our largest gas-producing state in detail. American Gas Association Rate

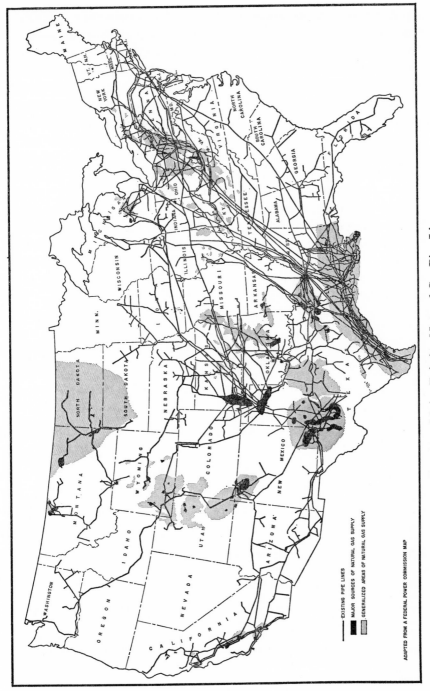

Fig. 32.—Major Existing Natural Gas Pipe Lines
in the United States, June 30, 1959.

Supreme Court has consistently interpreted the purpose of this act as "the prevention of the exploitation of the consumer at the hands of the natural gas companies" and has construed the act to require a comprehensive system of controlling the natural gas industry from the individual gas well to the burner tip.

The statute contains provisions regarding jurisdiction, certificates of public convenience and necessity, rate control, commission power and procedure, and judicial review.[32] Section 1 provides that the act shall apply to three things: (1) the transportation of natural gas in interstate commerce; (2) the sale in interstate commerce of natural gas for resale for ultimate public consumption for domestic, commercial, industrial, or any other use; and (3) to companies engaged in such transportation and sale; and that provisions of the act shall not apply to four things: (1) any other transportation or sale of natural gas; (2) the local distribution of natural gas; (3) the facilities used for such distribution; or (4) the production or gathering of natural gas.[33]

Committee, *Gas Rate Fundamentals,* discusses comprehensively the rate-making side of gas utility regulation. Note also Joseph A. Kornfeld, *Natural Gas Economics.*

There is no comprehensive treatment, from a legal standpoint, of federal natural gas regulation. The authoritative articles on this subject are: Charles I. Francis, "Federal Regulation of Interstate Shipment and Sale of Gas," a paper presented at the Fourth Annual Institute on Oil and Gas Law and Taxation as It Affects the Oil and Gas Industry, Dallas, Texas, January 21–23, 1953, and published in *Proceedings, q.v.,* 103; Francis, "Rate Regulation of Natural Gas Companies by the Federal Power Commission," *Law and Contemporary Problems,* Vol. XIX, No. 3 (Summer, 1954), 413; Raymond N. Shibley and George B. Mickum, III, "The Impact of Phillips Upon the Interstate Pipelines," *Georgetown Law Journal,* Vol. XLIV, No. 4 (June, 1956), 628; and John T. Miller, Jr., "Competition in Regulated Industries: Interstate Gas Pipelines," *Georgetown Law Journal,* Vol. XLVII, No. 2 (Winter, 1958), 224. The Miller article is concerned with competition between interstate gas pipe lines and the antitrust laws. Other material of interest will be found in the *Annual Report* of the Mineral Law and Public Utility sections of the American Bar Association, and in the periodical *Public Utilities Fortnightly.*

[32] See Justin R. Wolf, "The Independent Producer and the Federal Power Commission," a paper presented at the Sixth Annual Institute on Oil and Gas Law and Taxation as It Affects the Oil and Gas Industry, Dallas, Texas, January 19–21, 1955, and published in *Proceedings, q.v.,* 2, for a detailed description of the provisions of the Natural Gas Act.

[33] Section 1(c) of the act, which exempts intrastate distribution activities from control, is discussed on page 281.

Under Section 3 of the act, the Federal Power Commission is given control of the export of gas from the United States and of the import of natural gas into the United States. See Falck and Welch, *Federal Regulation of Natural Gas in the United States,* 80–100.

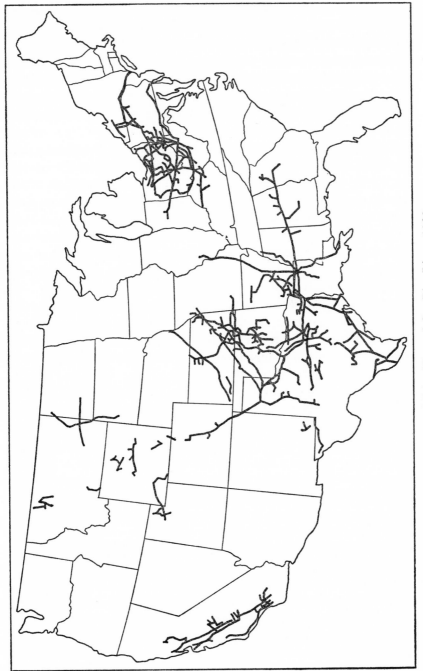

FIG. 33.—Major Natural Gas Pipe Lines, 1930.

Section 7 of the act controls the issuance of certificates of public convenience and necessity and provides that a person may not carry out a jurisdictional sale or transportation of natural gas without first obtaining a certificate of public convenience and necessity. Section 7(a) gives the commission power to compel a natural gas company to provide service to a distributing company whether or not the natural gas company so intended. Section 7(b) gives the commission control of all abandonment of jurisdictional services. Sections 7(c) through 7(e) cover the issuance of certificates of public convenience and necessity. Once an initial certificate is obtained, any extension, enlargement, or acquisition of facilities for the transportation or the sale of natural gas in interstate commerce for resale requires additional certification by the Federal Power Commission.

Sections 4 and 5 of the act grant the Federal Power Commission powers of complete control over any rates and charges made in connection with jurisdictional business. Any rates and charges and the terms and conditions of any service provided by a natural gas company must be just, reasonable, and nondiscriminatory, and such rates and charges must be publicly posted and open to public inspection. Section 4(d) of the act provides that no rate or charge may be changed, nor may a change be made in the terms and conditions of service, without the approval of the commission. Increased charges sought by a natural gas company may be suspended by the commission for a period of five months (during which the company may not collect the increased rate). At the end of the suspension period, the increased rate may be put into effect under bond. Under Section 5 of the act the commission has the authority, upon complaint or upon its own motion, to investigate the rates and charges being made by any natural gas company. If the commission finds the existing rates to be unjust or unreasonable, it may prescribe the just and reasonable rates to be charged in the future.

Sections 6, 8, 9, 10, and 14 of the act give the commission specific powers necessary to make regulation effective. Under these sections the commission has the power to prescribe a Uniform System of Accounts to be followed by natural gas companies. The commission also possesses the power to investigate and to require the filing of periodic reports. Sections 20, 21, and 22 of the act set forth the means by which the commission may compel compliance with its orders from

276

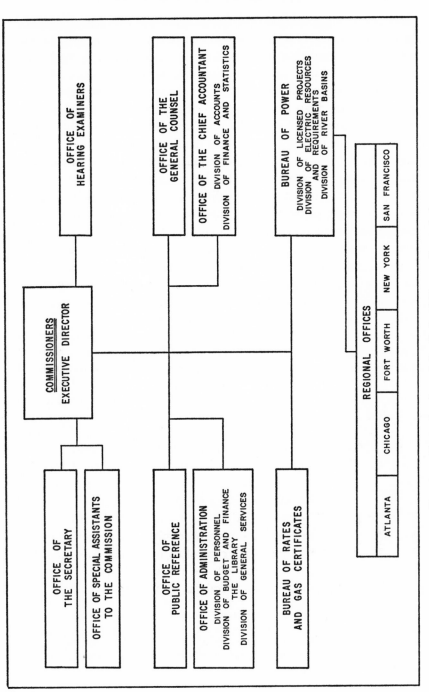

Fig. 34.—Organization of the Federal Power Commission.

the rules and regulations. Provisions are made for fines, imprisonment, and injunctive relief. Section 19 of the act provides for judicial review of Federal Power Commission orders, rules, and regulations by the United States Circuit Court of Appeals.

The most important decisions by the United States Supreme Court interpreting the Natural Gas Act are the Natural Gas Pipeline case, and Hope Natural Gas case, the Phillips Petroleum case, the City of Detroit case, the Mobile and Sierra decisions, the City of Memphis case, and the Sunray-Midcontinent Oil Company case. In the Natural Gas Pipeline case,[34] 1942, the Court upheld the constitutionality of the Natural Gas Act and the validity of a Federal Power Commission order reducing natural gas rates of a pipe-line company on the basis of an original cost depreciated rate base with a 6.5 per cent annual rate of return. In 1944 the Court again upheld a Federal Power Commission order reducing wholesale rates for natural gas in the Hope Natural Gas case.[35] In this decision the Court announced the "end result" approach to its review of rate orders saying:

> . . . under the statutory standard of "just and reasonable" it is the result reached and not the method employed which it is controlling . . . It is not theory but the impact of the rate order which counts. If the total effect of the rate order cannot be said to be unjust and unreasonable, judicial inquiry under the Act is at an end. The fact that the method employed to reach that result may contain infirmities is not then important . . .

In the Phillips Petroleum case,[36] 1954, the Supreme Court reversed the Federal Power Commission and held that the Natural Gas Act applies to sales of natural gas in interstate commerce which are made during the producing and gathering phases of production for resale. Thus, the producing and gathering exemption of Section 1 of the act does not apply to sales made during producing and gathering operations. The Court held that such control of field sales was necessary under the primary aim of the act—to protect consumers from exploitation at the hands of the natural gas companies.

[34] *Natural Gas Pipeline Company of America* v. *Federal Power Commission,* 315 U.S. 575 (1942).

[35] *Federal Power Commission* v. *Hope Natural Gas Co.,* 320 U.S. 591 (1944).

[36] *Phillips Petroleum Company* v. *State of Wisconsin,* 347 U.S. 672, 74 Sup. Ct. 794, 98 L.Ed. 1035, 3 O.& G.R. 745 (1954).

In the City of Detroit case,[37] 1955, which the Supreme Court affirmed by refusing writ of certiorari, the Court of Appeals for the District of Columbia set aside and remanded to the Federal Power Commission a rate order permitting increased rates for Panhandle Eastern Pipe Line Company, an interstate pipe-line transporter subject to the Natural Gas Act. In authorizing increased rates the Commission had departed from the earlier established cost-of-production standard by permitting Panhandle Eastern to incorporate in its cost of service the "fair field price" for all natural gas produced by the company from its own leases, "reflecting the weighted average arms-length payments for identical natural gas in the fields . . . ." At the same time the commission excluded all of Panhandle's production and products extraction facilities from its rate base net investment. The commission also treated Panhandle's natural gasoline extraction business as nonjurisdictional. In reversing the commission, the court held that the commission was not prohibited, under the act, from using the fair field price rather than a utility type cost-of-production standard in setting the rates for gas produced from company-owned leases and that the commission has the right to consider the advantages to the public or having pipe-line companies own production facilities. Nevertheless, the commission must relate its action to the primary aim of consumer protection, and its order must contain findings showing that the rates allowed are no more than is reasonably necessary to achieve the purposes. Here the court enunciated the "point of departure" standard for measuring field prices, saying:

> Furthermore, it is seen that when we refer to an "increase" we mean an increase in the rates above those which would result from the conventional rate-base method. For though we hold that method not to be the only one available under the statute, it is essential in such a case as this that it be used as a basis of comparison.

In the instant case there were no such findings so the matter was remanded to the commission. The court also held that Panhandle's processing operations were jurisdictional.

[37] *City of Detroit, Michigan* v. *Federal Power Commission, et al.,* 230 F. 2(d) 810, 5 O.& G.R. 279 (D.C. Cir. 1955) ; cert. den. 352 U.S. 289, 6 O.& G.R. 897 (1956) ; rehearden. 352 U.S. 919, 6 O.& G.R. 1289 (1956).

The Supreme Court held, in simultaneous decisions, in the Mobile and Sierra cases,[38] 1956, that a fixed rate in a long-term contract for the sale of gas could not be changed by the unilateral filing of a new rate under Section 4 of the Natural Gas Act, even though such sales are subject to the Natural Gas Act. In this case United had agreed to sell gas under a long-term contract to Mobile at specified prices. The sales were sales in interstate commerce for resale, and the contract contained no provisions permitting unilateral price changes by United under the Section 4 procedures of the Natural Gas Act. The Court held that the parties to the contract were bound by the contracts, which made no provisions for unilateral filings, even though under the Natural Gas Act the Federal Power Commission had the power to change the contract as would be necessary in the public interest. In the City of Memphis case,[39] 1958, the Supreme Court upheld the right of a seller to a municipal distributing company to file unilateral rate increases in accordance with Section 4 of the Natural Gas Act, where the contract between seller and the municipal distributing company provided that both parties agreed to abide by rates on file with the Federal Power Commission. This latter provision in the contract differentiated the Memphis case from the Mobile case.

In the Sunray-Midcontinent Oil Company case,[40] 1960, the Court held that the commission might issue a certificate of public convenience and necessity unlimited as to term to an "independent producer" even though a limited time certificate was requested coeval with the term of the underlying gas purchase contract. In effect the Court held that the sale of natural gas in the field is the rendering of a utility service rather than the sale of a commodity. Consequently, the protection of the consumer requires that the cessation of such service may occur only by commission order in accordance with Section 7(b) of the act and not automatically at the end of a term provided in a certificate.

[38] *United Gas Pipeline Co.* v. *Mobile Gas Service Corp. and FPC,* 350 U.S. 322, 76 Sup.Ct. 373, 5 O.& G.R. 808 (1956); *Federal Power Commission* v. *Sierra Pacific Power Company,* 350 U.S. 348, 5 O.&G.R. 803 (1956).

[39] *United Gas Pipeline Co.* v. *Memphis Light, Gas and Water Division, et al.,* 358 U.S. 103, 9 O.& G.R. 967 (1958).

[40] *Sunray-Midcontinent Oil Co.* v. *Federal Power Commission,* 364 U.S. 137, 12 O.& G.R. 804 (1960).

Distribution activities have, for all practical purposes, been removed from Natural Gas Act jurisdiction by the 1954 amendment known as Section 1(c). This section exempts any interstate transportation or sale for resale within the boundaries of a state if all the gas under consideration is ultimately consumed within that same state, provided such exempted sales and services are under the control of a state commission. To effect the exemption, the state commission must certify to the Federal Power Commission its control over the sales and services to be exempted from the act.

Control of the interstate transportation phase of the natural gas industry under the Natural Gas Act is complete. The act applies to all "transportation of natural gas in interstate commerce," and to the "sale in interstate commerce of natural gas for resale" for all uses. No facilities for interstate transportation may be built, operated or expanded without a proper certificate of public convenience and necessity from the Federal Power Commission. Indeed the coverage of the act is so complete that, although gathering lines are probably nonjurisdictional, it is common practice for interstate pipe lines to obtain annual "blanket authorizations for construction" in the form of certificates of public convenience and necessity from the Federal Power Commission permitting the construction of a fixed dollar sum of small lines. The pipe lines account to the Federal Power Commission at the end of each year for construction under the certificates and include the cost of gathering line construction in the accounting.

Pipe-Line Certificates

Federal Power Commission rules and regulations describe the great bulk of the written material which must be filed by an applicant in a pipe-line certificate proceeding.[41] Notice, the right of any interested party to intervene, and hearing are provided for. Hearing is followed by an examiner's decision, the filing of exceptions to the decision, argument before the commission, and the commission's decision. The latter may be appealed to the circuit court of appeals. The entire procedure through commission decision takes about one year, and provision is made for the issuance without notice or hearing, meanwhile, of temporary certificates in case of emergency. The issuance and

[41] See Francis, "Rate Regulation of Natural Gas Companies by the Federal Power Commission," *Law and Contemporary Problems,* Vol. XIX, No. 3 (Summer, 1954), 415.

acceptance of a temporary certificate in no way limits the commission's powers of conditioning the final certificate under its broad rights in Section 7(e) of the act which empowers it "to attach to the issuance of the certificate . . . such reasonable terms and conditions as the public convenience and necessity may require." This section contains the following standards for the issuance of a certificate:

> A certificate shall be issued to any qualified applicant therefore, authorizing the whole or any part of the operation, sale, service, construction, extension, acquisition covered by the application, if it is found that the applicant is able and willing properly to do the act and perform the service proposed and to conform to the provisions of the Act and the requirements, rules, and the regulations of the Commission thereunder, and that the proposed service, sale, operation, extension or acquisition to the extent authorized by the certificate, is or will be required by the present or future public convenience and necessity; otherwise such application shall be denied. . . .

In practice the commission has established four requirements with which a certificate applicant must comply.[42] First, the applicant must show evidence of an adequate gas supply for the project. A reserve life of eighteen to twenty years is required, together with a deliverability study which shows that the daily system requirements can be met by the sources of supply for at least twelve years.[43] Second, a pipe-line design must be presented which is adequate, from an engineering standpoint, to meet the demands inherent in the proposed

[42] These requirements were first established by the Commission early in its administration of the Natural Gas Act. See *In the Matter of Kansas Pipeline and Gas, et al.,* 2 FPC 29 (1940).

[43] See R. D. Grimm, "Factors Affecting Gas Supply Control," a paper presented before the Interstate Oil Compact Commission, December 4, 1961, for a discussion of the burdens imposed upon the gas consumer through the twelve-year availability rule and the take-or-pay-for supply contract. Under the twelve-year availability rule, a pipe-line applicant for a Natural Gas Act certificate to sell additional gas must show a twelve-year availability of gas supply for existing and new service. Mr. Grimm points out the possible deleterious effect of this rule and demonstrates that maintaining the twelve-year availability with one to seventy-three hundred supply contracts will cost the consumer from three to ten cents per thousand cubic feet.

See Bruce C. Netschert, "Economic Aspects of Natural Gas Supply," in *Economics of the Gas Industry, q.v.,* I, 27. Mr. Netschert advocates amelioration of the twelve-year availability and the twenty-year reserve index rules.

sales. A market for the gas must be proved, and fourth, the project must be economically feasible. It must be one that can be financed, and the gas must be marketable at a competitive price. If these four requirements are met, the commission will find that the public convenience and necessity requires the issuance of a certificate.

Gas for Industrial Uses

One area of continuing interest under the Natural Gas Act lies in the control of the transportation and sale of gas for industrial uses. By the wording of the act, the control of gas for such uses is the same as the control for any other use except that rate increases for industrial sales may not be suspended (the effectiveness of the increase postponed) for five months by commission order as is the case for any other type of sale,[44] and that, when the consuming industry buys its gas in the field, there is no resale involved with the consequence that the purchase in the field is nonjurisdictional, and only the interstate transportation comes under the Federal Power Commission.[45]

Industrial sales, especially summertime sales at low prices to electricity generation plants (the so-called "dump gas" sales), are necessary in order to minimize the cost of gas to the wintertime, house-heating consumer. At the same time industrial sales are decried by the conservationists who see low priority industrial consumption as adverse to a public interest which dictates that natural gas—an exhaustible, irreplaceable natural resource—should be saved for high priority house-heating and chemical feedstock uses. Under the Natural Gas Act, the problems go to the extent of the Federal Power Commission's power to consider "end use" in the issuance or denial of certificates of public convenience and necessity. The decisions make it clear that the Federal Power Commission has not received, under the Natural Gas Act, any over-all powers to dictate priorities of end uses of natural gas. On the other hand, the commission may consider end use as one of the factors involved in the question of

44 Section 4(e) of the Natural Gas Act.

45 See *Consolidated Edison Co. of N. Y.* v. *Federal Power Commission*, 365 U.S. 1, 13 O.& G.R. 861 (1961). The proceedings in this case before the Federal Power Commission are styled *In the Matters of Transcontinental Gas Pipeline Company, et al.*, 21 FPC 138, 9 O.& G.R. 1199 (1959).

whether or not a particular certificate should be issued, or issued with conditions.[46]

The commission has authorized the interstate transportation and sale of industrial gas where the industrial sale is made at a sufficiently high price that the sale carries its fair share of the expenses of the pipe-line system.[47] When the circumstances so require, the sale is made through the local distributing company on an interruptible basis, thereby providing the industrial gas to satisfy winter, peak-load demand of house owners.[48]

Pipe-Line Rates

The commission's jurisdiction over pipe-line rates may be considered from the standpoint of initial rates and rate changes.[49] Under the Natural Gas Act the commission has no power to change an initial rate; however the commission controls initial rates indirectly through its certificate conditioning power[50] by requiring the filing of a proper initial rate as a condition to the issuance of a certificate. Changes in existing rates may be initiated either by the seller under Section 4 of the act or by the commission under Section 5 of the act. As a matter of practice the commission makes routine audits of natural gas companies' books. If such a routine check so indicates, or if a proper complaint is filed with the commission, it may order the investigation of any existing rate. If an existing rate is found to be unjust, unduly

[46] *Federal Power Commission* v. *Hope Natural Gas Co.,* 320 U.S. 591 (1944), and see discussion of end use control in the Con-Ed case cited above in footnote 45.

[47] *Charleston and W.C. Ry.* v. *FPC* 234 F 2(d) 62, 5 O.& G.R. 1261 (D.C. Cir. 1956); *In the Matter of Northern Natural Gas Co.,* 15 FPC 682, rev'd 15 FPC 1634, 6 O.& G.R. 528 (1956), aff'd sub nom., *National Coal Association* v. *Federal Power Commission,* 247 F 2(d) 86 (D.C. Cir. 1957)—Northern Natural's sale to the Black Dog Power Plant.

[48] *In the Matter of El Paso Natural Gas Company,* 22 FPC 900, 11 O.& G.R. 410 (1959). The presiding examiner's decision, issued May 12, 1959, in this case (Docket No. G–12580), contains a detailed discussion of reserve estimation methods.

[49] Excellent detailed discussions of the control of pipe-line rates under the Natural Gas Act are to be found in the following: Francis, "Rate Regulation of Natural Gas Companies by the Federal Power Commission," *Law and Contemporary Problems,* Vol. XIX, No. 3 (Summer, 1954), 413; Lloyd J. Klein, "Accounting Aspects of Utility Rate Regulation," *Law and Contemporary Problems,* Vol. XIX, No. 3 (Summer, 1954), 435; and American Gas Association Rate Committee, *Gas Rate Fundamentals,* 111ff. See also Francis X. Welch, *Preparing for the Utility Rate Case,* and Francis X. Welch, *Conduct of the Utility Rate Case.*

[50] Section 7(b) of the Natural Gas Act.

discriminatory, preferential, or otherwise unlawful, the commission has the power to order a decrease in the rate. If a natural gas company seller desires to change existing rates, Section 4 of the act requires thirty days' notice to the commission and to the public. Such notice is given by publicly filing the new rate with the commission. Commission regulations require the filing of voluminous correlative supporting data by the proponents. The volume of these materials is such that it requires nineteen pages of the rules and regulations to describe the material to be filed. The commission may, and invariably does when the case involves a major pipe line, order public hearing and may suspend the proposed rate for as many as five months. During the suspension period the old rate remains in effect. At the end of the suspension period, the increased rate may be put into effect under bond if the proponent so desires. Although the commission may not retroactively adjust rates, it may order the refund of any amount collected under the bond upon final determination of the justness and reasonableness of the proposed rates.

After the initiation of any rate proceeding, a time-consuming, full-scale investigation of the natural gas company's books is made by the Federal Power Commission; and this investigation serves as a basis for the Federal Power Commission staff's position and testimony at the subsequent hearing. The hearing is public and any interested party may intervene. Consequently the hearings are lengthy and complex. Their purpose is to provide a basis upon which the commission can determine whether the proposed rate is "fair and reasonable." Following staff investigation and hearing, briefs are filed, a written examiner's decision is handed down, exceptions to the decision are taken, arguments may be had before the commission itself, and the commission's decision is issued. A rehearing of the commission's decision may be had, after which the decisions may be appealed to a circuit court. All of this takes a great deal of time, often from one to seven years. In any event, a major rate proceeding is never concluded by the end of the five-month suspension period, so sizable amounts are collected under bond subject to refund plus 7 per cent interest. The amounts collected under bond by pipe-line companies represent a major problem to the transmission companies and their customers.

From a substantive point of view the Federal Power Commission allows rates which equal the total cost-of-service of the natural gas

285

company. Therefore the first step in a rate proceeding is to determine the total cost-of-service. The cost-of-service may be represented by the formula:

$$R = E + r(I-D) + d + T$$

where

R = total cost of service

E = annual operating expense

r = rate of return, expressed as a fraction

$I-D$ = original cost of the physical property less accumulated depreciation

d = current annual depreciation

T = taxes incurred by the utility

The test period for determining the cost of service is the last known twelve-month period adjusted, as the proponent may bear the burden of proof, to reflect future changes. The principal rulings regarding the Federal Power Commission determination of cost of service follow:

Operating expense includes allowance for operation and maintenance expenses and entails, according to the Federal Power Commission regulations, ". . . the most recently available actual experience, adjusted for changes . . . which are known and measurable with reasonable accuracy. . . . the twelve months' experience shall be adjusted to eliminate nonrecurring items, but this shall not preclude the replacement of the nonrecurring item with another of nonrecurring nature which the natural gas company anticipates will be realized, including the provision for the normalizing of such items as rate case expenses."[51]

Rate base is defined as the original cost of the plant which is used or useful in the natural gas business less accrued book depreciation plus working capital. *Original cost* is the cost in the hands of the holder at the time the property was "first devoted to public service." The *working capital allowance* equals forty-five days operating expense less cost of gas and certain other costs and is reduced by 75 to 100 per cent of annual income tax accruals. Interest during construction may be capitalized.

Depreciation is calculated by the straight line method at rates of 3 to 4 per cent per annum. No allowance is made for the effect of inflation on depreciation requirements.

[51] Federal Power Commission, *General Rules and Regulations,* amended Rule 154.63 (b) (3).

Rate of return should compensate for pure interest expense, risks of doing business, and costs associated with marketing securities and raising capital. The commission most recently considers the historical cost of money as the most important of the factors determining the rate of return. Rates from 5.5 to 6.25 per cent annual return have been set for interstate pipe-line systems depending primarily upon the financial structure of the natural gas company and on the amount of producing and exploration properties involved. In 1960 the commission refused to recognize pipe-line arguments that a rate of return of 7 per cent per year was necessary in order to attract capital to the interstate pipe-line business. The commission also recognizes that, because of the different risks involved, a higher rate of return is necessary on producing and exploration activities than on transportation activities.

Under *taxes* the principal questions are concerned with whether the tax to be included in the cost-of-service is an income tax calculated at normal corporate tax rate, or the actual income tax paid by the corporation. It has been decided[52] that since accelerated depreciation is really deferred taxation, the natural gas company need not take accelerated depreciation into account in calculating income taxes for cost-of-service purposes. This is true regardless of how the natural gas company may handle accelerated depreciation in calculating the income tax it actually pays to the Internal Revenue Service. However, tax benefits (depletion and the intangibles deduction) growing out of exploration for and production of natural gas from company-owned leases must be credited against the tax allowance for cost-of-service purposes, as would any saving in another item making up the cost of service (e.g., a saving in operating expenses).

Once the total cost-of-service has been determined it is necessary to make allocations between jurisdictional and nonjurisdictional business, and then between the several customers and types of service sold by the natural gas company. This latter allocation primarily involves an allocation of expenses between the commodity and demand components of the natural gas company's tariffs. *Allocation* is a very complex matter[53] involving many judgments. The Federal Power

[52] See *El Paso Natural Gas Company* v. *Federal Power Commission*, 281 F 2(d) 567 (5th Cir., 1960), and *In the Matters of Phillips Petroleum Company*, 24 FPC.

[53] See *In the Matters of Atlantic Seaboard Corp., et al.*, 11 FPC 43 (1952); *In the Matter of Canadian River Gas Co.*, 3 FPC 32, 61 (1943), aff'd as *Colorado Interstate Gas Co.* v. *Federal Power Commission*, 324 U.S. 581, 586 (1945); *In the Matter of Cities Service Gas Co.*, 3 FPC 459, 485 (1943), aff'd as *Cities Service Gas Co.* v. *Federal*

Commission practice basically requires grouping of operating and facility costs by the "functions" of producing and gathering (including gas purchased and producing expenses), long-distance transmission, and delivery from the line to the customer. Within functions, costs must be allocated to the demand and commodity components of the tariffs and to the customers involved. *Commodity costs* are those which vary in proportion to the volume of gas delivered.

In allocating producing and gathering function charges between commodity and demand, certain rules are generally followed. Gas obtained from the various supply sources of the pipe-line system and intermingled in the main transmission lines is charged at its average cost to all customers. Revenues from gas-processing operations are credited against the cost of gas production or purchase. The cost of gas produced from the pipe line's own leases may be, depending upon the Commission's determination in a particular case, priced on a strict utility cost-of-service basis or on a commodity-price ("fair field price") basis. Cost of purchased gas is allocated entirely to the commodity component unless the terms of the gas purchase contracts indicate that part of the expense should be allocated to the demand component. In the transmission function certain expenses, such as compressor fuel and supplies that are directly related to the flow of the gas through the lines are completely allocated to the commodity component. However, the large portion of transmission expenses, the so-called fixed charges made up of depreciation, taxes, and return, must be allocated between demand and commodity. The Federal Power Commission has consistently allocated 50 per cent of such expenses to demand and 50 per cent to commodity.[54] In the delivery-from-the-line-to-the-customer function, expenses such as the cost of measuring stations and gathering lines generally do not involve difficult allocation problems. Usually such costs may be allocated directly to the customer or service involved.

In a pipe-line system which renders only one type of service, the

Power Commission, 155 F 2(d) 694, 704 (10th Cir., 1946), cert. den., 329 U.S. 773 (1946). Allocation is descussed in detail by Klein, "Accounting Aspects of Utility Rate Regulation," *Law and Contemporary Problems,* Vol. XIX, No. 3 (Summer, 1954), 450–53; and also in American Gas Association Rate Committee, *Gas Rate Fundamentals,* 216ff. And see Raymond A. Ransom, "Value of Service and Pipeline Rates," *Public Utilities Fortnightly,* Vol. LXIX, No. 3 (February 1, 1962), 162.

[54] See the Atlantic Seaboard decision of the Federal Power Commission.

rate to be charged would be equal to the total cost-of-service divided by the expected volume of gas to be sold, with a proper allocation between demand and commodity components of the tariff. Actually the problem is made much more complex by the fact that most pipe lines have different rates in each of the several sales zones, and, that, in any particular zone, a pipe line usually sells several types of service, varying from high load-factor gas, which must be taken by the buyer every day, to low load-factor, winter-peaking service gas, which is delivered out of storage. In setting a company's rates the commission necessarily must consider all the types of service being rendered by the pipe-line company.

Processing Operations

Processing operations, the removing of liquefiable components from the natural gas stream, are carried out on the gas flowing in the natural gas company's facilities by plants which may or may not be owned by the natural gas company. If the processing plant is owned wholly by the natural gas company, the processing operation is jurisdictional whether or not the operation is a prerequisite to pipe-line transportation.[55] As a consequence any revenues received from processing must be credited to the jurisdictional cost of service. Similarly any amounts received by a pipe-line company from a third party for processing must so be credited. If a majority or complete interest in the processing plant is owned by a third party, the processing operation is nonjurisdictional.[56] Under these circumstances the question

[55] *City of Detroit* v. *Federal Power Commission,* 230 F 2(d) 810, 5 O.& G.R. 279 (D.C. Cir., 1955) ; cert. den. 352 U.S. 829, 6 O.& G.R. 897 (1956) ; rehear. den. 352 U.S. 919, 6 O.& G.R. 1289 (1956). In its opinion No. 338 issued September 28, 1960, *In the Matters of Phillips Petroleum Company* in Docket Nos. G–1148, *et al.,* 24 FPC 753, 13 O.& G.R. 343, the commission held that processing plants from which jurisdictional sales of residue natural gas are made are not subject to the jurisdiction of the commission where such plants are owned by a natural gas company which is an independent producer. The commission distinguished independent producer from pipe-line ownership of processing plants on the basis that the pipe line operates such plants, in part, to improve its transmission operation, whereas with the independent producer the processing is carried out as an independent business without regard to the efficiency of subsequent transportation of the residue gas. See Wendell J. Doggett, "Marketing by Producer of Natural Gas," in *Economics of the Gas Industry, q.v.* I., 226.

[56] *In the Matters of Texas Eastern Transmission Corporation and Wilcox Trend Gathering System, Inc.,* 11 FPC 434 (1952); *In the Matters of Panhandle Eastern Pipe Line Company, et al.,* 12 FPC 686 (1953).

becomes one of the proper allocation between jurisdictional pipe-line cost-of-service and the nonjurisdictional processing operation, of the cost involved in the pipe-line operations between the wells and the processing plant. Generally the Federal Power Commission refuses to adopt an allocation based on the volume reduction of the gas stream through the processing plant, but has adopted an allocation based on the Btu reduction through the plant in one case[57] and an allocation based on the relative market value of the plant products and the residue natural gas in another case.[58]

Company-produced Gas

Producing gas from its own properties, as opposed to purchasing gas from others, has the advantages to the gas company and the consuming public of enhancing the gas company's bargaining power when purchasing from others, of the comparatively wide variations permissible in the amounts of gas taken from a company-owned property, and of surety of long-term supply. These advantages are recognized by the Federal Power Commission and by the courts.[59] Consequently many gas companies have acquired gas-producing, or possibly productive, properties ranging from wildcat acreage to proven gas fields.

Many gas companies maintain gas exploration departments which acquire potentially productive acreage by lease or farm-out. No ap-

[57] The City of Detroit decision required that the net gasoline plant revenues of Panhandle be credited back to the cost of service. Such net gasoline plant revenues were calculated using a Btu allocation factor in allocating field gathering expenses. More recently, the commission, in its decision *In the Matters of Phillips Petroleum Company*, again used a Btu allocation factor in allocating expenses between residue gas and plant products at processing plants.

[58] *Federal Power Commission* v. *Colorado Interstate Gas Co.*, 348 U.S. 492 (1955) involved a factual situation in which the Federal Power Commission had made an allocation of gathering system expenses on a relative products value basis. See Jacobs, "Governmental Regulation of Gas Production—1956," *Fourth Annual Institute on Mineral Law* (1956), 43, 51.

[59] *City of Detroit* v. *Federal Power Commission* 230 F 2(d) 810, 5 O.& G.R. 279, 285 (D.C. Cir., 1955); cert. den. 352 U.S. 289, 6 O.& G.R. 897 (1956); rehear. den. 352 U.S. 919, 6 O.& G.R. 1289 (1956). For FPC proceedings see *In the Matter of Panhandle Eastern Pipe Line Co.*, 13 FPC 53 (1954), Opinion No 269 in Docket Nos. G–1116 *et al.*; *In the Matter of El Paso Natural Gas Co.*, 13 FPC 421 (1954), Opinion No. 278 in Docket No. G–2018; and *In the Matter of Olin Gas Transmission Corporation*, 17 FPC 685 (Order of May 15, 1957, in Docket No. G–8559) where a fair field price of 10¢/MCF was allowed.

proval under the Natural Gas Act is required for the consummation of such transactions. The Federal Power Commission has not asserted jurisdiction over the moneys received by lessor or "farmer" companies and recognizes gas-company expenditures in connection with such leases as a part of the cost-of-service. Some gas companies acquire semideveloped gas properties in consideration for cash, assuming a drilling obligation and paying an overriding royalty on production. A sizable, overriding royalty income from a farm-out of San Juan Basin semideveloped acreage was treated in the Phillips case as nonjurisdictional income with the concurrence of the trial examiner and the commission.[60] Other gas companies purchase fully developed properties. In the Rayne transaction, which, as shown in Table 18, is one of several trillion-cubic-feet reserve purchases made by gas companies in the 1959–61 period, sellers received cash on closing, a production payment out of separator and processing plant liquids, and notes maturing over three-fourths of the expected life of the property. The title transfer was made through an intermediary corporation so that the gas company is not liable on the notes.

In certificating facilities to tie the property into the purchaser's pipe-line system, the Federal Power Commission[61] recognized: (1) the consumer advantages in the property purchase of fixed price over the life of the property, (2) no effect of this purchase on prices paid for other gas either through favored-nations-clause triggering or price redetermination, and (3) an initial price below gas purchase contract levels. On appeal the commission was reversed on the grounds of inadequate proof of the initial price;[62] however, the nonjurisdictional status of the property transfer under the Natural Gas Act was confirmed. The leading case on the nonjurisdictional status of property

[60] *In the Matter of Phillips Petroleum Company,* 24 FPC 753, 13 O.& G.R. 343 (Opinion No. 338, issued September 28, 1960). And see the presiding examiner's decision *In the Matter of Phillips Petroleum Company,* Docket Nos. G–1148 *et al.,* issued April 6, 1959, pp. 107–11 of mimeograph edition.

[61] The Rayne Field Case—*In the Matters of Texas Eastern Transmission Corp., et al.,* 21 PFC 860 (1959); Order denying application for rehearing issued August 21, 1959, in Docket Nos. 12446 *et al.,* 22 FPC 451.

[62] *Public Service Commission of the State of New York* v. *Federal Power Commission, et al.,* 287 F 2(d) 143 (D.C. Cir., Opinion of December 8, 1960, in No. 15,412). See Jacobs, "In-Place Purchases of Gas Reserves," in *1962 Symposium on Petroleum Economics and Valuation, q.v.* 79, for the most recent discussion of five large reserve purchases by gas pipe-line companies.

TABLE 16
MAJOR PROVED PROPERTY PURCHASES BY NATURAL GAS COMPANIES

Field	State	Date	Buyer
Rayne	Louisiana	1959	Texas Eastern
MCN*	Louisiana (Offshore)	1960	Tennessee
Bastian Bay	Louisiana	1960	Tennessee
Ship Shoal	Louisiana (Offshore)	1961	Tennessee
King Ranch Area	Texas	1961	Monterey (For Resale to Columbia)

(Source: FPC)
*MCN and CATC are mining partnerships.

transfers is the Panhandle case[63] wherein the Supreme Court over-ruled Federal Power Commission objections to the transfer of developed and undeveloped leases from an interstate pipe-line company to its stockholders without authorization under the Natural Gas Act.

From the accounting point of view, exploration and development costs incurred by a natural gas company must, according to the Uniform System of Accounts prescribed by the Federal Power Commission, be expensed in the case of dry-hole drilling, delay rentals, and other nonproductive exploration and development costs. Amounts invested in acreage held for future use are to be capitalized.[64]

[63] *Federal Power Commission* v. *Panhandle Eastern Pipeline Co.,* 337 U.S. 498 (1949).
[64] See Klein, "Accounting Aspects of Utility Rate Regulation," *Law and Contemporary Problems,* Vol. XIX, No. 3 (Summer, 1954), 442.

Seller	Gas Reserve Billion Cu. Ft.	Total Consideration Dollars	Title Transfer	Status March 1, 1962 Natural Gas Act
Continental, Sun, Marr and General Crude	990.0	138,025,685	Closed	Approved and Remanded (G–12446)
Mobil, Continental, and Newmont	499.5	68,339,272	Sale Contract Terminated	Gas Purchase Contract Substituted (G–1456)
Pan American	759.0	159,463,500	Closed	Hearing Pending (CP61–106 and CI62–1034)
CATC*	533.0	97,333,333	Closed	Hearing Pending
Humble	6,645.0	994,732,035	Pending	Hearing Pending (CP62–88)

A major controversy centers about whether gas from company-owned leases should enter the cost-of-service calculations at commodity value or at a cost calculated according to utility rate-making principles. After years of following the utility rate cost approach, the Federal Power Commission in 1954 used the fair field price approach in two cases.[65] In one appeal, the City of Detroit case, the District of Columbia Circuit Court of Appeals reversed the Federal Power Commission holding that the commission is not restricted from the use of the fair field price method for company-produced gas either by the statute or the Hope decision and that the commission may properly give consent to encouraging the exploration and development and to the ownership by pipe-line companies of their own gas-producing properties as being in the public interest in fixing rates for a pipe-

[65] See footnote 59, above.

line company. The court recognized the use of the fair field price for company-produced gas as one method of giving such consideration; however, any rates determined on the foregoing basis must not lift the rates above the "just and reasonable" standard of the statute, and the commission must always relate its action to the primary aim of the statute which is to protect consumers against excessive rates. Consequently there must be findings based on the record to show that the allowed increase in the rates is no more than is reasonably necessary for these purposes. The order in the instant case did not contain such findings. Concluded the court:

> Furthermore, it is seen that when we refer to an "increase" we mean an increase in the rates above those which would result from the conventional rate-base method. For, though we hold that method not to be the only one available under the statute, it is essential in such a case as this that it be used as a basis of comparison. It has been repeatedly used by the Commission, and repeatedly approved by the courts, as a means of arriving at lawful—"just and reasonable"—rates under the Act. Unless it is continued to be used at least as a point of departure, the whole experience under the Act is discarded and no anchor, as it were, is available by which to hold the terms "just and reasonable" to some recognizable meaning.

FEDERAL CONTROL OF INDEPENDENT PRODUCERS

Jurisdiction Over Field Sales

After much discussion as to the meaning of the Section 1(b) concerning jurisdictional exemption of "the production or gathering of natural gas" and several attempts to amend the act to clearly exempt field sales of natural gas, in 1954 the Supreme Court of the United States in its Phillips decision[66] reversed the Federal Power Commis-

[66] *Phillips Petroleum Company* v. *State of Wisconsin*, 347 U.S. 672, 3 O.& G.R. 745 (1954).

The question of regulating field prices of natural gas is discussed at length in *Natural Gas Investigation* (Docket No. G–580), a two-volume work issued by the Federal Power Commission as its report. Neuner, *The Natural Gas Industry,* is an economics study which concludes that competitive conditions, rather than monopoly conditions, exist in field sales of natural gas. James W. McKie, *The Regulation of Natural Gas,* is an economics study which concludes that the regulation of field prices is unnecessary. Paul H. Douglas, "The Case for the Consumer of Natural Gas," *Georgetown Law Jounal,* Vol. XLIV, No. 4 (June, 1956), 566, concludes that the consumer interest can be protected only through Federel Power Commission control of field prices.

From the legal point of view important papers concerning the regulation of field sales

sion and ordered the commission to take jurisdiction of the sales made by an independent producer at the completion of producing and gathering. Subsequent court decisions have made it clear that Natural Gas Act jurisdiction over field sales, whether made before, during, or at the completion of producing and gathering, is complete. These de-

of natural gas appear as part of a symposium entitled "The Regulation of Natural Gas," in *Law and Contemporary Problems,* Vol. XIX, No. 3 (Summer, 1954), 323–412. A symposium on the federal regulation of natural-gas producers appears in the *Georgetown Law Journal,* Vol. XLIV, No. 4 (June, 1956), 551–693. See also Edward L. Atkinson, "Federal Regulation of Natural Gas—The Independent Producer's Status," *Southwestern Law Journal,* Vol. XIII, No. 4 (Fall, 1959), 425.

A great amount of material relating to the pro's and con's of the regulation of field sales is set forth in the hearings which were held relative to the Natural Gas Act in 1955. See, *Amendments to the Natural Gas Act,* "Hearings Before the Committee on Interstate and Foreign Commerce," 84 Cong., 1 sess. on Sen. Bill 712, *et al.,* to amend the Natural Gas Act, May 10–June 9, 1955; and *Natural Gas Act (Exemption of Producers),* "Hearings Before the Committee on Interstate and Foreign Commerce," 84 Cong., 1 sess., on H.R. Bill 4560, to amend the Natural Gas Act, March 22–April 18, 1955 (Part I), and April 19–May 2, 1955 (Part II).

Articles describing the gas purchase contract and its regulation are: William S. Richardson, "Producer Contracts for Sale of Natural Gas in Interstate Commerce," a paper presented at the Eleventh Annual Institute on Oil and Gas Law and Taxation, Dallas, Texas, February 10–12, 1960, and published in *Proceedings, q.v.,* 201; Ben R. Howell, "Natural Gas Purchase Contracts," a paper delivered at the Fifth Annual Rocky Mountain Mineral Law Institute, Boulder, Colorado, July 31–August 1, 1959, and published in *Proceedings, q.v.,* 221; Ben R. Howell, "Gas Purchase Contracts," a paper presented at the Fourth Annual Institute on Oil and Gas Law and Taxation as It Affects the Oil and Gas Industry, Dallas, Texas, January 21–23, 1953, and published in *Proceedings, q.v.,* 151; John C. Jacobs, Jr., "What Every Landman Should Know About Gas Purchase Contracts," *National Institute for Petroleum Landmen,* Vol. III (1962), 155; D. H. Gregg, "Negotiating and Drafting Gas Purchase Contracts on Behalf of Seller," a paper presented at the Thirteenth Annual Institute on Oil and Gas Law and Taxation, Dallas, Texas, February 14–16, 1962, and published in *Proceedings, q.v.,* 87.

The following articles are of particular interest: Robert E. May, "Preparation for Gas Rate Hearing Before the Federal Power Commission," a paper presented to the Eleventh Annual Institute on Oil and Gas Law and Taxation, Dallas, Texas, February 10–12, 1960, and published in *Proceedings, q.v.,* 123; Gene M. Woodfin, "Recent Developments in Federal Power Commission Control of Independent Producers," a paper presented at the Tenth Annual Institute on Oil and Gas Law and Taxation as It Affects the Oil and Gas Industry, Dallas, Texas, February 11–13, 1959, and published in *Proceedings, q.v.,* 25; Charles V. Shannon, "Recent Developments Affecting Production, Transportation and Sale of Gas," a paper presented at the Eighth Annual Institute on Oil and Gas Law and Taxation as It Affects the Oil and Gas Industry, Dallas, Texas, January 30–February 1, 1957, and published in *Proceedings, q.v.,* 219; Thomas Fletcher, "The Gas Producer and the Federal Power Commission: Cases, Statutes and Rulings," a paper presented at the Seventh Annual Institute on Oil and Gas Law and Taxation as It Affects

cisions are in accord with the Supreme Court's finding that the purpose of the Natural Gas Act is consumer protection.[67] Serious questions still remain unanswered regarding the standards to be used in determining whether field sales prices are "fair and reasonable."

Court decisions point out that, under the Natural Gas Act, the status of the independent producer is the same as that of any other natural gas company. Nevertheless, in its rules and regulations governing certificate and rate filings by independent producers,[68] the Commission has greatly simplified, as compared with pipe-line companies, the nature and quantity of supporting data required to be filed with the Federal Power Commission in a certificate application or rate increase filing. The commission has allowed the independent producer to file his gas purchase contract with the Federal Power Commission as a rate schedule, whereas pipe-line companies must reduce gas sales agreements to a specified book-form gas tariff for filing. No standard system of accounts has been promulgated for in-

---

the Oil and Gas Industry, Dallas, Texas, February 1–3, 1956, and published in *Proceedings, q.v.,* 95; Wolf, "The Independent Producer and the Federal Power Commission"; Jacobs, "Problems Incident to the Marketing of Gas"; W. Page Keeton, "Federal Regulation of Independent Gas Producers—Developments Since the Phillips Decision," a paper presented at the Fifth Annual Rocky Mountain Law Institute, Boulder, Colorado, July 31–August 1, 1959, and published in *Proceedings, q.v.,* 193; Justin R. Wolf, "Current Decisions and Problems in the Regulation of Independent Natural Gas Producers," a paper presented at the Second Annual Rocky Mountain Mineral Law Institute, Boulder, Colorado, August 2–4, 1956, and published in *Proceedings, q.v.,* 199.

The important decisions regarding independent producers are reviewed each year in the *Annual Report* of the Mineral Law Section of the American Bar Association. Also the Mineral Law and Public Utilities sections publish the speeches which are presented before them at each annual meeting. Since 1954 important speeches regarding control of independent producers have been given before each section. Decisions of importance to independent producers are reported monthly, with comments, in the *Oil and Gas Reporter* which is published by the Southwestern Legal Foundation of Dallas, Texas.

And see Federal Power Commission, *General Rules and Regulations, Including Rules of Practice and Procedure,* 18 CFR sec. 154 (1948).

[67] This opinion is not shared by John A. Crichton who believes that the Natural Gas Act was never intended to include producers.

For recent enunciations of this aim by the Supreme Court, see the Catco decision, *Atlantic Refining Co.* v. *Public Service Comm. of N.Y.,* 360 U.S. 378, 391, 79 Sup. Ct. 1246, 1255 3 L.Ed. 2nd 1312, 1320, 10 O.& G.R. 1021 (1959). See also *Federal Power Commission* v. *Hope Natural Gas Co.,* 320 U.S. at 610 (1944); *Phillips Petroleum Company* v. *Wisconsin,* 347 U.S. 672, 685, 3 O.& G.R. 745, 752 (1954).

[68] Federal Power Commission Orders No. 174–B, Order 187, Order 190, Order 198.

dependent producer bookkeeping, although pipe-line companies are bound by a specified system of accounts.

The complete nature of the jurisdiction over field sales is borne out by decisions which hold that certificates of public convenience and necessity are required for sales in interstate commerce for resale made at the outlet of processing plants,[69] at the outlet of gathering systems,[70] at individual well separators,[71] at the Christmas tree of a well,[72] inside the well bore,[73] and of casinghead gas to a processor.[74] Jurisdiction attaches to royalty interest gas sold in interstate commerce,[75] to a non-operator's share of gas from a unit marketed on a day-by-day basis by the operator in accordance with the terms of the operating agreement even though such nonoperator's gas is sold under operator's gas purchase contract to which the non-operator is not a party,[76] and to all of the stream of gas from a well if any part of the stream is subject to a jurisdictional sale.[77]

Not all sales made in the field are jurisdictional. As discussed above, the sale of a property to a natural gas company is nonjurisdictional from the seller's standpoint. Sales which are currently non-

---

[69] See the Phillips case cited above in footnote 66.

[70] *J. M. Huber Corp.* v. *FPC,* 236 F 2(d) 550, 6 O.& G.R. 519 (3rd Cir., 1956).

[71] *Deep South Oil Company of Texas* v. *FPC,* 247 F 2(d) 882, 7 O.& G.R. 1539 (5th Cir., 1957); *Humble Oil & Refining Co.* v. *FPC,* 247 F 2(d) 903 7 O.& G.R. 1561 (5th Cir., 1957). cert. den. 355 U.S. 930, 78 Sup.Ct. 410, 2 L.Ed. 2nd 413, 8 O.& G.R. 834 (1958); *Shell Oil Company* v. *FPC,* 247 F 2(d) 900, 7 O.& G.R. 1562 (5th Cir., 1957), cert den. 355 U.S. 930, 78 Sup.Ct. 410, 2 L.Ed. 2nd 413, 8 O.& G.R. 844 (1958); *Continental Oil Co.* v. *FPC,* 247 F 2(d) 904, 7 O.& G.R. 1534 (5th Cir., 1957).

[72] *Saturn Oil & Gas Company, Inc.* v. *FPC,* 250 F 2(d) 61, 8 O.& G.R. 365 (10th Cir., 1957), cert. den. 355 U.S. 956, 2 L.Ed. 2nd 532, 78 Sup.Ct. 542, 8 O.& G.R. 843 (1958).

[73] *Continental Oil Company* v. *FPC,* 266 F 2(d) 208, 10 O.& G.R. 601 (5th Cir., 1959), cert. den. 361 U.S. 827, 11 O.& G.R. 305 (1959).

[74] *Shell Oil Co.* v. *FPC,* F. 2(d) 900, 7 O.& G.R. 1562 (5th Cir., 1957); *Continental Oil Co.* v. *FPC,* 247 F 2(d) 904, 7 O.& G.R. 1534 (5th Cir., 1957).

[75] *In the Matters of Northern Natural Producing Company, et al.,* —— FPC ——, 6 O.& G.R. 538 (1956), letter of August 30, 1956, in Docket Nos. G–10,001 and 10,184.

[76] *In the Matters of Dixie Pipeline Company, et al.,* 14 PFC 106, 4 O.& G.R. 1837 (1955); *In the Matter of Nelson Bunker Hunt Trust,* 16 FPC 831, 5 O.& G.R. 1412 (1956); *Sun Oil Company* v. *Federal Power Commission,* 256 F 2(d) 233, 9 O.& G.R. 422 (5th Cir., 1958).

[77] *In the Matters of Deep South Oil Company of Texas, et al.,* 14 FPC 83, 4 O.& G.R. 1815 (1955), affirmed *Deep South Oil Co.* v. *FPC,* 247 F 2(a) 882, 888, 7 O.& G.R. 1539 (5th Cir., 1957).

jurisdictional from both buyer's and seller's standpoints are the sale in intrastate commerce and the non-resale type of sale. If the gas involved is produced and consumed within a single state, sales prior to consumption are sales in intrastate commerce. The nonjurisdictional status of such sales could be changed by amendment of the act or by court interpretation based on the effect of intrastate commerce rates upon interstate commerce rates.[78] If the gas involved is purchased at the well by the ultimate consumer, the sale is nonjurisdictional even though the gas moves in interstate commerce because no resale is involved. Illustrative of the act as it has been applied to this type of sale is the Consolidated Edison proceeding which involved the electricity-generating company's purchases in the field for its own use. The Federal Power Commission refused to permit the transportation of such gas from field to power plant by an interstate pipe line as being against the public interest and was upheld by the United States Supreme Court.[79] In some instances the purchaser in a non-resale sale is an interstate pipe line buying gas to be used for compressor fuel. In 1961 such sales were ruled jurisdictional on the basis of the predominantly interstate commerce nature of the commingled stream of gas.[80]

The Natural Gas Act's injunction against the termination of any jurisdictional service without commission approval applies to field sales by independent producers also. For purposes of this rule the independent producer's sales of natural gas are considered a utility service rather than the sale of a commodity. Sales may not be discontinued because the underlying gas purchase contract provides for termination if the sales are subjected to Federal Power Commission jurisdiction,[81] nor because the term of the gas purchase contract has

[78] *Shreveport Rate Cases,* 234 U.S. 342, 354–55 (1914).

[79] *Consolidated Edison Co. of N.Y. v. Federal Power Commission,* 365 U.S. 1, 13 O.& G.R. 861 (1961). The proceedings before the Federal Power Commission are styled *In the Matters of Transcontinental Gas Pipeline Company et al.,* 21 FPC 138, 399, 9 O.& G.R. 1199 (1959).

[80] See *In the Matters of Oklahoma Natural Gas Company, et al.,* 23 FPC 291, 23 FPC 531, 11 O.& G.R. 1046 (1960). Cf. *State of North Dakota Public Service Commission v. Federal Power Commission,* 247 F 2(d) 173 (8th Cir., 1957). Jurisdiction was declared in the matters of *Lo-Vaca Gathering Company, et al.,* 26 FPC ——, 15 O.& G.R. 577 (1961).

[81] *In the Matters of Argo Oil Corporation, et al.,* 15 FPC 601, 1221, 5 O.& G.R. 824 (1956); *J. M. Huber v. Federal Power Commission,* 362 F 2(d) 550, 6 O.& G.R. 519 (3rd Cir., 1956), cert. den. 352 U.S. 971, 6 O.& G.R. 1407 (1957).

expired.[82] Although the commission has the power to issue certificates for a limited term, it is not required to do so, and may issue certificates unlimited in time even though the applicant requested a certificate which would terminate in accordance with the underlying gas purchase contract.[83] As a matter of practice all certificates issued to independent producers by the Federal Power Commission are unlimited as to duration. Termination requires a future petition by independent producer under Section 7(b) of the act and approval by the Federal Power Commission. The Federal Power Commission has permitted termination of service under a showing that the public interest will not be adversely affected even in cases where the gas would be resold at higher prices in intrastate commerce[84] and where the gas would be resold in interstate commerce.[85] The commission has denied termination where the gas would be shifted from one interstate commerce buyer to another at higher prices.[86]

Initial Prices

In view of the great demand for gas supply, certificate applications by independent producers which involve the most recently executed gas purchase contracts also involve the highest field prices. Under its powers to condition certificates, the commission can, and does, condition initial prices to lower levels. However, in 1960, there was no certainty as to the standard to be used in conditioning such initial

---

[82] See *Continental Oil Company and Charles B. Wrightsman* v. *United Gas Pipe Line Co.*, No. 18494 in the Fifth Circuit Court of Appeals. In this yet undecided proceeding, proponent producers seek review of a district court order which refused to require the pipe line to purchase gas from the producers at increased rates unilaterally filed by the producers at the end of the term of the gas purchase contract. The pipe line has refused to purchase at the higher rate, and the producers may not lawfully sell to anyone else. This same proceeding is before the Federal Power Commission in applications to abandon sales in Docket Nos. CI 60–131, –132 and CI 60–126.

[83] *Sunray-Midcontinent Oil Co.* v. *Federal Power Commission*, 364 U.S. 137, 18 O.& G.R. 804 (1960). *Sun Oil* v. *Federal Power Commission*, 364 U.S. 170, 12 O.& G.R. 799 (1960).

[84] *In the Matter of the Atlantic Refining Company*, 16 FPC 1010, 6 O.& G.R. 733 (1956); *In the Matter of P. R. Rutherford, et al.*, 23 FPC 357, 11 O.& G.R. 1068 (1960).

[85] *In the Matters of Phillips Petroleum Company, et al.*, 24 FPC 897, 13 O.& G.R. 133 (Order of October 21, 1960, in Docket Nos. G–18533, *et al*).

[86] *In the Matters of Dixie Pipe Line Company, et al.*, 14 FPC 196, 4 O.& R.G. 1837 (1955).
··

rates. The Supreme Court has remanded, for further proceedings regarding initial price, two cases in which initial prices of 21.4[87] and 21.5¢/MCF[88] (excluding tax reimbursement) were certificated without condition for field sales of natural gas in South Louisiana. In the former case the Court said that where a proposed initial price "is not in keeping with the public interest because it is out of line or because its approval might result in triggering of general price rises or an increase in the applicant's existing rates by reason of 'favored nation's clauses' or otherwise, the Commission in the exercise of its discretion might attach such conditions as it believes necessary."

The Ninth Circuit Court of Appeals recently remanded[89] another South Louisiana gas sales certificate involving an initial price of 21.5¢/MCF because the Commission, in deciding to not condition the 21.5¢ price, relied on other South Louisiana initial prices which, though certificated, were under appeal at the time. The Commission is now faced with the difficult problem of reconciling the "hold-the-line" rule of CATCO,[90] the nonreliance on appealed certificate prices of the Ninth Circuit,[91] and, possibly, the cost-of-service as a point of departure rule of the City of Detroit case[92] in its handling of initial prices. The courts have recognized that under a Section 7 certificate proceeding the question is whether certificating the initial rate is "in the public interest," rather than whether the initial rate is "fair and reasonable." The decisions state that the commission is not bound to any particular formula under the act in judging whether an initial rate is consonant with the public interest. The statutory "fair and reasonable" standard applies in Section 4 and 5 rate proceedings. The beginning price in a new gas purchase contract filed by a nonoperating

[87] *Atlantic Refining Co.* v. *Public Service Commission of New York,* 360 U.S. 378, 10 O.& G.R. 1021 (1959).

[88] *United Gas Improvement Company, et al.* v. *Federal Power Commission, et al.,* 361 U.S. 195, 11 O.& G.R. 423 (1959), affirming *United Gas Improvement Company, et al.* v. *Federal Power Commission,* 69 F 2(d) 865, 11 O.& G.R. 418 (3rd Cir., 1959).

[89] *United Gas Improvement Company* v. *Federal Power Commission,* 283 F 2(d) 817, 13 O.& G.R. 555 (9th Cir., 1960).

[90] *Atlantic Refining Co.* v. *Public Service Commission of New York,* 360 U.S. 378, 10 O.& G.R. 1021 (1959).

[91] *United Gas Improvement Company* v. *Federal Power Commission,* 283 F 2(d) 817, 13 O.& G.R. 555 (9th Cir., 1960).

[92] See footnote 59, above.

owner of working interest is not an initial price, where prior deliveries were made by operator on behalf of non-operator.[93] Further, the commission may not suspend an initial rate.[94]

In September 1960 the Federal Power Commission promulgated *area prices*[95] at or below which it will issue unconditioned certificates for field sales. One of the reasons for the adoption of area prices as an answer to the field pricing problem was to avoid the complications inherent in applying cost-of-service pricing to gas producers. The use of area prices should also make it possible to reduce the large backlog of undecided producer certificate and rate cases on file with the Federal Power Commission.

[93] *Sun Oil* v. *Federal Power Commission,* 281 F 2(d) 275, 12 O.& G.R. 1207 (5th Cir., 1960, opinion issued July 22, 1960, in No. 17432).

[94] *Phillips Petroleum Company* v. *Federal Power Commission,* 227 F 2(d) 470, 5 O.& G.R 300 (10th Cir., 1955).

[95] *Statement of General Policy No. 61–1* entitled "Establishment of Price Standards to Be Applied in Determining the Acceptability of Initial Price Proposals and Increased Rate Filings by Independent Producers of Natural Gas," issued September 28, 1960, as amended, see 12 O.& G.R. 1227, 14 O.& G.R. 209, 14 O.& G.R. 211, 15 O.& G.R. 413. The prices promulgated in Statement No. 61–1 are set forth in Table 17, below. See David T. Searles, "Decision of Federal Power Commission in Phillips Petroleum Case," a paper presented at the Twelfth Annual Institute on Oil and Gas Law and Taxation, Dallas, Texas, February 8–10, 1961, and published in *Proceedings, q.v.,* 1. Statement 61–1 was issued without notice, but it has been upheld on review. *State of Wisconsin, et al.* v. *Federal Power Commission,* 292 F 2(d) 735 (D.C. Cir., 1961), 15 O.& G.R. 209.

In September, 1962, two general area price hearings were under way covering the Permian Basin of Texas and South Louisiana to develop a record from which an area price, which will give the consumer gas at the lowest price consistent with continued exploration for and development of reserves, can be established. See Oliver L. Stone, "Federal Power Commission Developments of Significance to Independent Producers of Natural Gas," a paper presented at the Thirteenth Annual Institute on Oil and Gas Law and Taxation, Dallas, Texas, February 14–16, 1962, and published in *Proceedings, q.v.,* 1. Illustrative of the broad economic data presented at the area price hearings are the following articles: Ira H. Cram, "Introduction to the Problem of Developing Adequate Supplies of Natural Gas," in *Economics of the Gas Industry, q.v.,* I,1; Netschert, "Economic Aspects of Natural Gas Supply," *Economics of the Gas Industry, q.v.,* I, 27. Mr. Cram concludes that higher prices are necessary to engender the discovery of reserves required by future demand, while Mr. Netschert believes that future gas supply will be adequate if present prices are maintained.

Joseph C. Swidler, "The Natural Gas Act and Free Enterprise," a paper presented before the 41st Annual Meeting of the American Petroleum Institute, Chicago, Illinois, November 15, 1961, describes the propriety and advantages of area pricing from the administrative point of view.

301

Price Increases

The area price order also sets forth prices at which rate increases will be allowed to independent producers without suspension. Rate increases by independent producers are subject to the procedures of Section 4 of the act which involves thirty days' notice, hearing, five months' suspension, and collection of the increase under bond with possible refunds upon final determination of the fairness and reasonableness of the proposed increase. The primary problem involved in the control of independent producer rate increases under the Natural Gas Act has been whether such rate increases are to be judged by a cost-of-service standard or by some other standard such as area prices.[96]

The courts have ruled that the commission is not bound by state issued minimum price orders in its handling of independent producer price increases[97] and that the commission may properly hold that no price increase can be held to be fair and reasonable on a record which contains no cost-of-service data.[98] In its use of gas purchase contracts as the filed tariff, the commission must interpret the price provisions to determine if a proper filing has been made; however, such interpretation is not a matter of administrative expertness, and the reviewing court may freely interject its own judgment as to the proper contractual interpretation.[99] All rate increase filings will be judged by the same standards, if properly filed, regardless of whether such increase is based on a favored nation's clause, a price redetermina-

[96] See "Are 'Conventional Methods' Necessary in Natural Gas Rate Regulation?" *Cornell Law Quarterly*, Vol. XLI, No. 3 (Spring, 1956), 438.

[97] *Natural Gas Pipeline Company* v. *Panoma Corporation, et al.*, 349 U.S. 44, 4 O.& G.R. 905 (1955) ; *Cities Service Gas Company* v. *State Corporation of Kansas, et al.*, 355 U.S. 399, 8 O.& G.R. 673 (1958) ; *Michigan Wisconsin Pipe Line Company* v. *Corporation Commission of Oklahoma, et al.*, 355 U.S. 423, 9 O.& G.R. 417 (1958).

[98] *Bel Oil Corporation* v. *Federal Power Commission*, 255 F 2(d) 548, 9 O.& G.R. 319 (5th Cir., 1958), cert. den. 358 U.S. 804 (1958) ; *Associated Oil & Gas Company* v. *Federal Power Commission*, 255 F 2(d) 555, 9 O.& G.R. 407 (5th Cir., 1958) ; *Gulf Oil Corporation* v. *Federal Power Commission*, 255 F 2(d) 556, 9 O.& G.R. (5th Cir., 1958); *Sun Oil Company, et al.* v. *Federal Power Commission*, 255 F 2(d) 557, 9 O.& G.R. 420 (5th Cir., 1958). But see *Forest Oil Corporation, et al.* v. *Federal Power Commission*, 263 F 2(d) 623, 10 O.& G.R. 242 (5th Cir., 1959), where the court said that the Federal Power Commission, in ruling on independent producer rate increases, need not require the use of a conventional rate base method of rate making.

[99] *Texas Gas Transmission Corporation, et al.* v. *Shell Oil Company*, 363 U.S. 263, 12 O.& G.R. 828 (1960).

tion provision, or a fixed-step increase proviso of the gas purchase contract.

The independent producer rate increase decisions to January 1, 1961 by the Federal Power Commission may be grouped as follows:

(1) Cases involving low prices and low volumes in which no cost-of-service data have been placed to record and in which the price increase has been allowed.[100]

(2) Cases wherein cost-of-service data have been introduced and the increase allowed if the evidence is adequate or the increase disallowed if the evidence is inadequate.[101]

(3) Cases where no cost data have been introduced into the record but the increase allowed as a part of a settlement under which the indeterminate pricing clauses (favored nation's and price redetermination clauses) have been deleted from the gas purchase contracts.[102]

(4) Cases wherein cost data have been introduced into the record and the price increases allowed as a part of a settlement wherein

[100] *In the Matter of Pan American Petroleum Corp.,* 19 FPC 463, 8 O.& G.R. 981 (Order of April 4, 1958, in Docket No. G–8549); *In the Matters of Shamrock Oil and Gas Corporation,* 22 FPC 882, 11 O.& G.R. 915 (1959), which FPC ruling has been appealed, *Minneapolis Gas Co.* v. *Federal Power Commission,* Court of Appeals for the District of Columbia, No. 15,452.

[101] Increase granted: *In the Matter of Wunderlich Development Co.,* 15 FPC 690, 5 O.& G.R. 1090 (1956); *In the Matter of Davidor and Davidor,* 15 FPC 1236, 5 O.& G.R. 1081 (1956); *In the Matter of Christie, Mitchell & Mitchell,* 15 FPC 751, 6 O.& G.R. 385 (1956); *In the Matters of William Negley, et al.,* 17 FPC 550, 7 O.& G.R. 521 (1957); *In the Matter of Bayview Oil Co.,* 21 FPC 405 (1959); *In the Matter of Sinclair Oil Co.,* 22 FPC 53 (1959); *In the Matter of Harper Oil Company,* 17 FPC 803, 7 O.& G.R. 664 (1957); *In the Matter of Hassie Hunt Trust,* 21 FPC 27 (1959); *In the Matter of Monsanto Chemical Company,* 22 FPC 1077 (1959).

Increase disallowed: *In the Matter of H. L. Hunt,* 19 FPC 748 (Order of May 19, 1958, in Docket No. G–9553); *In the Matter of United Carbon Company,* opinion of presiding examiner of August 5, 1957, in Docket No. G–9572, reversed and remanded by the Federal Power Commission for further proceedings, 19 FPC 242 (Order of February 19, 1958, in Docket No. G–9572).

[102] *In the Matter of Jake L. Hamon, et al.,* 23 FPC 471, 11 O.& G.R. 906 (1960); *In the Matters of Champlin Oil & Refining Co., et al.,* 23 FPC 861, 12 O.& G.R. 776 (1960).

This type of settlement has been recognized as a standard in the commission's Second Amendment to *Statement of General Policy No. 61–1* (issued December 20, 1960), which amends the nationwide area price order to provide for settlements of the type being discussed here.

indeterminate clauses are deleted from the gas purchase contract, additional gas is dedicated to the jurisdictional market and the settlement price is below the level originally proposed in the Section 4 proceeding.[103]

The Phillips rate case,[104] which constitutes the rate determination portion of the "grandfather" Phillips jurisdictional proceeding under which independent producers were first subjected to Federal Power Commission jurisdiction, involved a Section 5 company-wide rate investigation consolidated with numerous Section 4 applications for price increases which had been suspended. Lengthy hearings were

---

[103] *In the Matters of Union Oil Company of California and Louisiana Land and Exploration Company*, 23 FPC 73, 11 O.& G.R. 929 (1960).

In the categories of rate decisions under consideration here, it should also be noted that in a number of instances the proposed increase has been disallowed by the Federal Power Commission for the failure to introduce cost-of-service data in the record. See *In the Matter of Cities Service Gas Company*, 14 FPC 134, 5 O.& G.R. 428 (Order of November 28, 1955, in Docket No. G–2569) ; *In the Matters of Continental Oil Company, et al.*, 15 FPC 735, 5 O.& G.R. 1409 (Order of June 14, 1956, in Docket No. G–6503) ; *In the Matter of Sun Oil Company*, 17 FPC 501, 6 O.& G.R. 1412 (Order of February 6, 1957, in Docket No. G–8288) ; *In the Matter of Crow Drilling Company*, 17 FPC 226, 7 O.& G.R. 131 (Order of February 6, 1957, in Docket No. G–6622) ; *In the Matter of Forest Oil Corporation*, 17 FPC 586, 7 O.& G.R. 659 (Order of February 11, 1957, in Docket No. G–5510) ; *In the Matter of H. F. Sears*, 18 FPC 244, 7 O.& G.R. 1147 (Order of September 3, 1957, in Docket No. G–6502). The right of the Federal Power Commission to deny rate increase where no cost-of-service data are introduced was affirmed in *Bel Oil Corporation* v. *Federal Power Commission*, 255 F 2(d) 548, 9 O.& G.R. 319 (5th Cir., 1958), cert. den. 358 U.S. 804 (1958) ; *Forest Oil Corporation, et al.* v. *Federal Power Commission*, 263 F 2(d) 623, 10 O.& R.G. 242 (5th Cir., 1959).

[104] *In the Matters of Phillips Petroleum Company*, 24 FPC 537, 13 O.& G.R. 343 (Opinion No. 338 issued September 28, 1960, in Docket Nos. G–1148, *et al.*) 24 FPC 1008 ; affirmed *State of Wisconsin, et al.* v. *Federal Power Commission, et al.*, 303 F 2(d) 380 (D.C. Cir., 1961), cert. granted 369 U.S. 870 (1962). See Searles, "Decision of Federal Power Commission in Phillips Petroleum Company Case."

The Commission has also terminated Section 5 (a) proceedings against independent producers in three cases in which the producers prices were shown to be justified on a cost basis. *In the Matter of Gillring Oil Co.*, 20 FPC 770 (1958) ; *In the Matter of Ralph E. Fair, et al.*, 20 FPC 810 (1958) ; *In the Matter of C. V. Lyman*, 22 FPC 557 (1959).

For a comprehensive commentary on the trial examiner's decision in this case, see Samuel Joseph, "Background and Analysis of Trial Exaniner's Decision in Phillips Case," a paper presented at the Eleventh Annual Institute on Oil and Gas Law and Taxation, Dallas, Texas, February 10–12, 1960, and published in *Proceedings, q.v.*, 1.

304

carried out in which many intervenors participated and at which a record was developed containing a company-wide cost-of-service study of Phillips' jurisdictional operations. The studies were aimed at applying the cost-of-service formula to a major independent producer of natural gas. Using the cost-of-service standard, the trial examiner found that Phillips' cost-of-service was less than its revenues and ordered a rate increase under a plan which would have established uniform rates for the company without regard to the geographical area in which the gas was sold. In its decision the commission first stated that, based on its experience of regulating independent producer rates for five years, the "traditional original cost, prudent investment rate base method of regulating utilities is not a sensible, or even a workable method of fixing the rates of independent producers of natural gas," and simultaneously issued a policy statement declaring area prices to control independent producer rates.[105] Since a complete cost-of-service record was before it, the commission, nevertheless, proceeded to analyze Phillips' rates against traditional cost-of-service standards and found that the rates did not provide enough revenue to meet Phillips' cost-of-service. Rather than order rate increases, in light of its promulgation of area prices, the commission dismissed the Section 5 investigation and allowed the Section 4 proposed rate increase to become effective without refund.

In applying the cost-of-service standards to Phillips' operations, the commission found that, although Phillips is an independent producer and the largest seller of natural gas in the United States, natural gas revenues constituted only 6 per cent of Phillips' total income in the test year of 1954. It approved the use of 1954 as a representative test year. The commission declared that, in calculating operating expenses, it is not necessary that part of the expenses be allocated to "excess" reserves discovered. It allowed increases in the cost of gas Phillips purchased under gas purchase contracts with other companies which automatically share, through a percentage arrangement, in any rate increases to Phillips. In the calculation of income tax, benefits to Phillips growing out of depletion allowance and out of the expensing of intangible drilling costs were ordered passed on to the consumer. The commission agreed with Phillips in allowing a low-

[105] See footnote 95 on page 301.

interest adjustment in the calculation of taxes. Phillips was allowed to keep the benefits arising from its taking rapid amortization under the income tax laws.

The commission allocated producing costs between jurisdictional gas and nonjurisdictional oil on leases where both are produced by the use of a relative cost method. In this method the cost of producing gas is obtained from other leases in which gas only is produced and the cost of producing oil is obtained from other leases in which oil only is produced. These costs are then applied to the actual volumes of gas and oil produced on the joint leases and the allocation based on the values obtained. It is not necessary to make an adjustment because of the fact that gas is used in lifting oil. The commission decided to allocate exploration costs between jurisdictional gas and nonjurisdictional oil on the basis of a Btu allocation factor times four. The result was that the cost of finding one barrel of oil was twenty-four times the cost of finding one MCF of gas. A proper adjustment was made for reserves which had been sold in place to the Pacific Northwest Gas Pipeline Company. Using a straight Btu factor, the commission allocated between jurisdictional natural gas and nonjurisdictional extracted liquids. This allocation applies to expenses between the well and the gasoline plant. The commission found that Phillips' gasoline plant operations were nonjurisdictional.

In determining Phillips' rate base, the commission approved the use of a year-end balance instead of an average balance over the year. An 11 per cent rate of return on the depreciated rate base was allowed to Phillips by the commission. This was made up of a 12 per cent return on equity capital and a cost-of-money return on debt. Phillips' capitalization was 11.6 per cent debt and 88.4 per cent common equity. The rate of return was set to include an allowance to promote the continued exploration for the production of gas in addition to the usual other aims of making available sufficient money to attract capital to the enterprise. Phillips' cost-of-service was found to be 11.309¢/MCF which was greater than Phillips' average rate for the sale of gas to its customers.

FEDERAL CONTROL UNDER OTHER STATUTES

The natural gas industry in the United States is also subject to direct federal control under the Public Utility Holding Company Act of 1935,[106] the Securities Act of 1933,[107] and the Securities Exchange Act of 1934.[108] Since practically all security issues by natural gas companies are sold to the public, such securities are issued in accordance with the provisions of the Securities Act and the Securities Exchange Act. The provisions of these acts, designed to protect the purchasing public, provide for full business disclosures in a prospectus available to the public and for the filing of substantial supporting data with the Securities Exchange Commission. The Public Utility Holding Company Act of 1935 vested broad powers in the Securities Exchange Commission to carry out the primary purpose of reducing the holding company systems in the natural gas and electricity industries through national action to such size that the states could regulate them effectively and the secondary objective of policing the financial and operating aspects of holding company systems so as to strengthen state regulation. A reduction in the size of holding company systems now has been largely completed. Holding company regulation brought about the elimination of all but one of the four large holding companies of 1935 from the natural gas holding company field, the reduction of the remaining large company to an integrated natural gas system, the elimination of oil companies as public utility holding companies, the divorcement of major electric power and natural gas systems, and an end to the drift toward the concentration of control in superholding companies.

Articles of particular interest regarding the ratable taking of gas are Lee Cameron, "Effect of Gas Proration on Recent Special Orders," *Journal of Petroleum Technology,* Vol. XII, No. 3 (March, 1960), 22; Dee Kelly, "Gas Proration and Ratable Taking in Texas," *Texas Bar Journal,* Vol. XIX, No. 11 (December, 1956), 763; and Robert McGinnis, "The Texas Common Purchaser Statute as Related to Natural Gas," a paper presented before the Mineral Law Section of the State

---

[106] 49 Stat. 803 (1935), 15 U.S.C. sec. 79. See Huitt, "Natural Gas Regulation Under the Holding Company Act," *Law and Contemporary Problems,* Vol. XIX, No. 3 (Summer, 1954), 455; Barnes, *The Economics of Public Utility Regulation,* 628ff.; Clemens, *Economics and Public Utilities,* 486ff.

[107] 48 Stat. 74 (1933).

[108] 48 Stat. 881 (1934).

See, regarding the Securities Acts, Barnes, *The Economics of Public Utility Regulation,* 683ff.; and Clemens, *Economics and Public Utilities,* 464ff.

Bar of Texas, July 4, 1958, and later published in the *Texas Bar Journal,* Vol. XXI, No. 8 (September, 1958), 521.

Recent decisions of interest regarding the setting of allowables and ratability include: *In Re Conservation and Prevention of Waste of Crude Petroleum and Natural Gas in the Blue Basin Field, Wharton County, Texas,* Railroad Commission of Texas, Oil and Gas Docket No. 128, No. 3–32,805, January 30, 1956, 5 O.& G.R. 1100, wherein field rules were established for the determining of individual well allowables by multiplying actual production by a promulgated set of percentages; *In the Matter of Promulgation and Establishment of Field Rules to Govern Operations in the "J" Sands of the Adena Field, Morgan County, Colorado,* Colorado Oil and Gas Commission, Cause No. 26, Order No. 26–30, July 31, 1956, 6 O.& G.R. 511, where field rules were established prorating oil production between wells on the basis of reserves originally in place; *Railroad Commission of Texas and The Atlantic Refining Company* v. *Permian Basin Pipeline Company,* 302 S.W. 2(d) 238 (Tex.Civ.App., 1957), where the court upheld a Texas Railroad Commission order requiring a pipe line to purchase gas ratably from a field even though the pipe line's gas purchase contracts negated the right to purchase ratably, 7 O.& G.R. 525 and 6 O.& G.R. 898, 1409; *Murray, et al.* v. *R&M Well Servicing & Drilling Company, et al.,* 297 S.W. 2(d) 225 (Tex.Civ.App., 1956, writ ref.) upholding limited production for a gas cap well under statewide Rule 6(b), 7 O.& G.R. 357; *Special Order Pertaining to the Matter of Requiring Purchase and Take of Gas in the Emperor (Devonian) and Emperor (Ellenburger) Field, Winkler County, Texas,* Railroad Commission of Texas, Oil and Gas Docket No. 126, No. 8–39,851, February 24, 1959, 10 O.& G.R. 239, pipe-line purchaser ordered to take gas legally tendered to it for purchase in conformity with the proration schedule allowables issued by the Railroad Commission; *Deep South Oil Company of Texas* v. *Texas Gas Corporation,* 328 S.W. 2(d) 987 (Tex.Civ.App., 1959, writ ref.), 12 O.& G.R. 597, where it was held that, in the absence of field rules, ratability is not based on 25 per cent of each well's potential capacity.

13

THE GAS PURCHASE CONTRACT[1]

by John C. Jacobs

THE BULK of gas marketed is purchased in the field under contracts between pipe-line buyers and producer sellers. Some additional gas is purchased from pipe-line companies, some is produced into pipe lines from pipe-line-owned properties, and some is sold by independent producers directly to the consumer. The contract for the sale of gas in the field between the producer and the pipe line is a legal document called a *gas purchase contract*. Operating under the great freedom of contract which exists in our Anglo-Saxon-derived common law tradition, the gas purchase contract has developed as an equitable and comparatively simple solution to the complicated problem of buying and selling gas. Complications grow out of the fact that the contract must reflect the rights and duties of many parties other than buyer and seller. Such other parties include the buyer's bond holders, the buyer's customers, the federal regulatory authority, the seller's banker, the seller's mineral property lessor, and the state regulatory authorities. A second complicating factor is that gas is sold for a term of twenty years. This is true of no other commodity, but is necessary in the natural gas industry to provide the long-term reserves required by the Federal Power Commission and necessary to the financing of the interstate pipe lines.

During the history of the natural gas industry, the gas purchase contract has developed from a short-term contract in which the seller undertook the legal liability of supplying the buyer's require-

[1] This chapter contains no references to authorities. The reader is referred to the extensive footnotes of Chapter 12, above, and especially to footnote 66 of that chapter. Also see Wendell J. Doggett, "Marketing of Natural Gas Through Means Conventional and Unconventional," a paper presented at the Institute on the Economics of the Gas Industry, International Oil and Gas Education Center, Dallas, Texas, 1962.

ments to the modern, long-term, guaranteed annual payment contract in which deliveries are adjusted annually to maintain an agreed-upon life of the reserves dedicated under the contract. Under this latter contract the seller receives a minimum annual payment based upon the specified reserve life regardless of the actual volume of deliveries. The reserve life and minimum annual payment features satisfy the banking requirements of both buyer and seller, and cognizance is taken in the contract of the possible effect of state and federal regulation on the contractual provisions. The very comprehensive state and federal regulation of natural gas is described above in Chapter 12. State control goes to the completion and drilling of gas wells and to the volume of gas which may be taken from wells. Federal control under the Natural Gas Act goes to the right to commence or to terminate sales in interstate commerce for resale, and to the prices to be paid for gas sold under these conditions.

The contract discussed in the following paragraphs and included in this chapter is typical of those used in the Gulf Coast area to purchase natural gas produced from gas wells for interstate transport and sale. A similar form of contract is used in the purchase of casinghead gas; however, it provides that the casinghead gas will be taken as available. Availability of casinghead gas depends upon the oil well allowables assigned by the state regulatory authority. Writing the contract in this manner eliminates the flaring of casinghead gas, but the buyer loses the right to vary the volumes purchased to fit his market demand. Usually the price for casinghead gas is lower than the price of gas well gas, reflecting this loss in flexibility.

Fundamentally the parties to a gas purchase contract are the pipeline buyer and the gas well operator-seller. It is customary that all persons owning any part of the working interest of the mineral rights represented by the leases covered in the gas purchase contract join the contract as parties seller. It is not customary that royalty owners sign the gas purchase contract as sellers.

The contract begins with *recitals*—the so-called "whereas" clauses —stating that buyer has a pipe line and wishes to purchase gas and that seller owns gas-productive properties and wishes to sell gas. These clauses are followed by definitions in which basic contractual terms such as "year," "gas well gas," "MCF," and "seller's gas reserve" are defined.

310

Under "Scope of Agreement" there is specified, usually by a land description attached as Exhibit A (see page 336), the properties covered by the gas purchase contract. In many cases the properties covered by the contract will be limited to that depth at which exists the deepest presently known producing horizon. *Precedent conditions* include provisions for obtaining certificates from regulatory authorities as may be necessary and for the construction of such facilities as may be necessary to permit deliveries as contemplated by the contract. Usually these provisions provide that the contract may be terminated by either party if the regulatory authority permit has not been obtained or the construction of facilities completed within a specified period of time.

The seller customarily reserves the right to operate the leases free from any control by the buyer, the right to use gas produced on the property for such lease operation, the right to process the gas for the recovery of liquefiable hydrocarbons, the right to sell surplus gas not covered by the contract to others, and the right to pool and unitize leases covered by the contract with other leases.

Under the modern gas purchase contract the seller does not undertake a legal obligation to deliver a fixed amount of gas over the life of the contract. Instead, he dedicates a certain reserve of gas to the contract, and provision is made to adjust average deliveries over the life of the contract to maintain an agreed-upon reserve life. In the usual situation reserves are jointly determined by buyer and seller once each year or, in the case of disagreement, the determination is made by an arbitrator. This reserve is then divided by the number of days in the agreed-upon reserve life to determine the so-called "daily contract quantity." The *daily contract quantity* represents the average daily volume which the pipe-line buyer guarantees to take averaged over each year of the contract. In the late 1940's and early 1950's, the divisor was usually 10,000 days, which is the equivalent of approximately a twenty-seven-year reserve life. Competition for gas supply in the Gulf Coast area has reduced this reserve life to the point that, in 1960, most contracts used a divisor of 8,000, which represents the number of days in approximately twenty-two years; and some contracts were written with a divisor of 7,300, which represents the exact number of days for a twenty-year reserve life. The contract also provides that, if in any year the pipe line has taken and paid for a lesser volume of gas than the effective daily contract quantity times 365 days, the pipe line will make a payment at the end of the year to the seller representing the deficiency. The pipe-line buyer, however, reserves the right to take additional gas in succeeding years, without payment to the seller, in an amount equal to the deficiency paid for in the previous years. Such daily contract quantity provisions based on reserves are conditioned so that the daily contract quantity will never exceed a certain percentage of the seller's delivery capacity. *Seller's delivery capacity,* which is the ability of the seller's wells to deliver gas into the buyer's pipe line, is determined by periodic tests. Contracts provide that delivery capacity must be from 120 to 150 per cent of the daily contract quantity. This limitation to delivery capacity is necessary from the buyer's standpoint to protect him from being forced to pay for gas that is physically unavailable, to provide him with some flexibility in volume to cover failure in some other part of his gas supply, and to reflect in the field purchases the seasonal variations in the buyer's market for the gas being purchased in the field. For example, a daily contract quantity based upon the reserves type of field purchase essentially represents a 100 per cent load-factor purchase requirement on the pipe-line buyer. On the other hand, few pipe-line buyers sell into a market with a composite load factor of better than 70 per cent. The daily contract quantity is further conditioned not to exceed a quantity which, to a prudent operator, would represent good engineering practice and which will not exceed the volumes permitted to be withdrawn, the allowable, established by any regulatory authority having jurisdiction. Provisions may also be included to require buyer to take the allowable, if it is greater than the daily contract quantity. This provision is necessary to protect seller's property against drainage on a ratable basis.

The contract should specify the point and pressure at which the gas will be delivered by the seller to the buyer. The obligation to compress gas as wellhead pressures decrease over the life of the contract should be specified. Sometimes provision is made for a reduction in the buyer's line pressure at the end of ten years; and sometimes it is provided that either party may elect to compress, but, that if neither so elects, the contract will be terminated with regard to the low-pressure well.

Quality specifications are included in most contracts. These cover the Btu content of the gas, the maximum delivery temperature, and the maximum amount of such components as hydrogen sulfide, sulphur, oxygen, carbon dioxide, and water that may be contained in the gas. If the gas does not meet the standard specified in the contract, the seller may be required to make it meet the contract specifications. Some contracts provide that if the buyer elects not to take delivery of nonspecification gas the contract will terminate with regard to the wells or well producing the nonspecification gas. A usual provision states that if the gas falls below the minimum of 1,000 Btu's, the buyer may elect to discontinue buying gas, or may elect to continue buying with a reduction in prices to reflect the lower Btu content. Provisions are also included which describe in detail the measuring stations to be constructed, name the party at whose expense they are to be installed, and explain the method by which the charts and data from the measuring station are to be used in calculating the amount of gas passing through the station.

Prices in gas purchase contracts are expressed in cents per MCF of gas sold. The contract specifies the initial price at which gas deliveries will be commenced and also specifies the methods by which such initial price may be adjusted over the life of the contract. The provisions regarding price adjustments grow out of the pipe-line buyer's requirement of a twenty-year-term contract for financing purposes and the Federal Power Commission reserve life and availability standards. Both initial prices and price adjustments for gas sales covered by the Natural Gas Act are within the control of the Federal Power Commission. Table 17 sets forth the area prices recently promulgated by the Federal Power Commission.

The most widely used price adjustment clauses are the fixed-step escalation clause, the tax reimbursement clause, the two-party favored-nations clause, and the price redetermination clause. By its Order No. 242 of February 8, 1962, the Federal Power Commission "outlawed" price escalation clauses other than fixed-step clauses, tax reimbursement clauses, and certain price redetermination clauses. The *fixed-step escalation clause* is one which describes a definite cents-per-MCF increase at a definite date in the future. For example, contractual provision may be made for an increase of one cent per MCF every five years. In theory this type provision allows the pipe line to purchase gas at lower initial prices when its market is small and when its bonded indebtedness is at its maximum. Also, this type provision

313

TABLE 17

AREA PRICE LEVELS FOR NATURAL GAS SALES BY INDEPENDENT PRODUCERS

Area	Ceiling for Initial Rates Under New Contracts		Ceiling for Rate Increases Under Existing Contracts	
	@ 14.65 psia	@ 15.025 psia	@ 14.65 psia	@ 15.025 psia
Texas				
District 1	15.0	----	14.0	----
District 2	18.0	----	14.0	----
District 3	18.0	----	14.0	----
District 4	16.0	----	14.0	----
District 5	14.5	----	14.5	----
District 6	15.0	----	14.0	----
District 7b	14.5	----	11.5	----
District 7c	16.0	----	11.0	----
District 8	16.0	----	11.0	----
District 9	14.5	----	14.5	----
District 10	17.0	----	11.0	----
Louisiana				
Southern	20.72	21.25	13.7	14.0
Offshore	19.01	19.5	----	----
Northern	16.6	17.0	13.7	14.0
Mississippi	20.96*	21.5*	13.7	14.0
Oklahoma				
Panhandle Area	17.0	----	11.0	----
Carter-Knox	16.8	----	11.0	----
Other	15.0	----	11.0	----
Kansas	16.0	----	11.0	----
New Mexico				
Permian Basin	16.0	----	11.0	----
San Juan Basin	12.7	13.0	12.7	13.0
Colorado	14.6	15.0	12.7	13.0
Wyoming	15.0	----	12.7	13.0
West Virginia	26.8	28.0	23.9	25.0

(Source: Federal Power Commission, Statement of General Policy No. 61–1, as amended through August 30, 1962.)

* Plus tax reimbursement. All other prices include tax reimbursement except Louisiana Offshore where severance tax is not applicable.

gives the seller some protection against increased value of gas in the future which could reflect increased cost of finding replacement gas or a general inflation.

The *tax reimbursement clause* provides that seller shall be reimbursed for a portion (ranging from 50 to 100 per cent) of additional taxes levied on the severance of gas from the ground or on the production and gathering of natural gas. Again, the provision represents an effort to measure the future value of gas during the twenty-year term of the contract.

The name of the *favored nations clause* is borrowed from the phrase "most favored nation" in international law. This phrase refers to a treaty between two nations in which one promises to give the other as favorable treatment as the first extends to any other nation in the world. The so-called "two-party favored-nations clause" in gas purchase contracts is a provision wherein the pipe-line-buyer promises to increase the specified prices in the contract to equal those which the buyer pays to any other party from which is purchases gas within a designated area. Practically nonexistent today is the so-called "third-party favored-nations clause" in which the buyer promised to increase the contract price to the highest price paid by any buyer to any seller within a given area.

The *price redetermination clause* is one in which buyer and seller agree that at specified times during the life of the contract (usually every five years) the parties will determine the average of the three highest prices then being paid for gas of similar quality, volume, and delivery conditions in the specified area. This price becomes effective under the gas purchase contract for the next five-year period.

Only a few contracts include *price adjustment provisions* which would move the contract price up or down periodically with some index, such as the Bureau of Labor Standards Index of the Price of Wholesale Commodities. Also, a very few gas purchase contracts contain the so-called "spiral escalation clause" by which pipe-line-buyer agrees to increase the price under the gas purchase contract if the buyer's own rates at which it sells gas to its customers are increased. Finally, a few gas purchase contracts provide that the price will be increased in accordance with the Btu content (heating value) of the gas above the specified minimum of 1,000 Btu's per cubic foot.

During 1960, in face of the complete Federal Power Commission

315

control of price adjustments on gas moving in interstate commerce, a few contracts appeared containing price adjustment clauses of the following type:

> It is agreed by and between the parties hereto that for any reason whatsoever and at any time either party may file with or apply to the Federal Power Commission under any applicable provision of law, including, without limitation, the provisions of the Natural Gas Act, specifically Sections 4 and 5 thereof, or to any other body or court having jurisdiction, for an increase or decrease in the rates for gas sold and services rendered hereunder, and each party consents to the making of any such filing or application by the others; it being understood, however, that neither party waives any right to contest the level of such rates or basis upon which such rates shall be fixed by the Federal Power Commission or other body or Court having jurisdiction.

The price provisions may also include paragraphs by which the pipeline buyer will be reimbursed for the installation of facilities which would ordinarily be built by the seller, and paragraphs whereby the seller will be paid an additional amount for gathering, dehydrating, and compressing gas prior to delivery to the pipe-line buyer.

Gas purchase contracts are nearly always written on a twenty-year term which may be extended on a year-by-year basis by the parties thereto. This is true even though, under the Natural Gas Act, jurisdictional sales may not be discontinued without commission approval. This provision in the act means that the term of a jurisdictional gas purchase contract is completely within the hands of the Federal Power Commission.

Other contract provisions cover such things as force majeure, default, notice, warranty of title, method of billing and payment, and arbitration and may be examined in detail in the gas purchase contract which follows.

GAS PURCHASE CONTRACT[2]

THIS AGREEMENT, made and entered into as of the _____ day of _____, by and between _____ _____, hereinafter referred to as "Seller," and _____

[2] The form of the gas purchase contract printed here is the property of Texas Eastern Transmission Corporation and is reprinted by permission of that firm.

_____, hereinafter referred to as "Buyer,"

WHEREAS, Buyer owns and operates a natural gas transmission system, together with the facilities and properties used in connection with said pipe lines; and

WHEREAS, Seller owns and or controls oil, gas and mineral leaseholds and/or lands in the _____ Field in _____

_____, described in Exhibit A attached hereto, and made a part hereof, and Seller will have a supply of gas available from said field and is desirous of selling such gas to Buyer; and

WHEREAS, Buyer desires to purchase such gas from Seller for a portion of the requirements of its said system; and

WHEREAS, the parties hereto have agreed that, except where the context otherwise indicates another or different meaning or intent, the following terms are intended and used herein and shall be construed to have meanings as follows:

1. The term "day" shall mean a period of twenty-four (24) consecutive hours beginning and ending at eight o'clock a.m. Central Standard Time.

2. The term "month" shall mean a period beginning at eight o'clock a.m. on the 1st day of a calendar month and ending at eight o'clock a.m. on the 1st day of the next succeeding calendar month.

3. The term "year" shall mean a period of twelve (12) months beginning on the day on which the delivery of gas to Buyer is commenced hereunder or any anniversary of such date.

4. The term "gas" shall mean natural gas including both gas well gas and casinghead gas, and the residue gas therefrom, of merchantable quality as described in Article VIII hereof.

5. The term "MCF" shall mean one thousand (1,000) cubic feet.

6. The term "Seller's Gas Reserve" shall mean the estimated total quantity of economically recoverable gas which will be available for delivery to Buyer hereunder, and contained in the portions of the various gas and/or oil bearing formations or reservoirs which underlie the leaseholds and/or lands owned or controlled by Seller and covered by this Agreement on the date of any estimate or determination of Seller's Gas Reserve, plus the total quantity of gas theretofore delivered by Seller to Buyer under this contract.

7. The term "Seller's Delivery Capacity" shall mean the maximum quantity of gas which can be withdrawn (subject to any valid rules, orders and regulations of any State or Federal regulatory body) daily from the leaseholds and/or lands of Seller covered by this Agreement and which is available for delivery to Buyer at the point or points of delivery hereunder at the pressure provided for in Article V hereof.

317

8. The term "Daily Contract Quantity" shall mean the quantity of gas per day, averaged over each year, which Buyer is required, by the provisions of Paragraph 1 of Article III hereof, to purchase from Seller hereunder.

NOW, THEREFORE, in consideration of the premises and the mutual covenants and agreements herein contained, the parties hereto do hereby covenant and agree as follows:

I. *SCOPE OF AGREEMENT*

1. Subject to all of the terms, conditions and limitations hereinafter set forth, Seller agrees to sell and deliver or cause to be delivered to Buyer, and Buyer agrees to purchase and receive from Seller, gas, in the quantities hereinafter provided, which may be produced from the leaseholds and/or lands which Seller now owns or controls or may hereafter acquire or control in said _____ Field.

2. Each of the parties hereto agrees to proceed with due diligence in a good faith effort to obtain such Governmental authorizations and Certicates of Public Convenience and Necessity as may be necessary to enable it to perform its obligations under this Agreement. In the event either party should fail to obtain any such Governmental authorizations and Certificates of Public Convenience and Necessity upon terms and conditions satisfactory to it within _____ (__) days after the date of this Agreement, then either party shall have the right and option to terminate and cancel this Agreement by serving written notice upon the other party within the next suceeding thirty (30) days, whereupon both parties shall be relieved of any further liability hereunder. Upon receipt and acceptance by both Buyer and Seller of the necessary Governmental authorizations and Certificates of Public Convenience and Necessity referred to above, Seller agrees to commence and prosecute with due diligence the construction of a gathering system and all other necessary facilities to enable Seller to deliver at the point or points of delivery hereinafter specified, the quantities of gas contemplated by this Agreement and Buyer agrees to construct with due diligence any facilities necessary to enable Buyer to receive such gas at said point or points of delivery. The delivery of gas hereunder shall commence on the date on which such facilities of both Seller and Buyer are completed.

3. Seller has furnished Buyer with complete data regarding the productive status of each leasehold or tract of land described in said Exhibit A, and Seller agrees to keep Buyer informed as to any additions to or reductions of the leaseholds and/or lands covered by this Agreement and any substantial changes in the productive status of any such leaseholds and/or lands. Nothing herein shall preclude Seller from pooling or unitizing any of said lease-

318

holds and/or lands with those of others, provided that the interests of Seller in any such unit so formed shall be subject to this Agreement, nor shall Seller be precluded from abandoning any wells or leaseholds or permitting to lapse any leases or mineral rights which, in Seller's judgment, are deemed to be unproductive or without substantial value.

4. Seller has furnished Buyer with an estimate of Seller's Gas Reserve showing that such reserve amounts to _____ MCF of gas. Buyer has accepted such estimate and concurs therein. Not less than thirty (30) days prior to each anniversary date of the initial delivery of gas under this Agreement, Seller shall furnish Buyer with a written estimate of Seller's Gas Reserve as of such anniversary date. If Buyer fails to give Seller written notice that Buyer questions any such estimate within thirty (30) days after Buyer's receipt of same, it shall be conclusively presumed that Buyer concurs therein. If Buyer questions any such estimate by giving written notice to Seller within said thirty (30) day period, and Buyer and Seller are unable to agree upon the quantity of Seller's Gas Reserve, then the determination of the quantity of said reserve shall be submitted to and determined by arbitration in the manner provided in Article XVI hereof. Each such estimate or determination, as the case may be, shall be effective as of the anniversary date for which it is made or the date the same is concurred in by Buyer or determined by arbitration, whichever shall occur later, and shall remain in effect until superseded by a later estimate concurred in by Buyer or by a determination by arbitration.

5. Seller shall, with due diligence, develop the lands and leaseholds subject to this Agreement in a skillful and reasonably prudent manner to the end that Seller's Delivery Capacity shall be maintained at a volume not less than one hundred fifty per cent (150%) of the Daily Contract Quantity in effect from time to time under the provisions of Article III hereof, provided, however, that nothing herein shall be construed to require Seller to produce any well or wells in a manner which would not constitute good operating practice, nor shall Seller be obligated to drill additional wells or to deepen or rework any existing wells when it is not required to do so under the express or implied covenants of Seller's leases.

II. *RESERVATIONS OF SELLER*

Seller hereby expressly reserves the following rights with respect to the leaseholds and/or lands subject to this Agreement:

1. The right to use gas produced from said leaseholds and/or lands for the following purposes:

(a) For the development and operation of such leaseholds and/or lands;

(b) For delivery to the lessors in Seller's leases of the gas which such lessors are entitled to use under the terms of such leases; and

(c) For the operation of the facilities which Seller may install in order to deliver gas hereunder in accordance with the terms hereof.

2. The right to process the gas for the recovery of liquefiable hydrocarbons (including the right to use the gas for fuel in the operation of any gasoline plant in which the gas is processed); and the right to produce gas from wells on leaseholds and/or lands covered by this Agreement and return such gas to the formation from which it was produced or other formation under the leaseholds and/or lands covered by this Agreement after extracting, or causing to be extracted, therefrom any or all liquefiable hydrocarbons capable of extraction, absorption, or separation from said gas and contained in, and produced with, said gas, provided that in the exercise of such rights Seller does not in any way interfere with the delivery of gas to Buyer in the quantity and of the quality provided for herein.

3. The right to sell and deliver to parties other than Buyer the surplus gas which may be produced by Seller from the leaseholds and/or lands covered by this Agreement and which is available for sale to such other persons after compliance with the provisions of Paragraph 1 of Article III hereof.

III. *QUANTITY OF GAS*

1. (a) Subject to the provisions of this Agreement Seller agrees to sell and deliver to Buyer and Buyer agrees to take and pay for, or pay for if available and not taken, the Daily Contract Quantity hereinafter provided for in this Paragraph 1, averaged over each year of the term of this Agreement. Until increased or decreased pursuant to the provisions of this Paragraph 1, the Daily Contract Quantity hereunder shall be _____ MCF of gas, hereinafter called the "Original Daily Contract Quantity."

(b) If at any time during the term hereof the quantity of gas in Seller's Gas Reserve on the last previous anniversary of the date of initial delivery of gas under this Agreement, as shown by the estimate or determination thereof then in effect in accordance with the provisions of Paragraph 4 of Article I hereof, shall exceed or shall be less than a quantity equal to ten million (10,000,000) MCF of gas for each one thousand (1,000) MCF of the Daily Contract Quantity then in effect under the provisions of this Paragraph 1 of Article III, then the Daily Contract Quantity shall be increased or decreased, as the case may be, to a quantity of gas equal to one thousand (1,000) MCF for each ten million (10,000,000) MCF of gas so estimated or determined to be contained in Seller's Gas Reserve on such anniversary date of this Agreement; provided that

(i) if Seller's Delivery Capacity (unless reduced by unavoidable accident as hereinafter defined) is then less than one hundred fifty per cent (150%) of the Daily Contract Quantity thus determined, such Daily Contract Quantity shall be reduced to a quantity equivalent to two-thirds (⅔) of Seller's Delivery Capacity, and

(ii) the Daily Contract Quantity shall never exceed one hundred fifty per cent (150%) of the Original Daily Contract Quantity.

(c) If at any time the Daily Contract Quantity then in effect hereunder shall be the maximum Daily Contract Quantity permitted by the provisions of Subdivision (ii) of Subparagraph (b) of this Paragraph I of Article III, and the quantity of gas in Seller's Gas Reserve, as shown by the estimate or determination thereof then in effect in accordance with the provisions of Paragraph 4 of Article I hereof, shall exceed a quantity equal to ten million (10,000,000) MCF of gas for each one thousand (1,000) MCF of the Daily Contract Quantity then in effect, then Seller shall be considered to have surplus reserve to the extent of such excess; and Seller shall have the right to sell gas from such surplus reserve, provided and to the extent that Seller's Delivery Capacity exceeds one hundred fifty per cent (150%) of the Daily Contract Quantity then in effect hereunder. Whenever Seller has gas for sale from surplus reserve and desires to sell such gas, Seller shall give Buyer written notice of such fact. Within thirty (30) days after receipt of such notice Buyer shall notify Seller in writing whether or not Buyer elects to purchase all or any part of such quantity of surplus gas under this Agreement. If Buyer does so elect to purchase all or any part of such quantity of surplus gas, the Daily Contract Quantity shall be increased, effective at the beginning of the month following such election, by a quantity equal to one thousand (1,000) MCF for each ten million (10,000,000) MCF of such surplus gas as Buyer elects to purchase. If Buyer does not elect to purchase all of such quantity of surplus gas, then Seller shall have the right to sell such quantity of surplus gas as Buyer does not elect to purchase to parties other than Buyer; provided, however, that in no event shall Seller have the right to sell surplus gas to parties other than Buyer unless and except to the extent that Seller's Delivery Capacity is in excess of one hundred fifty per cent (150%) of the Daily Contract Quantity then in effect hereunder.

(d) If at any time Seller's Delivery Capacity shall be less than one hundred fifty per cent (150%) of the Daily Contract Quantity then in effect hereunder (and such condition shall not be the result of unavoidable accident as hereinafter defined), then at the option of Buyer the Daily Contract Quantity then in effect hereunder shall be reduced in proportion to the reduction in Seller's Delivery Capacity below a quantity equal to one hundred fifty per cent (150%) of such Daily Contract Quantity; and thereafter such reduced Daily Contract Quantity shall be in effect unless and until further reduced or increased in accordance with the provisions of this Paragraph 1 of Article III; provided, however, that if at any time Seller's Delivery Capacity shall be less than twenty-five per cent (25%) of the Original Daily Contract Quantity, Buyer shall have the right to terminate this Agreement by giving Seller one hundred fifty (150) days written notice of Buyer's election to terminate the same; and provided, further, that Seller shall have the right to prevent such termination by increasing Seller's Delivery Capacity to at least tyenty-five per cent (25%) of the Original Daily Contract Quantity before the expiration of said one hundred fifty (150) day period.

2. Seller's Delivery Capacity shall be determined at least twice each year by actual measurements and calculations and shall be estimated or calculated for each month in the months in which no actual tests are made, using the result of the last actual test as the basis of the estimation.

3. For the purposes of this Article III, the term "unavoidable accident" shall mean acts of God, strikes, lockouts, or other industrial disturbances, acts of the public enemy, wars, blockades, insurrections, riots, epidemics, landslides, lightning, earthquakes, fires, storms, floods, washouts, arrests and restraints of governments and people, civil disturbances, explosions, breakage or accidents to wells, machinery, or lines of pipe, the necessity for making repairs or alterations thereto, freezing of wells or lines of pipe, and any other causes, whether of the kind herein enumerated or otherwise, not within the control of the party claiming the existence of an unavoidable accident; provided, however, that said term shall not mean or include any cause which by the exercise of due diligence the party claiming the existence of an unavoidable accident is able to overcome; and provided, further, that in no event shall said term mean or include partial or entire failure or depletion of gas wells or sources of supply of gas. It is understood and agreed, however, that the settlement of strikes or lockouts shall be entirely within the discretion of the party having the difficulty and that any obligation, express or implied, on the part of either party to remedy any "unavoidable accident," if within such party's control, with reasonable dispatch shall not require the settlement of strikes or lockouts by acceding to the demands of opposing party when such course is inadvisable in the discretion of the party having the difficulty.

4. Seller recognizes that due to operating conditions, varying market demands and the difficulty of apportioning receipts of gas from various sources, Buyer may not be able to take gas from Seller during any definite period at exactly constant rates. Buyer shall, however, to the best of its ability maintain as nearly a constant rate of takings of the quantities provided for in Paragraph 1 of this Article III as practicable and shall balance deficit

takings from Seller under this Agreement by an excess of takings from Seller hereunder as soon as practicable after such variations have occurred and shall have been ascertained, and Buyer may balance excess takings from Seller hereunder by curtailed takings from Seller hereunder. Nothing herein contained shall prevent Buyer from purchasing from Seller hereunder at any time and from time to time quantities of gas greater than the Daily Contract Quantity then in effect hereunder; provided that Seller shall not be obligated to deliver in any day a quantity of gas in excess of one hundred fifty per cent (150%) of such Daily Contract Quantity then in effect hereunder.

5. In the event Buyer is required by the provisions of this Agreement to pay Seller for a quantity of gas which Buyer shall not have actually taken during any year of the term hereof, then Buyer may make up for such deficient takings during the next succeeding year of the term hereof by applying against such deficiency the gas taken during such succeeding year in excess of the average daily quantity of gas Buyer is obligated to take or pay for during such year. Buyer shall not be required to pay Seller for gas applied in any year against a deficiency which shall have arisen during the previous year and for which payment shall have already been made.

6. It is understood and agreed that nothing in this Agreement shall be construed to require Seller to sell and deliver to Buyer or to require Buyer to purchase and receive from Seller or pay Seller for a quantity of gas in excess of the total quantity of gas per day which the wells on the leaseholds and/or lands covered by this Agreement are capable of producing into Buyer's line, when produced at their respective allowable rates of flow under the applicable rules, regulations and orders of regulatory bodies having jurisdiction.

IV. *POINT OF DELIVERY*

1. The point of delivery of the gas to be delivered by Seller to Buyer hereunder shall be at a point to be mutually agreed upon located on Buyer's _____ line in the _____ _____ .

2. As between the parties thereto, Seller shall be in control and possession of the gas deliverable hereunder and responsible for any damage or injury caused thereby until the same shall have been delivered to Buyer, after which delivery Buyer shall be deemed to be in exclusive control and possession thereof and responsible for any injury or damage caused thereby.

V. *PRESSURE*

1. The gas to be delivered hereunder shall be delivered by Seller into Buyer's _____ transmission line against the pressure existing therein from time to time at said point of delivery, provided, however, that

Seller shall not be required to deliver such gas at a pressure in excess of
_____ (_____) pounds per square inch gauge during the first ten (10) years from the date of the first delivery of gas hereunder or in excess of _____ hundred (_____) pounds per square inch gauge thereafter.

2. Seller shall make reports to Buyer, as often as may be necessary in practice, of the pressure at which the gas is being delivered hereunder and the rate of such deliveries. Seller shall have agents or employees available at all times to receive from Buyer's dispatchers advices and requests for changes in the rates of delivery of gas hereunder as required by Buyer from time to time.

VI. *MEASURING STATIONS*

1. Seller shall install, maintain and operate, at Seller's own expense, at or near the point of delivery, a measuring station properly equipped with orifice meters, flange connections, orifice plates, and other necessary equipment by which the volume of gas delivered hereunder shall be measured. Orifice meters shall be installed, maintained and operated and volumes computed in accordance with Gas Measurement Committee Report No. 3, including the Appendix thereto, dated April, 1955, of the American Gas Association. Buyer shall have access to such metering equipment at reasonable hours, but the reading, calibrating and adjusting thereof and the changing of charts shall be done only by Seller.

2. Buyer may install, maintain and operate, at its own expense, such pressure regulators and check measuring equipment as it shall desire and Seller, to the extent that Seller has the right to do so, hereby grants to Buyer, the right to install, maintain and operate such equipment in Seller's measuring station or stations, provided that such equipment shall be so installed as not to interfere with the operation of Seller's measuring equipment. Seller shall have access to such check measuring equipment at reasonable hours, but the reading, calibrating and adjusting thereof and the changing of charts shall be done only by Buyer.

3. Each party shall have the right to be present at the time of any installing, reading, cleaning, changing, repairing, inspecting, testing, calibrating, or adjusting done in connection with the other's measuring equipment used in measuring deliveries hereunder. The records from such measuring equipment shall remain the property of their owner, but upon request each will submit to the other its records and charts, together with calculations therefrom, for inspection and verification, subject to return within ten (10) days after receipt thereof.

324

4. In the event a meter is out of service, or registering inaccurately, the volume of gas delivered hereunder shall be estimated:

(a) By using the registration of any check meter or meters if installed and accurately registering, or in the absence of (a):

(b) By correcting the error if the percentage of error is ascertainable by calibration, test, or mathematical calculation or, in the absence of both (a) and (b), then:

(c) By estimating the quantity of delivery by deliveries during periods under similar conditions when the meter was registering accurately.

5. At least once each month Seller shall verify the accuracy of Seller's measuring equipment and Buyer shall verify the accuracy of its check measuring equipment. If either party shall notify the other that it desires a special test of any measuring equipment, the parties shall cooperate to secure a prompt verification of the accuracy of such equipment. If either party at any time observes a variation between the delivery meter and the check meter, it will promptly notify the other party thereof and both parties will then cooperate to secure an immediate verification of the accuracy of such equipment. Each party shall give to the other notice of the time of all tests of meters reasonably in advance of the holding of such tests in order that the other party may conveniently have its own representative present.

6. If, upon test, any measuring equipment, including recording calorimeter, is found to be in error not more than two per cent (2%), previous records of such equipment shall be considered accurate in computing deliveries hereunder; but such equipment shall be adjusted at once to record correctly. If, upon test, any measuring equipment shall be found to be inaccurate by an amount exceeding two per cent (2%), at a recording corresponding to the average hourly rate of flow for the period since the last preceding test, then any previous recordings of such equipment shall be corrected to zero error for any period which is known definitely or agreed upon, but in case the period is not known definitely or agreed upon such correction shall be for a period extending over one-half (½) of the time elapsed since the date of last test, not exceeding a correction period of sixteen (16) days.

7. Each party shall preserve for a period of at least five (5) years all test data, charts and other similar records.

VII. *MEASUREMENTS*

1. The sales unit of the gas deliverable hereunder shall be one (1) MCF of gas.

2. The volume of the gas delivered hereunder shall be determined as follows:

(a) The unit of volume for the purpose of measurement shall be one (1) cubic foot of gas at a base temperature of sixty degrees (60°) Fahrenheit and at a pressure of fourteen and sixty-five hundredths (14.65) pounds per square inch absolute with correction for deviation from Boyle's Law. Computation of volumes, including the deviation from Boyle's Law, shall be made in accordance with applicable rules, regulations and orders promulgated by the Texas Railroad Commission pursuant to the Standard Gas Measurement Law of Texas.

(b) The average absolute atmospheric pressure shall be assumed to be fourteen and seven-tenths (14.7) pounds to the square inch, irrespective of actual elevation or location of the point of delivery above sea level or variations in such atmospheric pressure from time to time.

(c) The temperature of the gas passing the meters shall be determined by the continuous use of a recording thermometer so installed that it may properly record the temperature of the gas flowing through the meters. The arithmetical average of the temperature recorded each twenty-four (24) hour day shall be used in computing gas volumes for that date.

(d) Unless the parties hereto agree to the use of a spot test method, the specific gravity of the gas delivered hereunder shall be determined by the continuous use of an Acme recording gravitometer, or other standard gravitometer agreed upon by the parties hereto, so installed that it may properly record the specific gravity of the gas flowing through the meters. The arithmetical average of the specific gravity recorded each twenty-four (24) hour day shall be used in computing gas volumes for that date. If the parties hereto agree to the use of a spot test method, such spot test shall be made with an Edwards type of gas balance, or by such other method as shall be agreed upon between the parties. If the spot test method is used, the specific gravity of the gas delivered hereunder shall be determined once monthly, or as much oftener as is found necessary in practice. The regular monthly test shall determine the specific gravity to be used in computation for the measurement of natural gas delivered, until the end of such month or until changed by special test; the special test to be applicable from the day made through the remaining days in such month.

VIII. *QUALITY OF GAS*

1. Seller agrees that:

(a) The gas delivered hereunder shall have a total heating value of not less than one thousand (1,000) British thermal units per cubic foot. In the event that the total heating value of the gas tendered for delivery hereunder falls below one thousand (1,000) British thermal units per cubic foot, Buyer shall have the option to accept said gas so long as said heating value remains below one thousand (1,000) British thermal units per cubic foot.

(b) The total heating value of the gas in British thermal units per cubic

326

foot shall be determined by Seller at intervals of not more than ninety (90) days by means of some approved method of general use in the gas industry. Buyer shall have the right to determine, at such time or times as it may desire, the total heating value of the gas in British thermal units per cubic foot by means of some approved method of general use in the gas industry. Each party shall conduct at its expense the test or tests made by it. Each party shall give to the other notice of the time of all tests for determining the British thermal unit content of the gas to be conducted by such party reasonably in advance of making the test in order that the other party may conveniently have its representative present. Should there be any material variance between tests by Buyer and by Seller, a joint test will be run and will be controlling, effective from the first day of the calendar month preceding such a joint test. The British thermal unit content per cubic foot shall be determined for a cubic foot of gas at a temperature of sixty degrees (60°) Fahrenheit when saturated with water vapor and at an absolute pressure equivalent to thirty inches (30″) of mercury at thirty-two degrees (32°) Fahrenheit.

2. Seller agrees that the gas delivered hereunder:

(a) Shall be dehydrated by Seller and shall in no event have a water content in excess of seven (7) pounds of water per million cubic feet of gas measured at a pressure base of fourteen and seventy-three (14.73) pounds per square inch and at a temperature of sixty degrees (60°) Fahrenheit, as determined by dew-point apparatus approved by the Bureau of Mines.

(b) Shall be commercially free from hydrogen sulphide and shall not contain more than one (1) grain of hydrogen sulphide per hundred (100) cubic feet of gas as determined by quantitative test after the presence of hydrogen sulphide has been indicated by qualitative test, which shall consist of exposing a strip of white filter paper recently moistened with a solution of one hundred (100) grains of lead acetate in one hundred (100) cubic centimeters of water to be exposed to the gas for one and one-half (1½) minutes in an apparatus previously purged, through which the gas is flowing at the rate of approximately five (5) cubic feet per hour, the gas from the jet not impinging upon the test paper, and which qualitative test shall be deemed to be satisfied, if after this exposure, the test paper is found not distinctly darker than a second paper freshly moistened with a solution not exposed to the gas.

(c) Shall not contain more than twenty (20) grains of total sulphur per one hundred (100) cubic feet of gas.

(d) Shall not contain in excess of:

(1) Three per cent (3%) by volume of carbon dioxide;

327

(II)   One per cent (1%) by volume of oxygen; or

(III) Two-tenths (0.2) gallons per MCF of gas, of those certain liquefiable hydrocarbons commonly referred to as natural gasoline,
as determined by absorption methods as prescribed from time
to time by the Natural Gasoline Association of America.

3. Except as otherwise specifically provided to the contrary in this Article
VIII, all measurements of gas required in this Article VIII shall be at a
temperature of sixty degrees (60°) Fahrenheit and at an absolute pressure
of fourteen and seventy-three hundredths (14.73) pounds per square inch.
In addition to meeting the above specifications, the gas delivered hereunder
shall be commercially free from dust, gums, gum forming constituents, or
other liquid or solid matter which might become separated from the gas in
the course of transportation through pipe lines.

IX. *PRICE*

1. Subject to the provisions of Paragraphs 2 through 4 below, the price
to be paid by Buyer to Seller for gas delivered to Buyer hereunder shall be
as follows:

_____ cents per MCF from date of initial delivery to _____;

_____ cents per MCF from _____, to _____;

_____ cents per MCF from _____, to _____;

_____ cents per MCF thereafter.

2. Any sales, transactions, occupations, service, production, severance,
gathering, transmission, export or excise tax, assessment or fee levied, assessed or fixed by the United States or any State or other Governmental authority and taxes of a similar nature or equivalent in effect (not including
income, excess profits, capital stock, franchise, or general property taxes) in
addition to or greater than those, if any, being levied, assessed or fixed on
_____, 19____, in respect of or applicable to the gas
to be delivered by Seller to Buyer hereunder and which Seller may be liable
for during any month either directly or indirectly through any obligation to
reimburse others, are hereinafter collectively referred to as an "additional
tax." It is expressly understood and agreed between the parties that there
shall be added to the prices provided for in this Article IX, so long as the
additional tax shall be in effect, an amount per MCF sufficient to reimburse
Seller for _____ of such additional tax. In the event
all or any part of such liability of Seller is not determined or not determinable by the end of any month, then such additional amount per MCF required in respect of such liability not determined or determinable shall be
set forth for all such months in any calendar year in a statement to be rendered by Seller to Buyer by April 1st of the following year and Buyer shall

pay the amount due pursuant to such statement on or before May 1st of such following year.

3. If at any time or times Buyer shall enter into a contract for the purchase of gas from a field or fields located in _____ for any part of the requirements of Buyer's system and such contract provides for a price to be paid for such gas during any calendar year which differs from the price payable under this Agreement during the same calendar year, Buyer shall promptly notify Seller thereof, giving full information as to the price provisions of such contract, the term thereof, and all other provisions of such contract which affect the remuneration to the Seller thereunder. Seller shall have the option, within thirty (30) days after receipt of such information from Buyer, to have such price provisions of such other contract applied to gas thereafter delivered hereunder for the term of this Agreement or the term of such other contract, whichever term is the shorter. Should such other contract have a shorter term than this Agreement, then, for the period following the expiration of the term of such other contract, the prices and provisions of this Agreement shall apply to gas delivered hereunder. Should Seller not elect to accept any such different price provisions, Seller shall thereupon be foreclosed as to such rejected provisions for the duration of this Agreement. Should Seller accept any such different price provisions, same shall be effective hereunder at the beginning of the calendar month immediately following the date of such election by Seller or at the time such different price becomes effective under such other contract, whichever event shall occur later, and shall remain in effect, as above provided, unless changed by subsequent election of Seller to have applied to gas delivered hereunder price provisions differing in any calendar year from the price provisions then in effect hereunder during the same calendar year and from all price provisions which Seller had previously been offered by Buyer. In determining whether the price payable under any such other contract differs from the price payable for gas under this Agreement, due consideration shall be given to the provisions of this Agreement as compared with such other contract as to quality of gas, delivery pressures, gathering and compressing arrangements, provisions regarding measurement of gas, including deviation from Boyle's Law, and taxes payable by Buyer and Seller, respectively, upon or in respect of the gas delivered. The provisions of this paragraph shall not apply to any contract for the purchase by Buyer from another pipe line company of gas which shall have been transported by such other pipe line company through its transmission pipe line system.

4. It is agreed that, in accordance with the following program, Seller may request a price redetermination of the prices hereinabove provided to be

paid to Seller for any one or more and/or all of the three-five year periods which begin _____, 19_____, _____, 19_____, and _____, 19_____, respectively. Any such request shall be given not less than six (6) months nor more than twelve (12) months prior to the beginning of the period for which such price redetermination is desired. Such redetermination shall be made by the parties hereto, or, if they are unable to agree, by arbitration in the manner provided in Article XVI hereof, and shall be completed not less than three (3) months prior to the beginning of such period. Upon such request being made, the parties hereto, or the arbitrators (in the event said parties are unable to agree) shall determine the three (3) highest prices per MCF to be paid at the beginning of the period for which the redetermination is to be made by interstate gas pipe line companies, including Buyer (if Buyer shall be one of the three companies paying the highest price) for substantial quantities of gas produced in District No. _____ of the Railroad Commission of Texas (as such District is constituted on the date of this Agreement), under contracts with producers under which deliveries of gas are being made at the time the redetermination is made, providing for deliveries over a period of time at least equal to the remainder of the primary term of this Agreement and upon substantially the same terms and conditions as to quality of gas, delivery pressures, gathering and compressing arrangements, measurement and taxes payable in respect of gas delivered, as those provided herein. The arithmetical average of such three highest prices per MCF shall be the price to be paid hereunder for gas delivered during the period for which such redetermination was made; provided, however, that in no event shall the price per MCF hereunder during such period be less than the arithmetical average of the prices per MCF for such period shown above in Paragraph 1 of this Article IX.

X. BILLING

1. Seller shall render bill to Buyer, at its office designated in or pursuant to Article XVII hereof, on or before the tenth (10th) day of each calendar month for all gas delivered hereunder during the preceding month. Buyer shall make payment to Seller, at its office designated in or pursuant to Article XVII hereof, by check on or before the twenty-fifth (25th) day of each calendar month, for all gas delivered during the preceding month and billed by Seller in statement for said month according to the measurements, computations and price herein provided. If presentation of bill by Seller is delayed after the tenth (10th) day of the calendar month, then the time of payment shall be extended accordingly unless Buyer is responsible for such delay.

2. In the event an error is discovered in the amount billed in any state-

ment rendered by Seller, such error shall be adjusted within thirty (30) days of the determination thereof, provided that claim therefor shall have been made within sixty (60) days from the date of discovery of such error, but in any event within twelve (12) months from the date of such statement.

3. If Buyer shall fail in any year of the term of this Agreement to take the quantity of gas Buyer is obligated to take under the provisions of Paragraph 1 of Article III of this Agreement, then Seller may, within thirty (30) days after the end of such year, render a bill to Buyer for the amount due Seller by reason of such deficient takings and Buyer shall make payment to Seller within fifteen (15) days after receipt of such bill, in the manner set forth in Paragraph 1 of this Article X, at the weighted average price per MCF in effect hereunder during the year in which such deficiency arose. In computing the amount due Seller for any deficiency in takings by Buyer occurring during any year, the following quantities shall be deducted from such deficiency:

(a) The total of the quantities of gas which Buyer requests (up to a daily maximum of one hundred fifty per cent (150%) of the Daily Contract Quantity) and which Seller fails to deliver on any day or days during such year.

(b) The total of the quantities of gas which Buyer is unable to take on any day or days during such year by reason of force majeure.

(c) The total of any deficiency in Seller's allowable for the wells covered hereby below the Daily Contract Quantity on any day or days during such year.

XI. *FORCE MAJEURE*

1. In the event of either party hereto being rendered unable, wholly or in part, by force majeure to carry out its obligations under this Agreement, other than to make payments due hereunder, it is agreed that on such party giving notice and full particulars of such force majeure in writing or by telegraph to the other party as soon as possible after the occurrence of the cause relied on, then the obligations of the party giving such notice, so far as they are affected by such force majeure, shall be suspended during the continuance of any inability so caused but for no longer period, and such cause shall as far as possible be remedied with all reasonable dispatch. The term "force majeure" as employed herein shall mean acts of God, strikes, lockouts or other industrial disturbances, acts of the public enemy, wars, blockades, insurrections, riots, epidemics, landslides, lightning, earthquakes, fires, storms, floods, washouts, arrests and restraints of governments and people, civil disturbances, explosions, breakage or accidents to machinery or lines of pipe, the necessity for making repairs to or alterations of machinery or lines of pipe, freezing of wells or lines of pipe, partial or entire failure of wells or

sources of supply of gas, and any other causes, whether of the kind herein enumerated or otherwise, not within the control of the party claiming suspension and which by the exercise of due diligence such party is unable to prevent or overcome; such term shall likewise include (a) in those instances where either party hereto is required to obtain servitudes, rights of way grants, permits or licenses to enable such party to fulfill its obligations hereunder, the inability of such party to acquire, or the delays on the part of such party in acquiring, at reasonable cost and after the exercise of reasonable diligence, such servitudes, rights of way grants, permits or licenses, and (b) in those instances where either party hereto is required to furnish materials and supplies for the purpose of constructing or maintaining facilities or is required to secure permits or permissions from any governmental agency to enable such party to fulfill its obligations hereunder, the inability of such party to acquire, or the delays on the part of such party in acquiring, at reasonable cost and after the exercise of reasonable diligence, such materials and supplies, permits and permissions. It is understood and agreed that the settlement of strikes or lockouts shall be entirely within the discretion of the party having the difficulty, and that the above requirement that any force majeure shall be remedied with all reasonable dispatch shall not require the settlement of strikes or lockouts by acceding to the demands of the opposing party when such course is inadvisable in the discretion of the party having the difficulty.

XII. *DEFAULT*

It is covenanted and agreed that if either party hereto shall fail to perform any of the covenants or obligations imposed upon it under and by virtue of this Agreement, then in such event the other party hereto may at its option terminate this Agreement by proceeding as follows: The party not in default shall cause a written notice to be served on the party in default stating specifically the cause for terminating this Agreement and declaring it to be the intention of the party giving the notice to terminate the same; thereupon the party in default shall have thirty (30) days after the service of the aforesaid notice in which to remedy or remove the cause or causes stated in the notice for terminating the Agreement, and if within said period of thirty (30) days the party in default does so remedy or remove said cause or causes and fully indemnify the party not in default for any and all consequences of such breach, then such notice shall be withdrawn and this Agreement shall continue in full force and effect. In case the party in default does not so remedy or remove the cause or causes or does not indemnify the party giving notice for any and all consequences of such breach, within said period of thirty (30) days, then, at the option of the party giving the notice, this Agreement shall become null and void from and after the expiration of said period. Any cancellation of this Agreement pursuant to the provisions of this Article XII shall be without prejudice to the right of Seller to collect any amounts then due Seller for natural gas delivered prior to the time of cancellation and shall be without prejudice to the right of Buyer to receive any gas for which it has paid but has not received, although entitled thereto, prior to the time of cancellation, and without waiver of any remedy to which the party not in default may be entitled for violations of this Agreement.

XIII. *TERM*

This Agreement shall be effective from the date hereof and shall continue and remain in full force and effect for a primary term of twenty (20) years from the date upon which Seller commences the delivery of gas to Buyer hereunder, and shall continue in force and effect thereafter for successive periods of one (1) year each unless or until terminated either by Seller or by Buyer upon twelve (12) months' prior written notice to the other party hereto specifying a termination date at the end of such primary term, or of any yearly period thereafter.

XIV. *WARRANTY OF TITLE*

Seller hereby warrants the title to all gas delivered by Seller to Buyer hereunder, the right to sell the same and that it is free from all liens and adverse claims, and agrees, if notified thereof by Buyer, to indemnify Buyer against all suits, actions, debts, accounts, damages, costs, losses, and expenses arising from or out of any adverse legal claims of any and all persons to or against said gas. Seller agrees to pay or cause to be paid all taxes and assessments levied on the gas prior to its delivery to Buyer, and to pay or cause to be paid to the parties entitled thereto all royalties, overriding royalties or like charges against said gas or the value thereof. In the event any adverse claim of any character whatsoever is asserted in respect to any of said gas, Buyer may retain the purchase price thereof up to the amount of such claim without interest until such claim has been finally determined, as security for the performance of Seller's obligation with respect to such claim under this Article XIV, or until Seller shall have furnished bond to Buyer, in an amount and with sureties satisfactory to Buyer, conditioned for the protection of Buyer with respect to such claim.

XV. *REGULATORY BODIES*

This Agreement is subject to all present and future valid orders, rules, and regulations of any regulatory body having jurisdiction.

XVI. *ARBITRATION*

Any dispute arising between Seller and Buyer out of this Agreement shall be determined by a board of three (3) arbitrators to be selected for each controversy so arising as follows: Either Seller or Buyer may, at the time such board of arbitration is desired, notify the other of the name of an arbitrator, and such other party shall, within ten (10) days thereafter, select an arbitrator and notify the party desiring arbitration of the name of such arbitrator. If such other party shall fail to name a second arbitrator within ten (10) days, then the party who first served the notice may, on reasonable notice to the other party, apply to the person who is then Senior Judge of the United States District Court for the Southern District of Texas for the appointment of such second arbitrator for or on behalf of the other party, and in such case the arbitrator appointed by the person who is such Judge shall act as if named by the other party. The two (2) arbitrators chosen as above provided shall, within ten (10) days after the appointment of the second arbitrator, choose the third arbitrator, and in the event of their failure so to do within said ten (10) days, either of the parties hereto may in like manner, on reasonable notice to the other party, apply to the person who is such Judge for the appointment of a third arbitrator and in such case the arbitrator appointed by the person who is such Judge shall act as the third arbitrator. The board so constituted shall fix a reasonable time and place for the hearing, at which time each of the parties hereto may submit such evidence as it may see fit. Such board shall determine the matters submitted to it pursuant to the provisions of this Agreement. The action of a majority of the members of such board shall govern and their decision in writing shall be final and binding on the parties hereto. Each party shall pay the expense of the arbitrator selected by or for it and all other costs of the arbitration shall be equally divided between the parties hereto.

XVII. *ADDRESSES*

Until Buyer is otherwise notified in writing by Seller, the address of Seller is and shall remain _____

_____

and, unless Seller is otherwise notified in writing by Buyer, the address of Buyer is and shall remain _____

_____. All notices required to be given in writing hereunder shall be given to the respective parties at such addresses or such other addresses as the parties respectively shall designate by written notice.

XVIII. *MISCELLANEOUS*

1. No waiver by either party hereto of any one or more defaults by the other in the performance of any provisions of this Agreement shall operate or be construed as a waiver of any future default or defaults, whether of a like or of a different character.

334

2. This Agreement shall be binding upon and inure to the benefit of the heirs, legal representatives, successors and assigns of the respective parties hereto and shall constitute a real right and covenant running with the lands and leasehold estates covered hereby, and shall be binding upon any purchaser of Buyer's transmission system and upon any purchaser of the properties of Seller which are subject to this Agreement; and Seller and Buyer both agree that no sale of said properties of Seller or any part thereof or of all or substantially all of Buyer's said system shall be made unless the purchaser thereof shall assume and agree to be bound by this Agreement insofar as the same shall affect and relate to the property or interest sold or conveyed. It is agreed, however, that nothing contained in this paragraph shall in any way prevent either party hereto from pledging or mortgaging its rights hereunder for security of its indebtedness.

3. It is agreed that this Agreement may be ratified and adopted by any owner of an interest in any lease or leases subject hereto or any lands or leases with which any lease or leases subject hereto may be pooled or unitized, by execution and delivery to Buyer of a special instrument in writing, ratifying and adopting this Agreement insofar as said owner's interest in any such land, lease or leases is concerned, whereupon such owner shall become a party Seller to this Agreement with like force and effect and to the same extent as though such owner had executed this Agreement at the time of its execution and delivery, and all of the terms and provisions of this Agreement shall thereupon become binding upon Buyer and any such other owner. Seller's Gas Reserve and the Daily Contract Quantity, as variously calculated and mentioned herein, contemplate the execution or the ratification and adoption of this Agreement by all parties owning working interests in the lands and/or leases described in Exhibit A attached hereto, and, in the event of the failure of all of such parties to execute or ratify and adopt this Agreement, Seller's Gas Reserve and such Daily Contract Quantity shall be proportionately reduced to reflect such failure.

4. In the event there are two or more parties Seller to this Agreement, each such party Seller agrees that all parties Seller will appoint one of their number as their representative hereunder for giving and receiving notices and requests, making and witnessing tests, delivering the quantities of gas deliverable, rendering bills for gas delivered, and receiving payments therefor, allocating, prorating and distributing such payments among the various parties Seller, and for doing and receiving all things provided for concerning Seller in this Agreement. Buyer may act, and shall be fully protected in acting, in reliance upon any and all acts and things done or performed by, or agreements with respect to all matters dealt with herein made by such representative in behalf of the parties Seller as fully and effectively as though each

335

had done, performed, made or executed the same. The parties Seller may change their representative and designate one of their number as the new representative from time to time by delivery of written notice of change and designation to Buyer. It is understood and agreed that each party Seller executing or ratifying this Agreement is selling its gas severally, and not jointly with other Sellers, to Buyer, that the parties Seller are not acting as partners, joint adventurers or otherwise jointly in this transaction and that nothing herein contained or provided for shall operate to, or be construed as creating any such relationship.

5. Pursuant to preceding Pragraph 4 of Article XVIII, the parties Seller hereto designate _____, as representative for the purposes as set out in such Paragraph 4 of Article XVIII.

IN WITNESS WHEREOF, the parties hereto have executed this Agreement in _____ (_____) originals on the day and year first above written.

ATTEST:

By_____   By_____
                                         Vice President

ATTEST: **BUYER**
By_____   By_____
                                         SELLER

EXHIBIT A

To be attached to Gas Purchase Contract, dated the _____ day of _____, between _____ _____, referred to as "Seller," and _____ _____, referred to as "Buyer," showing acreage covered by said Contract and listed as follows:

(Exhibit A Descriptions to Be Supplied by Seller)

336

14

THE NATURAL GAS INDUSTRY
IN FOREIGN COUNTRIES

*by Alfred M. Leeston
and John A. Crichton*

CANADA

THE discovery of Leduc oil field on February 13, 1947, in the western Canadian province of Alberta added new wealth to a great country already incredibly rich in natural resources. It made Canada an oil and gas country. It brought Canada nearer to the goal so highly valued by all nations but reached only by a privileged few, self-sufficiency in both precious fossil fuels. It stimulated investments in the oil and gas industry to some $2,397,000,000 within ten years. It aroused Wall Street and many of its customers to speculate in Canadian securities. It presented American and Canadian oil companies with a great opportunity for finding and producing oil and gas in surprisingly large quantities. It opened the way to supply Canada, the Pacific Northwest, and California with natural gas.[1]

Like the oil, gas is found in great abundance in Alberta, in smaller quantities in British Columbia, in Saskatchewan, and also in south-

[1] "Ten years ago there were only 600 producing wells producing 10 million barrels a year. Now there are 8,000 wells in Alberta producing 150 million barrels and a potential 75 million barrels additional limited only by available markets. The natural gas picture ten years ago was insignificant. Today, there are over 1,300 wells capable of production representing 20 trillion cubic feet of gas," said E. C. Manning, Premier of Alberta, in his address before the Forty-first Meeting of the Investment Dealer's Association of Canada, June 12, 1957. D. K. Yorath, president of Canadian Western Natural Gas Company, Limited, Calgary, and of Northwestern Utilities, Limited, and A. E. Grauer, president of British Columbia Power Corporation, Limited, Vancouver, also spoke. Mr. Yorath's speech was entitled "Natural Gas—What It Means to Canada," and Mr. Grauer spoke on the topic, "Recent Economic Trends in British Columbia." See the Investment Dealer's Association of Canada Convention Section of the *Commercial and Financial Chronicle,* Vol. CLXXXV, No. 5650 (June 27, 1957), 31ff.

western Ontario where gas has been known and used for about seventy-five years.

As early as July 1938, the Province of Alberta set up a Conservation Board, which was to be the regulatory authority for all operations in oil and gas and which has been of crucial importance for the entire oil and gas industry since 1947. No gas may leave the province of Alberta without previous permission of the board. Exports include not only transmission of gas to the United States but also shipments of gas within the various provinces of Canada proper. Thus the attitude of the Board is decisive. "While the question of permitting the export of gas was a provincial matter, it would become a federal one as soon as gas left Alberta. The federal government, through the Board of Transport Commissioners, exercised jurisdiction over the routes and construction of inter-provincial pipe lines. To export gas from Canada, a permit had to be obtained from the Department of Trade and Commerce. To import gas into the United States, the permission of the FPC must be sought."[2]

The board proceeded very carefully and slowly until it recognized that there was an exportable surplus of natural gas. In 1952 the board estimated established reserves of exportable gas at 6.8 trillion cubic feet. Although the consulting firm of De Golyer and MacNaughton in Dallas, Texas, had estimated the proven resources at nearly 8.6 trillion cubic feet in 1951 and the proven, probable, and possible reserves at 16 trillion cubic feet in 1952, the board held to its own low and conservative estimate.[3]

Years went by, and new prolific gas fields were constantly discovered. In 1959 the Conservation Board of Alberta revised its estimate to the following:

	Trillion Cu. Ft.
Established Reserves within Economic Reach	26.3
Alberta's Thirty-year Requirements	11.7
Portion to Be Supplied from Future Reserves	— 4.4
Net Requirements	7.3
Amount Already Approved for Export	+13.7
Total Amount Committed to Requirements and Export	21.0
Surplus to Alberta Requirements and Existing Permits	5.3

[2] Eric J. Hanson, *Dynamic Decade*, 226, 314ff. Professor Hanson's book is the first systematic survey of the first ten years of oil and gas operations in the Province of Alberta. This period began with the discovery of Leduc in 1947.

[3] *Ibid.*, 229–30.

Therefore, Alberta's requirements (11.7 trillion cubic feet) plus the approved export 13.7 trillion cubic feet), a total of 25.4 trillion cubic feet, fell within the estimated reserves of 26.3 trillion cubic feet. Out of the amount shown in the table above, the board recommended that the provincial government approve export permits in the following amounts:

	Trillion Cu. Ft.
Trans-Canada	6.83
Alberta and Southern	4.30
Westcoast (Peace River)	1.10
Westcoast (Southern Alberta)	1.10
Saskatchewan Power Corporation	0.59
Canadian Montana	0.32
Peace River Transmission Company	0.03
TOTAL	14.27

Two federal commissions, the Gordon Commission appointed by the previous Liberal government and one established by the Conservative government headed by Prime Minister Diefenbaker, made reports about the oil and gas situation in Canada. Henry Borden, chairman of the Royal Energy Commission which took his name, is a Conservative politically, a barrister by training, and a lawyer-industrialist by profession.[4] A Rhodes scholar, Mr. Borden was president of the Brazilian Traction Power and Light Company, Limited. The other members of the Borden Commission were: Leon J. Ladner, a lawyer; Robert Dudley Howland, who served on the Gordon Commission; Robert MacDonald Hardy; Jean Louis Levesque; and George Brinell.

The Borden Report was very optimistic on the subject of possible gas reserves in western Canada. It said that under favorable economic conditions ultimate recovery would be 300 trillion cubic feet of natural gas in the Western Canada sedimentary basin. The total area of this basin is over 750,000 square miles. It includes British Columbia, Alberta, Saskatchewan, Manitoba, Yukon, and the Northwest Territories. Presently proven gas reserves in this area are about 31.0 trillion cubic feet. Alberta has 27.7 trillion cubic feet. British Columbia has 2.3 trillion cubic feet, and Saskatchewan has 1.0 trillion cubic feet.

[4] "Meet the Men Behind the Borden Commission," *Oil and Gas Journal,* Vol. LVI, No. 44 (November 3, 1958), 46.

In British Columbia, oil and gas exploration is in the very early stage of development. Exploration is only about to commence in the Yukon, the Northwest Territories, and the Arctic Islands. In Alberta the gas discovery rate has been very high. Natural gas reserves are increasing at the rate of 2.7 trillion cubic feet per year in this province alone. This discovery rate exceeds the rate of growth of Canadian and export markets at a time when most companies are exploring for oil and not gas. "Sales of natural gas must be made at a rate which will give producers sufficient incentive to continue the exploration and drilling operations. The Canadian market is not large enough by itself to absorb the quantities of gas which are necessary to provide exploration companies with this incentive. It has already been proven many times that new discoveries of reserves in Canada are in direct proportion to the rate of exploratory drilling."[5]

The Borden Commission recommended the establishment of a National Energy Board of Canada. This board was created July 21, 1959. Ian N. McKinnon, the highly experienced chairman of the Alberta Oil and Gas Conservation Board, was appointed as chairman of the new energy board.[6] Mr. McKinnon served a two-year term while on leave of absence from his Alberta post. The other board members who have been named for seven-year terms are Robert D. Howland, Jules A. Archambault, H. Lee Briggs, and Douglas M. Fraser.

The law to authorize the creation of the National Energy Board provided for less stringent regulatory powers than those recommended by the Borden Commission. The new board, in addition to broad advisory functions, has the power for the construction of interprovincial and international pipe lines and has complete jurisdiction over the tolls charged. It also regulates, through the issuance of licenses, the export and import of gas, the export of electric power, and the prices charged for such energy.[7] An amendment to the law brought pipe lines for the transmission of sulphur and other gas by-products under

[5] Trans-Canada Pipe Lines, Limited, *Annual Report* (for 1959).

[6] "Canada's Top Oil-Gas Expert Is Named Energy Boss," *Oil and Gas Journal,* Vol. LVII, No. 38 (September 14, 1959), 72.

[7] Any gas or electricity license granted by the board becomes effective only after Cabinet approval. No license may be granted for longer than twenty-five years or, if the applicant holds a provincial license to remove gas or power from a province, for a period longer than the term of the provincial license. See *Petroleum Times,* Vol. LXIII, No. 1625 (November 20, 1959), 723.

the board's jurisdiction. Canada's natural gas reserves are mostly in the form of sour gas. They contain large amounts of sulphur which must be removed to obtain purified pipe-line gas. Light hydrocarbons such as ethane, propane, butane, and natural gasoline can also be extracted from the gas to support petroleum chemical plants.

A crucial point in the law is the provision that all tolls charged by pipe-line companies shall be "just and reasonable" and that the board's decisions in this respect are apparently not subject to appeal. In this connection, it is to be noted that the minister of trade and commerce, the Honorable Gordon Churchill, said in Parliament during the introduction of the bill, that the government's first premise with respect to the regulation of the rates of return of the pipe-line companies was that such returns "must be sufficient to attract capital for replacement and expansion."

On April 1, 1960, the Canadian government, on recommendation of the Canadian National Energy Board, authorized Trans-Canada Pipelines, Limited; Alberta and Southern Gas Company, Limited; West Coast Transmission Company, and Canadian-Montana Pipe-line Company to export 6.259 trillion cubic feet of natural gas to the United States and ushered in a new era for the gas industry in both Canada and the United States. No pipe line carrying gas from Canada to the United States had been built since Westcoast Transmission Company opened its pipe line on October 8, 1957, to carry gas from the Peace River country of northern British Columbia down to connect with the Pacific Northwest Pipeline Corporation line at Sumas on the international border in the State of Washington.

Meanwhile, Pacific Northwest merged with El Paso Natural Gas Company. El Paso Natural Gas owns approximately 18.6 per cent common stock interest in Westcoast Transmission. Westcoast's main interests are centered around the British Columbia part of the Peace River and in the adjoining Northwest Territories. More recently, great progress has been made in operations around Fort Nelson and other parts of northeastern British Columbia, and it is believed that this area will develop into one of Canada's major gas provinces. This opens up entirely new vistas for Westcoast's future deliveries into British Columbia and into the United States where it would join the huge El Paso Natural Gas system and supplement the gas supply available to California and the Pacific Northwest. Customers of Westcoast Pipeline in British Columbia are Inland Natural Gas Company, Limited, for communities in the interior of British Columbia, the British Columbia Electric Company for the lower mainland, and El Paso Natural Gas for the United States Pacific Coast states.

Although California is by far the greatest consumer of natural gas in the West Coast region, the states of the Pacific Northwest area,[8] Washington, Oregon, and Idaho, served by the Northwest Division of El Paso Natural Gas Company, must also be considered as rapidly expanding markets for natural gas. These northwestern states are growing at a rate well above the national average. The population of this region is increasing at a rate that is twice the national average and is expected to increase to 6.1 million by 1965. The largest utilities in the area are Northwest Natural Gas in Portland, Oregon, and Washington Natural Gas Company in Seattle.[9] In 1959, Northwest Natural Gas sold 30 billion cubic feet of gas and Washington Natural Gas 26 billion, of which about 19 billion were interruptible sales.

El Paso is constructing a transmission line from its main line near Camas, Washington, across the Columbia River and south up the Willamette Valley to the Eugene-Springfield area in Oregon. This opens up new residential, commercial, and industrial sales for the gas company. The conditions are favorable for progress of natural gas in the sprawling, fast-growing city of Seattle, Washington, where firm industrial sales have gained 283 per cent since 1955. It should be kept in mind that this development has been achieved in the face of vigorous challenge from competitive fuels, not the least of which is cheap, government hydroelectric energy.

The other companies involved in serving this last frontier for natural gas transmission are the Cascade Natural Gas Corporation, the Spokane Natural Gas Company, and Idaho's Intermountain Gas Company. Their load-building program is progressing quite satisfactorily with public reception to natural gas service at a high level, and new installations are running ahead of earlier schedules.

[8] William Iulo, *Natural Gas in the Pacific Northwest—Some of Its Economic Aspects,* 110ff.

[9] See the very favorable write up about Washington Natural Gas Company and the "unabated population growth of its service area with ensuing increase of gas consumption" in "Prospects of Washington Natural Gas Glow on Rapid Gains in Service Area," *Barron's,* Vol. XL, No. 47 (November 21, 1960, 34–35.

The main problem is still to provide an adequate gas supply for both the northern and southern parts of California where mushroom-like growth has steadily increased requirements for natural gas. In 1957, Kenneth E. Hill and John G. Winger estimated, in their book *Future Growth of the West Coast's Petroleum Industry,* that the over-all demand of the West Coast for gas in 1966 would be approximately 7.2 billion cubic feet a day—125 per cent more than was consumed in 1956. Of the total supply, 6 billion cubic feet a day would need to be brought in from outside the area—more than three times the volume that was "imported" in 1956. In 1959, the two principal utilities supplying California, Pacific Gas and Electric Company, and Pacific Lighting Corporation, imported about 736,083 billion cubic feet of natural gas from Texas. Should the Chase Manhattan Bank's estimate prove true, California will consume about 2.75 trillion cubic feet of gas in 1966. Of this tremendous quantity of natural gas, no less than 1.7 trillion cubic feet, according to the bank's forecast, will have to be imported. The tremendous quantities of natural gas consumed in California can be seen by comparing the 1956 and 1958 figures in Table 18 on page 344.

The authorization given by the Canadian government to the import of vast amounts of natural gas from Canada and the FPC-approved construction of a new pipe line provide an increased supply to meet burgeoning needs. The building of this new Transwestern Pipeline was authorized by the Federal Power Commission in August, 1955.[10] This system of 1,809 miles of pipe extends from near Roswell, New Mexico, to the Arizona-California border near Topock, Arizona, and includes a 252-mile lateral line from Puckett Field, Pecos County, Texas, to the Roswell terminal and a 298-mile line from Hemphill County, Texas, to the beginning of the main line. Pacific Lighting Gas Supply Company, the supplier of Los Angeles and other areas of southern California, received the full initial supply of 300 million cubic feet daily for resale through affiliated distribution companies in southern California. Pacific also had first call on additional gas volumes which became available from Transwestern.

[10] See "Gas Line to California Approved," *Oil and Gas Journal,* Vol. LVII, No. 34 (August 17, 1959), 94–95, and "Pipe Laying to Begin on Transwestern," *Oil and Gas Journal,* Vol. LVII, No. 44 (October 26, 1959), 56.

TABLE 18

NATURAL GAS CONSUMPTION IN CALIFORNIA
(Million Cu. Ft.)

Source of Supply		1956	1958
Indigenous Production		480,732,697	421,061,435
Import		577,732,835	649,435,106
	TOTAL	1,058,465,532	1,070,496,541
Gas Usage by Gas Companies			
Domestic and Commercial Sales		384,803,357	393,918,158
Industrial Sales		253,543,504	265,235,677
By Company as Power, etc.		11,414,500	9,995,672
Unaccounted For		29,188,820	15,566,066
	TOTAL	678,950,181	684,715,573
Gas Usage by Other Power Companies			
Steam Electric Generating Plants		146,336,770	202,236,205
Oil and Gas Producers		213,178,581	183,544,763
	TOTAL	1,038,465,532	1,070,496,541

IMPORTS
(Million Cu. Ft.)

		1956	1958	1959
Southern California				
Gas Company		293,024,796	359,723,183	392,643,000
Pacific Gas and Electric		264,708,039	289,711,923	343,440,000
	TOTAL	557,832,845	649,435,106	736,083,000

The pipe line was organized by Warren Petroleum Corporation, Monterey Oil Company,[11] and J. R. Butler and Associates, Houston. About 44.9 per cent of the reserves dedicated to the new system are committed by Gulf Oil Corporation's sale of Puckett-Ellenburger gas. Other suppliers are Richardson and Bass, Union Oil of California, Humble Oil, Sun Oil, British-American Oil Producing Company, C. H. Vaughan, Jr., Superior Oil Company, Magnolia Petroleum Company, and Hunt Oil Company. The Transwestern Pipeline project

[11] Northern Natural Gas bought Monterey's 16 per cent interest in Transwestern for $11,875,000 ($12.50 per share).

See "California: Growing Market for Gas," *Oil and Gas Journal*, Vol. LVII, No. 10 (March 2, 1959), 68, for a very interesting article about the demand for natural gas in California.

came to pass after the study of the Chase Manhattan Bank was written.

Of great importance to fuel-hungry California is the flow of natural gas from Canada which was authorized on April 1, 1960. The permit for the export of gas from Canada represents not only a large amount of gas to be imported into the United States but also a new attitude in gas export policy. As Lewis W. MacNaughton, president of Great Plains Development Company of Canada, remarked at the company's annual meeting in April, 1960, "The decision of the National Energy Board to permit export of natural gas has come at a time when the fortunes of the western Canadian petroleum industry are at a low ebb. . . . gas sales will grow very rapidly. . . ."

The Canadian gas scene, as it has developed since the export permit was given, is about as complicated as a modern abstract painting, but Canada probably "will end up with a natural gas system which will spread out over the United States like one of Canada's famed winter cold fronts." The largest of the Canadian-export-fostered projects is that of Pacific Gas and Electric Company.[12] "From a long-range point of view, by far the most important development . . . was the progress made toward obtaining the necessary governmental approvals for (the) project to transport natural gas from the Province of Alberta to the California market. In undertaking this project (PG&E) has been motivated by the desire to obtain direct accesss to the large reserves of natural gas in western Canada in order to take care of the future growth of its gas business."[13]

The wholly-owned Canadian subsidiary, Alberta and Southern Gas Company, Limited, has entered into contracts with producers to purchase gas for the project. One of the main producers is Shell Oil Company, which has important holdings in the Province of Alberta. Shell, for instance, supplies two hundred million cubic feet a day and plans

[12] A very good review of this vast project and its widespread ramifications is found in "Bids for Big Gas System Going out Soon," *Oil and Gas Journal,* Vol. LVIII, No. 35 (August 29, 1960), 47. See also "New Technique Specified for Big Gas Line," *Oil and Gas Journal,* Vol. LVIII, No. 46 (November 14, 1960), 116–117.

[13] *New York Times,* Saturday, July 13, 1957.

The entire line including laterals will be about 1,600 miles long. PG&E will have 296 miles in California; Pacific Gas Transmission Company, 614 miles in Oregon and Washington; Alberta Natural Gas Company, 107 miles in British Columbia; and Alberta Gas Trunk Line Company, 235 miles in Alberta. See "New Technique Specified for Big Gas Line," *Oil and Gas Journal,* Vol. LVIII, No. 46 (November 14, 1960), 117.

TABLE 19

A Postwar History of California Gas-import Projects

Company	Date Proposed	Volume Million Cu. Ft.	Date Completed	Date Authorized
El Paso Natural Gas	-----	May 1946	-----	305
	-----	1948	-----	250
	-----	Sept. 1948	-----	100
	-----	July 1950	-----	150
	-----	June 1952	-----	300
	-----	Dec. 1952	-----	300
	-----	Nov. 1955	-----	350
	-----	Dec. 1956	-----	150
	-----	March 1958	-----	150
	-----	-----*	-----	200
Transwestern	-----	-----	1960	300
Pacific Gas and Electric	-----	-----	1961	415
El Paso-Colorado Interstate	-----	Dec. 1960	-----	470
Tennessee Gas-Pemex	Jan. 1961	-----	-----	455
TOTAL (Constructed, Being Built, or Proposed)				3,895

* El Paso Natural Gas has applied to the FPC for authorization of this project.

to supply up to five trillion cubic feet from future discoveries in the next ten years. It was understood that Shell would receive an initial price of not less than thirteen and one-half cents per thousand cubic feet and that this would escalate up to around twenty cents.[14]

At a hearing before the Alberta Oil and Gas Conservation Board in late 1959, Alberta and Southern Gas wanted to include among its sources of supply the following oil and gas fields: Brazeau River, Burnt Timber, Caroline, Fox Creek, Fox Creek North, Fox Creek West, Kaybob, and Lobstick.[15] It also wanted to increase the deliv-

[14] The California Public Utilities Commission, through its attorney, objects to favored nations and fixed-step escalation clauses in gas contracts with Canadian producers who will supply the gigantic PG&E project. See "Canada-to-California Line Hits Snag," *Oil and Gas Journal,* Volume LVIII, No. 17 (April 25, 1960), 108. However, the California Commission gave its VFPC and approval. See "Alberta-California Line to Start Soon," *Oil and Gas Journal,* Vol. LVIII, No. 34 (August 22, 1960), 57.

[15] See R. A. Simpson and L. R. Borden, *A Survey of the Natural Gas Industry in Canada, 1957–1959,* Mineral Resources Division Mineral Information Bulletin MR39. Note especially Table 7.

eries from these and other fields from 400 million to 500 million cubic feet per day, from 135 billion to 168 billion cubic feet in a consecutive twelve-month period, and from 2,300 billion to 4,200 billion cubic feet during the term of the permit. The authorization of the National Energy Board was finally given for a total of 3,826 billion cubic feet over a twenty-five-year period—somewhat less than Alberta and Southern had asked for but still a large volume—to be transported to the Bay City.

The initial cost of the project was about 338 million dollars, of which 106 million represented the cost of facilities in the Province of Alberta which were financed and constructed independently by the Alberta Gas Trunk Line Company, which has an exclusive right to transport gas in the province of Alberta.[16] The section of the line through the Province of British Columbia is owned and operated in Canada by Alberta Natural Gas Company and from the international boundary to the California-Oregon boundary by Pacific Gas Transmission Company. Pacific Gas Transmission owns one-third of the stock of Alberta Natural Gas Company. The remainder of Alberta Natural Gas is held equally by Westcoast Transmission and by Canadians who can buy 310,000 common shares at ten dollars and fifty cents a share.

Pacific Gas and Electric owns 50 per cent of the equity securities of Pacific Gas Transmission. Nine per cent is owned by Canadian Bechtel, a branch of the world-wide San Francisco Construction Company. Seven per cent is owned by Bright and Company; 7 per cent by International Utilities Corporation, which owns the leading utilities in the Province of Alberta; 2 per cent by Montana Power; and 25 per cent by the public which bought that stock for an issue price of nine dollars and fifty cents a share. Canadians had first choice of that stock in Pacific Gas Transmission Company.

There are three segments[17] involved in the import project.[18] Pacific Gas Transmission buys 480 million cubic feet a day from Alberta and

[16] A. G. Bailey, a prominent Canadian oil and gas man, is president of Alberta Gas Trunk Line Company.

[17] The three segments of the import plan and their approval by examiner Robert M. Weston are described in the *Wall Street Journal* (Southwest Edition), Monday, May 2, 1940, p. 20.

[18] A very good survey and appraisal of the significance of the export permit granted April 1, 1960, can be found in an article entitled "Big Boost for Canadian Gas," which

Southern Gas Company, Limited, a wholly-owned subsidiary of Pacific Gas and Electric, which will receive gas from Pacific Gas Transmission at the California-Oregon border. Pacific Gas and Electric will sell the gas in California. This plan involves 640 miles of pipe line built at a cost of 133 million dollars to allow Pacific Gas Transmission to carry the gas from the international border to Pacific Gas and Electric.

Pacific Gas Transmission transports 136.5 million cubic feet of gas from the Canadian border to El Paso Natural Gas Company for use in its general system. El Paso, which constructed a $2,443,000 facility to receive the gas, bought the fuel in Canada from Westcoast Transmission Company, Limited. Westcoast made a contract with Husky Oil, one of the producers of the Savannah Creek gas field,[19] about 60 miles southwest of Calgary. Savannah Creek has, according to the conservation board's 1959 estimate, 550 billion cubic feet of disposable gas. The price under that contract was reported to have started at twelve cents per thousand cubic feet, escalating to twenty cents over a twenty-five-year period. Westcoast's permit foresees a daily volume of 152,000 MCF, with a total over a twenty-year period not to exceed 1,020 billion cubic feet. El Paso uses the gas it receives from Westcoast to replace fuel it currently gets from within its own system at Ignacio, Colorado. The gas supply being replaced is that gas El Paso is selling in California.

Gas imports from Canada put El Paso in the position "of having vast additional supplies of natural gas from fields in the southwest heading north and from Canada heading south." El Paso Natural Gas will get an additional 150 million cubic feet from Alberta. Conceivably, Alberta gas will find its way into the Los Angeles area as a result of this link. By *displacement*—freeing United States gas from demands in the Pacific Northwest—the Canadian gas increases the supply available for the Southern California area. As Canadian lines are built to this country for pickup by domestic lines, a large part of the

---

appeared in *Petroleum Press Service,* Vol. XXVII, No. 6 (May, 1960), 171–73. See "Effect of Canadian Gas on Balance of Payments," *Petroleum Press Service,* Vol. XXV, No. 12 (December, 1958), 471, for a discussion of the effect the project will have on the Canadian balance of payments deficit.

[19] "Gas Prices Climb in Western Canada," *Petroleum Week,* Vol. V, No. 10 (September 6, 1957), 9. Other producers are Northern Natural Gas Production Company (32.5 per cent), Phillips Petroleum Company (27.5 per cent), Canadian Anaconda Oils, Limited (5 per cent), and Target Petroleums, Limited (2.5 per cent). Husky Oil controls the other 32.5 per cent.

needs of California will be supplied from fields in Alberta. This source of supply should not be overestimated because the National Energy Board strongly emphasized that any future applications for export to the Pacific Northwest would receive most critical examination, unless the gas was to come from northern British Columbia. The board pointed out that the gas potential in that area needs to be explored.[20]

Canadian-Montana also plans to use Alberta and Southern lines to export to Montana up to 36,000 thousand cubic feet daily, or 273.7 billion cubic feet over twenty-five years. The parent company, Montana Power Company, will distribute the gas. The export of Alberta gas to Montana in 1952 was the first such export to be permitted by the Alberta Conservation Board.

It was in the Peace River area that Francis Murray Patrick McMahon pioneered the discovery of natural gas in Canada. This courageous wildcatter who hails from southwestern British Columbia "virtually single-handedly developed the natural gas of northwestern Canada."[21] As is often the case with oil and gas prospecting, success came only after many disappointing failures. The main discovery was the Fort St. John Field in British Columbia in 1952. Mr. McMahon realized from the day he planned the 650-mile, 30-inch pipe line from the Fort St. John Field through British Columbia to Sumas on the international border in the state of Washington that it could become profitable only if he could sell gas to the United States. British Columbia has a population of only 1.6 million in an area of 366,255 square miles (the size of Texas plus Colorado), and though the province has been showing a great boom it could not support such a costly undertaking as the big pipe line.[22]

Among the discoveries made in northeastern British Columbia

[20] The great discoveries in that area made this desire of the board a reality, as Francis M. McMahon, president of Westcoast Transmission Company, Limited, pointed out in his address, quoted in footnote 23.

Plans are being made by Westcoast for a 245-mile, 30-inch line that will provide an outlet for reserves in Northern Canada estimated at 2.5 trillion cubic feet. Costs will probably run as high as $400,000 per mile. The line is to be built (for $93,000,000) by Gas Trunk Line of British Columbia, Limited, and will tie in with Westcoast's system which carries gas from the Fort St. John area to the Canadian-United States border. This project, however costly, will be a boon for El Paso and the Pacific Coast region.

[21] "Pipeline Builder, a King of Sports," *New York Times,* October 9, 1957, p. 51.

[22] Hanson, *Dynamic Decade,* 240–42.

in March, 1959, were two which are considered to be two of the largest discoveries made in Canada. Both of these wells were tested on a restricted flow basis, but it is generally considered that they are approximately the same size as Berland River, one of the largest potential producers in Alberta. These wells were drilled in the Clarke Lake, Kotcho Lake, and Petitot River areas of northeastern British Columbia.[23]

When Trans-Canada Pipelines, Limited (Trans-Canada) was completed in 1958, it represented a high point in the planning, financing, construction, and operating history of natural gas transmission. In the United States there are natural gas transmission systems which have more mileage than Trans-Canada, but none of them runs a single line of such great length (about 2,294 miles or 3,700 kilometers).

The idea behind the line was conceived by the well-known Texas oilman and financier, Clint Murchison, in the wake of the Leduc discovery, which foretold the presence of huge natural gas reserves in western Canada. Western Canada had large reserves but small markets, and it was necessary to seek markets in eastern Canada and some adjacent areas across the border. The company was created by special act of Parliament in 1951. Mr. Murchison's idea was to establish an outlet for the wealth of gas in the prairies or great plains by founding a company that would, in the words of the charter, "own or lease and operate a natural gas pipeline system extending from the Province of Alberta across the Provinces of Saskatchewan, Manitoba, and through a portion of Quebec to Montreal."[24] Trans-Canada is the realization of Mr. Murchison's dream.

The fact that construction did not start until 1956 points to the fact that there were countless difficulties that had to be overcome before the company could go before the American and Canadian public to offer debentures and common shares for subscription. Dra-

[23] "Some of the gas wells that have been discovered (up to the northern boundaries of British Columbia and Alberta) particularly in the area around Fort Nelson, B. C., are among the most productive ever found anywhere in the world," said Frances M. McMahon, president of Westcoast Transmission Company, Limited, in an address delivered at the University of Toronto, Toronto, Ontario, October 24, 1960. This paper gives an excellent description of the development and future of the gas industry in Canada, especially in British Columbia.

[24] Mr. Murchison was the founder of Canadian Delhi Petroleum, Limited, a subsidiary of Delhi-Taylor Oil Corporation which he serves as chairman. For details, see Walter E. Skinner's *Oil and Petroleum Year Book*.

matic reading though it would make, we do not intend to write the story of Trans-Canada from its establishment to the beginning of construction, but being an important piece of living natural gas history, this undertaking deserves a more detailed description. As the *New York Times* put it:

> The Alberta to Montreal pipeline is one of the great sagas of post-war finance. Bogged down repeatedly in a diversity of vested interests, it was rescued first by one financial stroke then another. Frank Kernan was brought into the picture in the special capacity of financial adviser by holders of 51% of the ownership capital—Tennessee Gas Transmission, Hudson's Bay Oil Company, and British-American Oil Company.
>
> The deal came off only because the White, Weld (Company) partner (Mr. Kernan) achieved a meeting of minds with the big life insurance companies, and because another banking team—Lehman Brothers and Allen and Company—kept alive a costly option for acquiring certain gas distribution properties.[25]

Eventually, all requirements for successful operation of the Trans-Canada pipe line were met, and the determined promoters could carry out their grandiose design.

It was no easy task to line up the suppliers for a far-flung system like Trans-Canada. The gas producers wanted to be sure of having a regular, viable customer in the new pipe line. But finally the corporation executed forty-seven contracts with natural gas producers in fourteen fields in Alberta.[26] Some of the most prolific fields of the province including Pincher Creek, Cessford, Provost, Homeglen-Rimbey, and Nevis are contributing to the supply. Of course, supply is never complete in a giant system like this one. Fortunately new large fields have been discovered since, and the gas supply at the end of 1959 was estimated by Trans-Canada at 7.97 trillion cubic feet.

The Alberta Conservation Board granted Trans-Canada a permit to export up to a maximum of 4.35 trillion cubic feet until 1981 with a daily quantity of not higher than 620,000 thousand cubic feet and an annual maximum of 183,000,000 thousand cubic feet. On the basis of the higher future requirements already indicated by gas distrib-

[25] Paul Heffernan, "Personality: Builder of Pipelines in Wall Street," *New York Times,* Sunday, June 9, 1957, p. 3, financial section. This is a sketch of the successful transactions of Francis Kernan, partner of White, Weld and Company, in financing gas transmission systems.

[26] This was later increased to fifty-five contracts from fifteen fields.

utors and by big potential industrial consumers, Trans-Canada believes that by 1963 it will require twice the rate of off-take so far authorized by the Alberta Conservation Board and consequently also a double pipe-line capacity, which will entail building a new, parallel line. Meanwhile the board increased the original total of 4.35 trillion cubic feet by 1.1 trillion cubic feet, and there is little doubt that the board will permit further increases, especially in view of new prolific discoveries.

Trans-Canada paid originally ten cents per thousand cubic feet. The pipe line is now paying around 13½ cents per thousand cubic feet for its new supplies. It will receive the gas at the Alberta-Saskatchewan border from the Alberta Gas Trunk Line Company, Limited, a company unique in the history of natural gas transmission in several respects.[27]

Suggested by the Alberta Conservation Board and introduced by Premier Ernest C. Manning in the Alberta legislature, the Alberta Trunk Line Company was established on April 8, 1954. The company's function is to gather and transmit natural gas within the province of Alberta, both for domestic consumption and export. It is strictly a provincial institution, "a quasi-political amalgamation of producers, pipe-liners, and representatives of the Alberta Provincial Government."[28] Alberta Trunk Line maintains control of Alberta's gas by restricting voting shares in the corporation to the province and having two government representatives on the Board of Directors. Trans-Canada and other companies exporting gas from Alberta are entitled to name one director to the Board. Thus, Alberta's gas is guarded against outside invasion. For instance the gas for which the export permit was given on April 1, 1960, and which is being sent to the California market, will be transported in Alberta exclusively by Alberta Gas Trunk Line.

Alberta Trunk Line is not a Crown Corporation but is a government corporation which has sold shares on the public market. Indeed the public sale of 2,552,300 Class A non-voting shares priced at $5.25

27 See "Funnel for All New Gas Moving Out of Alberta," *Oil and Gas Journal*, Vol. LVIII, No. 2 (January 11, 1960), 46–47. This is an excellent article about the Alberta Gas Trunk Line.

28 See the Trans-Canada issue of *Gas*, Vol. XXXIII, No. 8 (August, 1957), for a comprehensive description of the great project and its checkered history. For additional factual information, see the *Prospectus* of Trans-Canada Pipelines, Limited, February 13, 1957.

each offered only in Alberta was "the heaviest financial rush of the Province's history."[29]

Board members of Alberta Gas Trunk Line are: B. F. Willson, representing the utilities; N. E. Tanner, representing gas exporters; A. G. Bailey, D. C. Jones, and J. Grant Armstrong, representing producers and processors; and R. J. Dinning, G. E. Church, the two government appointees. General Manager of Alberta Gas Trunk Line is Eldon Hunt.[30]

It is from this Alberta gathering system, one of the largest in the world, that Trans-Canada will receive the gas it has purchased from the producers at its western terminals. But Alberta Gas Trunk Line has expanded or is expanding its gathering system far beyond that initially devoted to transporting gas for Trans-Canada. Since there can be little doubt that Trans-Canada will greatly expand capacity and that more and more of Alberta gas will be exported, prospects for the growth of the Alberta Gas Trunk Line Company, Limited, appear to be bright.

The supply of natural gas being fully assured, the next important factor is a market. Canada's tremendous physical growth is not matched by her population figures. Her population density is quite low, and she could support several times her present population of 17 million. According to an estimate of the Gordon Commission, Canada may reach a population total of 25,770,000 in 1980 if net immigration per year is 50,000; 26,650,000, if net immigration is 75,000; or 27,-535,000, if net immigration is 100,000. These and other considerations may have some bearing on the market that Trans-Canada will supply with natural gas. The more important cities or metropolitan areas to be served by the company are: Regina, Brandon, Winnipeg, Fort Williams-Port Arthur, Toronto, Hamilton, Montreal, and Ottawa.[31]

The eastern-most market of the pipe line is the Quebec market. The utility distributing the gas is the Quebec Natural Gas Corporation

[29] There are 8,002,002 shares of Class A and Class B common stock with a par value of $5.00. Only 2,002 shares of Class A stock carry voting rights. See "Farmout Deal Scored," *Oil and Gas Journal,* Vol. LII, No. 47 (March 29, 1954), 62.

[30] "Eldon Hunt: A Busy Canadian Pipeliner," *Oil and Gas Journal,* Vol. LVIII, No. 2 (January 11, 1960), 144–45.

[31] A vivid description of what the development of natural resources such as natural gas can do in the vast, empty spaces of Canada can be found in Mr. McMahon's address, quoted in footnote 23 on page 350.

which is heir to the former gas distribution system of Quebec, Hydro-electric Commission, a provincial government agency. The financiers of Trans-Canada requested that this agency be acquired and made into a private corporation because there was little chance that Trans-Canada would be financially secure and profitable without the Quebec market. The shares of Quebec Natural Gas Corporation were picked up by the American and Canadian public with great enthusiasm, but the beginnings of the operations were somewhat disappointing. Neither the public in Montreal nor the industry were anxious to turn to natural gas particularly since heavy fuel oil prices in Montreal Harbor were very weak.

With the appointment of Leonard Milano as executive vice-president and chief officer, conditions improved generally and remarkably. He put together a highly efficient sales organization, and both residential heating and industrial fuel requirements increased remarkably. Quebec Natural is now well on the way to selling natural gas both for space heating and interruptible industrial purposes though it will be a little while before a noticeable increase in the consumption of natural gas with accompanying earnings can be realized. The following table presents a picture of Quebec Natural's gas sales and revenues:

	Actual 1959	*Estimate* 1963
Natural Gas Revenues (Thousands of dollars)	9,397	35,497
Natural Gas Sales (Million Cu. Ft.)		
Residential	3,283	12,300
Commercial	1,011	2,400
Industrial Firm	761	7,300
Industrial Interruptible	——	7,662
TOTAL SALES	5,055	29,662

The other great market is Toronto, center of Canada's most industrialized province, Ontario. There Trans-Canada deals with a long-established (1847), but youthfully aggressive gas utility, Consumer's Gas Company of Toronto, one of the fastest growing on the American continent.[32] Since 1954 the company has distributed natural gas carried to the international boundary by Tennessee Natural

[32] See the Trans-Canada issue of *Gas,* Vol. XXXIII, No. 8 (August, 1957), 56.

Gas Transmission from the Texas and Louisiana Gulf Coasts where a subsidiary of Consumer's, the Niagara Transmission Limited, buys it from the Marine Gathering Company, Phillips Petroleum Company, and Kerr-McGee Industries, Incorporated. In Canada Western Pipelines, a subsidiary of Trans-Canada, is the carrier.

The number of gas-heated homes in the Toronto metropolitan area grew from about four thousand in 1954 to more than thirty-eight thousand in 1958. About ten thousand homes were added to this number in 1959. Consumer's considers this early growth the prelude to a truly dramatic development in the sales volume of natural gas and is spending seventy-five million dollars on expansion.

Consumer's has contracted with Trans-Canada for 165,000 MCF daily between November 1, 1962, and October 31, 1963 and thereafter. It is not afraid of competition from other sources of energy. Having voluntarily cut the price of natural gas four times since 1955, the utility "hopes to make the biggest reduction of all when Trans-Canada comes on stream."[33] In 1958 Consumer's rates were still higher than those prevailing in the city of Buffalo, New York, but according to the *New York Times* the volume-consumer ratio is more favorable in Toronto. With Toronto and Ontario steadily growing, Natural Gas, Trans-Canada, and Consumer's Gas are to have a place in this favorable development.

Another first-rate customer of Trans-Canada in Ontario is Union Gas Company of Canada, Limited. Its market is the southwestern part of the province, and it is headquartered in the city of Hamilton. This promotionally active utility contracted with Trans-Canada for deliveries of 20 billion cubic feet of natural gas in the beginning which would build up to 64 billion cubic feet in the tenth year on a 75 per cent take-or-pay basis. High load factor operations are assured by Union's extensive storage facilities which provided 72 per cent of peak-day requirements during the winter of 1958–59. The present working storage capacity of 20 billion cubic feet can be greatly expanded through other undeveloped storage sites available to the company. This strong storage position provides several advantages. All industrial sales are made on a firm basis at an average price of eighty-five cents per thousand cubic feet. Furthermore, Union is now storing 7.5 billion cubic feet each year for the account of Consumer's

[33] "Natural Gas Use Sweeps Toronto," *New York Times,* January 8, 1958, p. 57.

Gas Company on a fee basis. Finally, these facilities enable Trans-Canada to deliver about two-thirds of its gas supply to Union during the off-peak months of April–October, thereby improving its own load-factor. In return, the pipe line sells gas to Union at a flat commodity price of thirty-nine cents per thousand cubic feet.

Natural gas is competitively priced for both residential heating and most industrial usage, and space-heating saturation is a relatively low 40 per cent. The company is capturing most of the new home market and expects to add ten thousand new space-heating customers annually over the next several years from conversions and new homes. The potential for increased industrial business is also attractive.

In the Province of Manitoba, the famous wheat region, metropolitan Winnipeg is the main market for natural gas which is distributed by the Winnipeg and Central Gas Company. Being a farming center, the city offers the greatest prospect for natural gas use in residential heating, but some is used by food processing enterprises for which controlled heat is especially suited. The Winnipeg utility has signed a contract with Trans-Canada for gas deliveries of 46,400 thousand cubic feet each year from November 1, 1962, on.

The province of Saskatchewan is called the center of the Prairie Market. There production of oil and gas have brought prosperity. In Saskatchewan there is also considerable production of uranium, and there are tremendous potash deposits. The enormous production of wheat and livestock has made agriculture the mainstay of this prairie province, but industry is coming. The province has an abundance of electrical power and says in a very attractive advertisement, "Low cost, efficient natural gas . . . is another prime attraction for expanding industry."[34] The capital is Regina. Another important city is Moose Jaw. Distributor of gas in this province is the Saskatchewan Power Corporation. This utility has natural gas reserves of its own but contracted with Trans-Canada for five billion cubic feet of gas for one year and three billion cubic feet for the remaining nineteen years of the contract—a Lilliputian quantity for a giant pipe line like Trans-Canada.

The Northern Ontario Section is the problem child of this great undertaking. Trans-Canada, like the Gaul of Caesar's accounts, is divided into three parts or sections: a western section consisting of

[34] *Ibid.*

about 586 miles of 34-inch pipe from the Alberta-Saskatchewan border to Winnipeg, Manitoba; a central section consisting of 1,251 miles of 30-inch pipe from the end of the Western Section to Toronto; and an eastern section from Toronto to Montreal, 308 miles of 20-inch pipe and a 33-mile, 24-inch extension to the present terminus of Western Pipeline, a wholly-owned subsidiary of Trans-Canada. A lateral line to Ottawa, the capital of the country, was constructed in 1958.

Part of the central section is the Northern Ontario Section, a thinly populated, heavily forested lakeland section.[35] This area has a population of about 307,000 people living in small towns and is typical of the thinly populated country which makes expensive pipe-line construction and marketing of gas economically difficult. There are about 50,000 homes in the service area of Northern Ontario Natural Gas Company, but the Northern Ontario Section also has eleven pulp and paper mills which supply newsprint to Canada and the United States. There, also, is situated the principal nickel production of the Free World. Although not many people live in this area, a rough climate assures the gas distributing utility, the Northern Ontario Natural Gas Company, Limited, a pretty high load factor through space-heating. The utility was assisted in its difficult job of organizing distribution by the experienced Fish Service Corporation of Houston, Texas, which belongs to the engineering firm that designed Pacific Northwest Pipeline Company. Geologically the area is part of the Pre-Cambrian or Canadian shield. Some of the towns being serviced are built on massive rock. Construction of the pipe line across the solid rock folds of the shield was difficult, and construction prices tended to skyrocket. Contracts awarded for five spreads covering 367 miles of 30-inch totaled $20,827,789, an average of $10.19 a foot. This compares with an average of $3.50 a foot in the flat prairie areas. "While drills, dynamite, and backhoes carve out the ditch foot by foot through rock in Ontario, the ditcher east of Toronto can make 20,000 feet a day."[36] The main obstacle to successful pipe-line operation is not the rock but the sparse population. Trans-Canada faced a formidable financial risk, but a solution was found in establishing a Government or Crown Corporation "that would build the Canadian Shield Section of the

35 See the Trans-Canada issue of *Gas,* Vol. XXXIII, No. 8 (August, 1957), 59.

36 *Oil and Gas Journal,* Vol. LV, No. 49 (December 9, 1957), 65.

pipeline to lease it to Trans-Canada, and provide a method whereby Trans-Canada would acquire ownership of the Crown Corporation when financially able to do so."[37] In early June, 1956, the Canadian Parliament in Ottawa approved formation of the Crown Corporation and an agreement that the corporation could loan Trans-Canada up to about $72,000,000 to be repaid by April 2, 1957, at 5 per cent interest. Trans-Canada subsequently borrowed $49,750,000 from the Crown Corporation. This was repaid with all costs and interests on February 26, 1957.

Northern Ontario Natural Gas Company, Limited, has made two contracts, one for the northern zone and another one for six cities in the western zone. Among them the the cities of Fort William and Port Arthur at the head of Lake Superior. These two places were fortunate in receiving Alberta's natural gas at the end of January, 1958, which marked completion of 60 per cent of Trans-Canada. According to the contracts, quantities in the northern zone began with 28,000 MCF daily, increasing to 60,200 MCF a day from November 1, 1962. In the western zone, the initial delivery was 25,000 MCF daily, increasing to 33,000 MCF from November 1, 1962.

The company was able to sign up all of its available large industrial customers by the middle of 1958, prior to completion of its basic system. High load-factor operations were thereby established at an early stage and were at around 93 per cent in 1959. The Borden Commission foresees for 1965 a maximum peak-day requirement for this market. The pulp and paper industry will probably require 75,000 MCF per day. Other industrial operations may take 16,000 MCF a day which will make a total of 91,000 MCF per day.

When Trans-Canada was struggling for financial support for its giant project, it had to show its prospective investors that it had firm customers that would take considerable quantities of gas. Tennessee Gas Transmission, always anxious to increase its supply of gas and to expand its system, entered, through its subsidiary Midwestern Gas Transmission Company, into agreements with Trans-Canada, giving Midwestern a 25-year contract to buy from Trans-Canada up to two hundred million cubic feet of natural gas a day. Tennessee Gas Trans-

---

[37] See *Prospectus* of Trans-Canada Pipelines, Limited, February 13, 1957, pp. 8–10. Trans-Canada expects that it will acquire the Northern Ontario section by the end of the fifth year of operation.

mission was to receive the gas at Emerson, Manitoba, some forty-eight miles from Winnipeg. Midwestern proposed to construct a pipe-line system from the Emerson delivery point across the states of Minnesota, Wisconsin, Illinois, Indiana, Kentucky and Tennessee to connect with the Tennessee Gas Transmission pipe-line system. The agreement provided that Tennessee Gas would receive excess gas from Trans-Canada at the international boundary at Niagara Falls to import into the United States. This would be gas for the Eastern Seaboard States. It strengthened considerably the Tennessee Gas position in that area. The FPC granted Midwestern permission to import the gas on October 31, 1959, provided that Trans-Canada receive permission to export the gas from Canada. This permission was given on April 1, 1960.

Trans-Canada also received permission to export at Niagara Falls, Ontario, on a completely interruptible basis to Tennessee Gas Transmission up to 204,000 MCF daily. In this case the twenty-year license period sought was shortened by fifteen years. The permit expires December 31, 1965.

Trans-Canada says in its annual report for 1959 that "export of natural gas can be a major factor in the improvement of Canada's adverse balance of trade with the United States. The stability of the sale over many years is a factor which makes the sale especially desirable. The financial strength which (Trans-Canada) will gain from export sales will enable (Trans-Canada) to serve and expand into new Canadian markets which it does not presently serve."[38]

Not the least of the difficulties besetting Trans-Canada before construction started was the financing of the new project. Investors were reluctant to risk their dollars in this great but untried venture, but once gas supply and gas sales appeared sufficiently large to warrant profitable operation of the pipe line, there were no obstacles to further delay financing. Supplies are more than adequate and will be so in the future if controls are released and the rate of return is not held to a bare minimum. As to the markets, the situation of Trans-Canada was different from that ordinarily found in the United States in that Trans-Canada proposed to supply a vast country where the thinly populated areas are the rule and populous sections are the exception.

[38] Average prices approved by NEB are: Trans-Canada, 30c/MCF; Alberta and Southern, 27.38c/MCF; Westcoast, 26.63/MCF; and Canadian-Montana, 24.96c/MCF.

TABLE 20
THE CAPITALIZATION OF TRANS-CANADA

Title of Class	Authorized or to be Authorized	Outstanding as of Dec. 31, 1956	Outstanding upon Completion of Financing
First Mortgage Pipe-line Bonds			
5.50 Per cent Series due 1978			
(Dollars)	——	——	23,010,000
5.25 Per cent Series due 1978			
(Dollars)	——	——	80,990,000
5.00 Per cent First Mortgage Bonds			
due Apr. 2, 1957 (Dollars)	80,000,000	43,750,000	——
5.25 Per cent Bank Loan due			
Mar. 1, 1962 (U.S. Dollars)	20,000,000	——	20,000,000
Subordinated Debentures due 1987			
5.85 Per Cent Canadian Series			
(Dollars)	54,166,700	——	54,166,700
5.60 Per cent United States Series			
(U.S. Dollars)	20,833,300	——	20,833,300
5.50 Per cent Subordinated Convertible Income Notes due 1987			
(Dollars)	21,000,000	——	——
Preferred Shares, $50 Par Value			
(Shares)	1,000,000	——	——
Common Shares, $1 Par Value			
(Shares)	10,000,000	1,928,184	5,823,184

The financing program was announced on February 14, 1957. It was a tremendous success in both the United States and Canada, and the offering was oversubscribed. A "package deal" was offered to the subscribers. The units consisted of $100 debenture and five common shares. The price per Canadian unit was $150 (Canadian) and per United States unit, $156 (United States). A total of $54,166,700 in 5.85 per cent subordinated debentures due 1987 (Canadian series) and $20,833,000 in 5.60 per cent subordinated debentures (United States Series) were offered. Thus, the Canadian character of the corporation was clearly preserved. The sum of $112,500,000 was realized from the sale of the units, and proceeds to the company totaled $108,048,077.

360

TABLE 21

Proceeds Received by Trans-Canada

	United States Dollars	Canadian Dollars
Canadian Series Bonds	------	23,010,000
Bank Loan*	20,000,000	------
United States Series Bonds	80,999,000	------
Canadian Units	------	78,000,480
United States Units	31,249,950	------
TOTAL	132,248,950	101,010,480†

* Lending banks: First City Bank of New York, Mellon National Bank and Trust Company, and J. P. Morgan and Company.
† Managing underwriters: Canada—Nesbitt, Thompson and Company, Limited, Montreal; Wood, Gundy and Company, Limited, Toronto; Osler, Hammond and Nanton, Limited, Winnepeg; and McLeod, Young, Weir and Company, Limited, Toronto; United States—Lehman Brothers, New York; Stone and Webster Securities Corporation, New York; and White Weld and Company, New York.

Breakdown of Ownership After Public Financing

	Per cent Owned
Trans-Canada Sponsors	33.11
Public in the United States	17.89
Public in Canada	46.51
Issued on Option to Attract and Hold Key Executive Personnel and for Employee Participation	2.49*
TOTAL	100.00

(Source: Trans-Canada issue of *Gas*, August, 1957.)
* Percentage represents a total of 5,823,184 common shares.

The capitalization of Trans-Canada, based on the company prospectus, is shown in Table 20.

According to the Trans-Canada issue of *Gas*, some fifty institutional investors took first mortgage pipe-line bonds at a cost of $94,-000,000. Canadian agencies were well represented on this list. The Canadianization of the huge undertaking is increasing. The number of Canadian-held shares has considerably increased since they first were issued, and there has been a complete change in ownership. The Americans have moved out, and the Canadians have moved in. Tennessee Gas and Hudson's Bay Oil and Gas Company (owned 75 per cent by Continental Oil Company) sold their stock to Home Oil Company,

361

Limited, of which R. A. Brown, Jr., one of Canada's leading oil men, is president. This purchase made Home Oil the largest single stockholder in Trans-Canada and resulted in the following ownership line-up: Home Oil, 19 per cent; Canadian Delhi Oil, Limited, 9.6 per cent; and British American Oil, Limited, 5.6 per cent. Canadian company holdings thus totaled 34.2 per cent. According to the *Oil and Gas Journal*, Canadians bought 78 per cent of the shares.

The first president of Trans-Canada was N. E. Tanner. He was succeeded in the presidency by Charles S. Coates, who was originally with Tennessee Gas and is a highly experienced gas engineer. James W. Kerr of Hamilton, Ontario, succeeded Mr. Coates. Mr. Kerr was formerly vice-president of the Canadian Westinghouse Company. Thus an electrical industry man took over the huge natural gas company. Mr. Tanner is now a director of the company and maintains his office in the company's Calgary branch. Other directors are: R. A. Brown, Jr., president of Home Oil Company, Limited; Frank A. Schultz, president of Canadian Delhi and director of Trans-Canada Pipe Lines, Limited; and James W. Kerr, who is president and chairman of the board. The other officers are N. John McNeill, vice-president, general counsel, and secretary; H. Dix Fowler, vice-president, engineering and operations; and George W. Woods, treasurer.

MEXICO

When, on August 22, 1957, Mexican natural gas entered the United States of America for the first time to add to its fuel supply, it was hailed as an event of great significance. From a historical point of view one could muse over changing times. Once Mexico was one of the most prolific exporters of oil from concessions operated by private concerns. It nationalized the oil industries in 1938 and has since expanded the oil industry primarily to meet domestic needs. In 1957 it returned to the international oil and gas scene as a supplier of gas to a prominent pipeline system in the United States of America. It was Texas Eastern Transmission Corporation that purchased the gas from Petroleos Mexicanos (Pemex), the government agency (a corporation) for the oil and gas industry. Under a twenty-year contract concluded in 1955, Mexico delivers an average of 140 million cubic feet of dry gas daily to Texas Eastern for about fifteen cents per thousand cubic feet, escalating two-tenths of a cent each year. In 1959, Texas Eastern sold 644 billion cubic feet of natural gas. Mexico's share amounts to only about 8 per cent of this volume; but it is a propitious beginning, and the amount can be increased in the future.

Possibilities for sales increases exist because Pemex gas comes from three fields in Mexico's northeastern, Reynosa district just across the Rio Grande. This district's proved reserves are estimated at 3.15 trillion cubic feet. The potential of this huge gas area is good. Another prolific gas district is the Macuspana district located in southeastern Mexico. It has proven reserves of 2.8 trillion cubic feet. A third district is Veracruz in the southern central part of the state of Veracruz. At least 2 trillion cubic feet of gas can be produced from Mexico's oil fields. Under the energetic management of Pascual Gutierrez Roldan, director-general of Pemex, exploration should continue to lead to new discoveries.

Pemex is constructing an extensive gas transmission system, chiefly for an energy-hungry industry. A very important Pemex project was completed in 1960 at a cost of $80,000,000. It is a 625-mile, 24-inch pipe line from Ciudad Pemex in southern Mexico to Mexico City. It was opened on May 22, 1961, by the President of Mexico, Adolfo López Mateos. An extension of this line is carrying gas to Salamanca.[39]

In the north, an existing pipe line from Reynosa to Monterrey and Saltillo will soon be expanded to Torreón and Chihuahua. Monterrey is Mexico's third largest city, while Saltillo is her second largest industrial center.

Pemex had, for 1960, a budget of eight billion pesos ($640,000,-000), almost as much as the Federal Government of Mexico. Such outlays give a mighty stimulus to further development.[40]

Under Gutierrez Roldan, Pemex has been highly successful in obtaining foreign loans for use in expanding the industry. A major project underway in 1962 was the creation of a petrochemical industry.

The Federal Power Commission held hearings in April, 1961, on a Pemex and Tennessee Gas project which proposes the building of a

[39] See the *Oil Daily,* Tuesday, May 23, 1961, p. 4.

[40] See Antonio Garcia-Rojas, "The Mexican Gas Industry," an address before the annual conference of the American Gas Association General Management Section, February 29–March 2, 1960, Pittsburgh, Pennsylvania. Mr. Rojas is the exploration manager of Pemex.

1,200-mile pipe line across northern Mexico from Reynosa on the Texas-Mexico border to Mexicali on the California-Mexico border at a cost of $165,000,000. Each day the line would transport 380,000 MCF of gas received from Tennessee Gas Transmission Company at the Texas border plus 75,000 MCF of Mexico-produced gas to the California border where the gas would be redelivered to Tennessee Gas. Tennessee Gas proposes to move the natural gas to Los Angeles for use by Southern California Edison Company in the generation of electricity.

EUROPE

Before World War II, Europe's production of natural gas was insignificant. Only the older oil-producing countries such as Poland and Rumania had any significant gas production. Russia, although possessing large potential gas resources, had only partially developed them. The situation changed in a startling way after the end of the war.

Italy

Italy, one of the poorest countries in natural resources, discovered and developed considerable deposits of natural gas. In 1959 reserves were estimated to be in excess of five trillion cubic feet.

So great has been the beneficial effect of this change on the entire economy of the country that the Economic Commission for Europe, in its 1957 "Report on the Position of Natural Gas in the European Economy," could say:

> Natural gas has thus proved a factor of fundamental importance to the Italian economy, and it can be said without exaggeration that it has provoked a veritable industrial revolution. . . . The exploitation of natural gas in Italy is a typical example of the use of methane (its main constituent) to improve the economic position of a region that is already heavily industrialized.

Natural gas in Italy occurs mainly in the valley of the Po River, where the large gas fields of Caviaga (1946) and Cortemaggiore (1949) have been discovered. About 70 per cent of Italy's industry is concentrated there. The famous industrial centers of Turin and Milan, known all over the world for the high quality of the goods they manufacture and export, are also located in this region. The finding of natural gas was of great importance to this busy area, which had

364

been short of power and forced to import expensive coal and oil to keep the wheels of industry moving. The availability of an excellent, indigenous fuel at an attractive price, speedily distributed by a closely-knit transport network throughout the Po Valley, constituted a powerful factor in further industrial development. This advantage was particularly striking during the reconstruction period when the ravages of war had to be removed, the economy rebuilt, and the extremely low standard of living raised. All this came about through a combination of energetic industrial and government leadership, maximum utilization of the newly found natural gas, and financial aid. Production of natural gas in Italy rose from 4 billion cubic feet in 1948 to 145 billion cubic feet in 1955, and 200 billion cubic feet in 1959.

Gas continues to be a stimulus to the economy. Investments needed to find and develop existing gas reserves have given a powerful impetus to many sectors of the country's economy. The rapid development of the gas industry has provided a body of experts and skilled workers, and it has been necessary to produce equipment for the exploitation of natural gas and for the institution of the consuming industries. It also made possible the creation of a petrochemical industry.

Italy had long possessed a chemical industry. A name like Montecatini was known all over, but now Italy stands in the forefront of the European nations in petrochemical production. The only other important consumption of methane for chemical synthesis is in Germany, where a third of the comparatively small natural gas production is employed for this end. The amount of natural gas consumed in Italy for what the Italians call "chemical transformation" rose from some seven billion cubic feet in 1954 to thirteen billion cubic feet in 1957. From natural gas the Italians produce synthetic ammonia from which nitrogenous fertilizers are made. Synthetic fertilizer production has been very beneficial to Italian agriculture. So much synthetic fertilizer can be produced from natural gas that Italy can even export some of her wide range of fertilizers. A substantial increase of fertilizers can be expected from Ravenna, where a nearby gas field supplies a natural gas containing approximately 99 per cent methane. This gas is used to make synthetic rubber and fertilizers. Reported production in 1960 was ninety thousand tons of synthetic rubber and about one million tons of fertilizers. This new plant, which was built with the technical assistance of Phillips Petroleum Company and Union Carbide, will provide Italy with all the synthetic rubber and fertilizer needed and leave some surplus for export. It is operated by A.N.I.C., a subsidiary of Ente Nazionale Idrocarburi.

Another desirable feature of a petrochemical industry using natural gas as raw material is the manufacture of a variety of products such as plastics. Plastics can be processed into a multitude of highly useful products which are frequently cheaper and better than goods made from Nature's own sources, which, with some exceptions, are scarce in Italy. Italy, a member of the Common Market Community, will considerably strengthen her competitive position with regard to the other five members—France, Germany, Belgium, Holland, Luxembourg—as she develops her natural gas industry.

It is interesting to note that the price of natural gas does not depend on the distance separating the consumer from the deposit but is the same throughout the area served by the network. The urge to establish a petrochemical industry led E.N.I. to accord it a lower price than that charged for thermal uses, a compensation for the high capital investment required in this industry and a supplying of a primary material on favorable terms. This policy helped to create and develop a strong petrochemical industry that will not only benefit the plants, private and state-owned alike, but the entire economy and the Italian people.

Of special interest is the organization of Italy's natural gas industry, which is quite unique in its strictly monopolistic position. A state organization known as Ente Nazionale Idrocarburi (E.N.I.) has been set up to promote and carry out projects of national importance in the fields of hydrocarbons and natural gases. Accordingly, all existing state interests in this field have been brought together in one integrated system. The E.N.I. controls a number of subsidiary companies, each company having its own branches and subdivisions. These include Aziendo Generale Italiana Petroli (A.G.I.P.) Mineraria, for the exploration and exploitation of deposits; Societa Nazionale Metanodotti (S.N.A.M.), which builds and operates natural gas pipe lines; Azienda Metanodotti Padani, which operates pipe lines in the Po Delta only; A.N.I.C., which operates the refinery and petrochemical business; and A.G.I.P. Gas, which distributes LPG products. In addition, there is a feeder line, managed by a private company, which serves Florence.

With its monopolist position, the E.N.I. controls relations between the gas-distributing companies and the natural gas producing and pipe-line industry. Free play of action is eliminated. Every detail of production and consumption is centrally planned—a system entirely alien to that in the United States. With reserves at about five trillion cubic feet and demand at two hundred billion cubic feet per year, a supply of twenty years is available. Since reserves are limited, it was felt necessary to establish an order of priority for users of natural gas in Italy.

There are three methods of gas distribution: it can be sold directly to gas-distribution enterprises, it can be sold through an E.N.I. subsidiary such as Metano Citta (City Gas), or it can be sold through joint companies in which Metano Citta holds 50 per cent of the shares and the municipal authorities hold the other 50 per cent.

The following table shows the consumption of natural gas in 1957 by economic sectors:

NATURAL GAS CONSUMPTION IN ITALY BY ECONOMIC SECTORS (1957)

Industrial	*Billion Cu. Ft.*
Food Processing	8.0
Textile	14.8
Paper	5.7
Metallurgical	32.2
Engineering	9.4
Non-metallic Ores	17.0
Chemical (Fuel)	20.6
Rubber	3.1
Other (Unclassified)	1.9
Total Industrial Consumption (Thermic)	112.7
Chemical Transformation	12.6
Thermo-electrical Industries	22.5
Civilian Uses	17.8
Compressed Gas (Motor traction)	8.1
Other Gas Ducts	.1
TOTAL	173.8

367

This general pattern of consumption was followed through 1959. During that year production was about two hundred billion cubic feet.

S.N.A.M. has accomplished a commendable feat. From a gas pipeline network of only about 220 miles in 1949, it built a 2,835-mile system by the end of 1957.

As in other fields of human endeavor, so in the natural gas industry, certain individuals excel in directing the development of industry, whether it is privately owned or is a public undertaking. The most notable individual in the Italian natural gas industry is the engineer, Enrico Mattei, chairman of E.N.I. He was in charge of building the widely ramified system that embraces all stages of the gas industry— production, transmission, and distribution. The distribution facilities were built jointly with existing municipal utilities, as is typical in Europe. This is in contrast to the United States where most of the gas-distributing companies are private enterprises with public utility character. Following the diversification pattern of American private transmission systems anxious to bolster their earnings with revenues from sources not controlled by the Federal Power Commission, Mr. Mattei has branched out into many related enterprises, including the synthetic rubber and fertilizer plant at Ravenna. This plant is equipped for an ultimate production of about 650,000 tons of fertilizers a year.

Although the recent accomplishments in the production and utilization of natural gas in Italy have been notable, the present large and expanding local fuel supplies are insufficient for all the country's needs. Either gas imported from North Africa or the Middle East by pipeline or tanker shipments will be required.

France

Of all countries in Western Europe, France had, at the end of 1959, the largest known natural gas reserves. The reserves were estimated at that time to be seven trillion cubic feet while production of natural gas at the wellhead during 1959 was reported to be about one hundred billion cubic feet. The large quantity of proven reserves enables this country to look for a sharp rise in gas production in the future.

France is in the second stage of an expanding gas industry. It is developing a full-fledged system like that of Italy. The two most important sources of supply in France are in the extreme southwest in

368

the Aquitaine Basin. The gas occurs in a relatively underdeveloped industrial area of France. This is in sharp contrast to the gas deposits of the Po Valley in northern Italy, which are located near the hub of the country's industry. The problem of utilizing the natural gas in France was, therefore, the reverse of that in Italy as it involved creating a new market rather than capturing one that already existed.

The two principal gas fields in France are the huge Lacq Field and the smaller St. Marcet Field, both located in the Aquitaine Basin. The Lacq gas field was discovered in 1951 and produces from formations of Neocomian, Portlandian, and Kimeridgian ages at depths of 11,200 to 12,000 feet. At the beginning of 1960, there were thirty-five wells in the field which were producing at a reported rate of five hundred million cubic feet daily. The reserves of the field are estimated to be more than six trillion cubic feet. Lacq field gas contains so much sulphur and other impurities that after treatment, it is greatly reduced in volume. The usual composition of the gas is: methane, 70 per cent; ethane, 3 per cent, propane, 1.4 per cent; butanes plus, 0.6 per cent; hydrogen sulfide, 15 per cent; and carbon dioxide, 10 per cent. There is also a severe corrosion problem, and specialized steel must be used for tubing.

During 1959, the treatment plant at Lacq yielded 530,000 barrels of natural gasoline, 150,000 barrels of butane and 125,000 barrels of propane. In addition, it yielded 420,000 tons of sulphur of which over 200,000 tons were exported, after satisfying all the demands of the home market. Some eighty billion cubic feet of gas were produced, and after processing, some forty-five billion cubic feet were sold from this field.

The sixteen-hundred-mile gas pipe line connecting the Lacq field to Paris has been completed. This line delivered about five hundred million cubic feet of gas daily during 1961.

The Lacq field is produced by the Société Nationale des Pétroles D'Aquitaine (S.N.P.A.); but, for the purpose of a common transport and sales policy, a new company, the Société Nationale des Gaz du Sud-ouest, was established. The shares in this new company are held as follows:

Régie Autonome des Pétroles	35%
Société Nationale des Pétroles D'Aquitaine	35%
Gaz de France	30%

This company transports and markets gas on behalf of the producers to private customers for industrial uses involving consumption exceeding five million therms per annum and to licensees of public distribution services, Gaz de France, and municipal authorities for consumption below that figure.

Outside the southwest area, the Compagnie Français de Methane, in which S.N.A.P. and Gaz de France each hold 50 per cent of the shares, is responsible for the transport and sale. However, the distribution mains are the property of Gaz de France, a government corporation.

The second largest field is the St. Marcet Field, situated about seventy miles east and slightly south of Lacq in the foothills of the Pyrenees Mountains. It was discovered in 1939 and has sixteen wells producing from five thousand feet. Its reserves are estimated to be 230 billion cubic feet, and its annual production is around 12 billion cubic feet. The gas is carried through a long-distance pipe line to the cities of Toulouse, Agen, and Bordeaux. The gas is sweet gas.

A third gas field, discovered in 1960, is the Charlas Field, producing from Lower Cretaceous formations at nine thousand feet. The extent of this field is not yet known.

The effect of natural gas on French industrial development has been considerable. Electricité de France has reserved for itself a third of the gas produced for thirty years to supply its power stations at Nantes, Bordeaux and Paris. Its new power station near Lacq will produce electricity for a new aluminum plant owned by Société Pechiney. The planned usage for 1962 was as follows:

	Billion Cu. Ft.
Electricité de France Power Stations	150
Southwestern Region	90
Nantes Region	18
East-Central Region	120
Paris Region	50

The possibility of importing additional gas from Algeria and the prospect of finding additional gas supplies in France make the future of the gas industry in France a bright one.

370

The Netherlands

A discovery in 1960 appears to have established a major gas reserve in the Netherlands. Royal Dutch-Shell and Jersey Standard operating through N. V. Nederlandse Aardolie Mij (N.A.M.) made the discovery in the northeastern Netherlands near Slochteren. The reservoir rock is called the Lower New Red and is reported to be of Carboniferous age. Initial estimates place the reserve at two trillion cubic feet. This magniture of reserve would make possible deliveries of two to three hundred million cubic feet daily, which would be extremely important to the industry of the Netherlands.

All natural gas produced in the Netherlands by N.A.M. is purchased by the government. The gas is delivered through state-owned pipe lines and resold to municipalities which use it to enrich town gas. Deliveries to the government in 1959 averaged about eighteen million cubic feet daily and totaled about six billion cubic feet that year.

Union of Soviet Socialist Republics

Gas was used in Russia as early as 1819 for illuminating the General Staff Headquarters in St. Petersburg (Leningrad). The year 1865 marked the construction of the Moscow gas works, but until comparatively recently the natural gas industry was of secondary importance. Now it has been given a high order of priority by the planning section of the communist government. The planned expansion of the natural gas industry apparently has been brought about by the discovery of sizable gas reserves, the advantages of gas as a fuel in relation to coal, the nearness of gas fields to consuming areas, and the political consideration that use of gas frees crude oil for the economic war with the Free World.

The reported expansion of the gas industry in the Soviet Union can be illustrated by the past and planned fuel balance:

	1950	1955	1960	1965	1972
Coal	65.0	64.8	59.0	41.7	30.0
Oil	12.0	22.4	25.0	33.0	38.0
Natural Gas	1.5	2.4	6.0	17.3	25.0
Other Fuels	21.5	10.4	10.0	8.0	7.0

It is interesting to note the change in the fuel balance in the United States from 1920 to 1960:

	1920	*1960*
Coal	78.4	23.5
Oil	13.5	45.8
Natural Gas	4.2	26.8
Other Fuels	3.9	3.9

It is evident that the Soviets plan to follow a similar trend in shifting from coal to natural gas and petroleum.

Production of natural gas in the Soviet Union during 1959 was about 1.5 trillion cubic feet. The plan calls for this to increase to 5 trillion cubic feet in 1965. The United States figure for 1959 was 12.5 trillion cubic feet.

The Soviet Union's principal gas-producing areas and their pipeline outlets are: the Dashava area in the Carpathians, from where gas is piped to Lvov, Kiev, and Moscow; the Shebelinka area near the Donets Basin, from where gas is piped to Moscow; the Stavropol area near the Black Sea, from where gas goes to Rostov and Moscow through two twenty-eight-inch diameter lines eight hundred miles long; the Saratov area, located on the Volga River between Kuibyshev and Stalingrad; the Stalingrad area, from where gas is piped to both Stalingrad and Moscow; the Baku area, an old oil- and gas-producing area in Russia; the Ufa-Tuimazy area, which is called "the second Baku"; the Gazli Bukhara area, a vast arid region east of the Caspian Sea which is often called "the third Baku"; and the Berezovo area which is located in the extreme north.

The Saratov area was the source of supply for the first gas trunk line in the Soviet Union. The 1,500-mile, 12-inch Saratov-Moscow line was completed in 1946 and provided a great many industrial plants and dwelling units with fuel.

About 80 per cent of Russia's oil now comes from the Ufa-Tuimazy area. Production is mostly from limestones and dolomites of Devonian age. From there, gas is piped to Gorky and the iron and steel center of Magnitorsk.

In the Gazli Bukhara area are the Kum-Dag, Central Kara-Kum, Gazli, Tadzhik, Murgab, and Fergana Valley districts. The Russians have reported the gas area around Gazli to contain the largest gas reserves in the Soviet Union, and possibly the world. Two 40-inch, 1,400-mile lines are planned from this area to the metallurgical and industrial centers of Chelyabinsk and Sverdlovsk in the Urals. Sverdlovsk will also be supplied by a line from the Berezova area.

The Communists have released several indications of reserve figures. It is impossible to know whether these are proved reserves, as in the United States method of estimating, or proved and possible reserves. Since the marine sedimentary basins in the Soviet Union exceed by a factor of 1.25 to 1.50 such basins in the United States, and since the status of gas exploration in the Soviet Union compares to that of this country in about 1915, large gas reserves can be expected. All these factors in relation to the reported production of 1.5 trillion cubic feet of gas in 1959, indicate that the Soviet Union should have at least 70 trillion cubic feet in our category of proved reserves.

Great expansion is reported in the fields of LPG, petrochemical plants, and underground storage. The role of underground gasification of coal is being studied. It is estimated that there are now 8,000 miles of gas trunk lines in Russia. A network of pipe lines totaling 25,000 miles is planned for 1965. This compares to 184,000 miles of gas trunk lines in the United States in 1960. There are many problems facing state-planned expansion of the natural gas industry. Procurement of enough compressors, large-diameter transmission pipe, valves, and allied equipment will pose a real problem in planning. Since the government of the Soviet Union plans to provide gas service to a total of sixty-eight million people in five hundred cities by 1965, construction of distribution systems will be a major concern if the plan is to be realized.

Rumania

Natural gas output in Rumania was 212 billion cubic feet for 1959. This figure represents a 20 per cent gain over production during 1958. Of this, 7 billion cubic feet went to Hungary, 40 billion cubic feet was for domestic use, and 165 billion cubic feet for industrial use. Gas accounted for 19 per cent of over-all energy consumption during 1959, and oil accounted for 53 per cent. Major gas lines in 1959 had a total length of 2,190 miles with a yearly carrying capacity of 350 billion cubic feet.

Austria

In western Europe, Austria is in a very fortunate position in the production of natural gas. This country, with an area of only 32,000 square miles, has considerable reserves of associated and non-associated gas that were estimated at one trillion cubic feet in 1958. The gas occurs in the three most geologically favorable oil and gas Zones of the country: the Molassa zone, the Inner Alpine Vienna Basin and the Graz Basin. These are the three most important Tertiary basins in Austria. In addition there are a number of smaller marine depressions. The largest field is Zeverndorf, which is only twenty-five miles from Vienna. Reserves there are estimated at some 500 billion cubic feet. Next comes the Matzen Field, with about 400 billion cubic feet of recoverable gas. Austrian gas is about 90 to 95 per cent methane.

Gas provides 15 per cent of the total energy supply in Austria, and gas production there is estimated to have been 35 billion cubic feet during 1959. The Austrian Mineral Oil Administration controls production. Gas is supplied to three principal customers: the City of Vienna, the Niogas for all consumers in lower Austria, and the Steirische Ferngas Company for all consumers in Styria. The Organization for European Economic Co-operation (OEEC) Gas Committee estimates that production will reach about 42 billion cubic feet yearly after completion of some pipe-line facilities. Of this, one-half will go to Vienna, one-sixth to lower Austria, one-sixth to Styria, and the remainder to the petrochemical industry.

A remarkable river crossing in the pipe-line system is the Barbara Pipe Bridge near Schechat, which crosses the Blue Danube. The construction of this bridge has incorporated new ideas in such structures.

Other European Countries

The Federal Republic of Germany (West Germany) is increasing its usage of natural gas. It is usually utilized as a mixture and is reformed at Dorster and Munich. The production for 1959 is reported to have been fourteen billion cubic feet.

Yugoslavia had a reported natural gas production during 1959 of ten and one-half billion cubic feet.

THE MIDDLE EAST

The Middle East includes the countries of Saudi Arabia, Iran, Iraq, Kuwait, Bahrein and Qatar. These countries produced about

4,500,000 barrels of oil and three billion cubic feet of gas daily during 1960. Thus one trillion cubic feet were produced in that year. Of this total, one-fourth was reinjected, one-tenth was used as fuel, and the remainder was surplus.

These countries have proved oil reserves of at least 160 billion barrels. It is estimated that the accompanying gas reserve must be at least 100 trillion cubic feet. This is one of the great sources of natural gas in the world.

Offers have been made by Aramco for sale at three and one-half cents per thousand cubic feet. To date no large markets have been discovered, but local markets such as cement plants and fertilizer plants are being developed. A project is under way for disposal of the liquefied petroleum gases, and petrochemical plants are envisioned.

SOUTH AMERICA

The natural gas industry in South America is in the early stages of development. Venezuela and Argentina have developed some of their gas resources, and will develop more in the future. There are several marine sedimentary basins, especially in Brazil, which have good possibilities of being gas productive.

Venezuela

Venezuela's gas is found in three principal areas. The primary reserves are in the Anaco trend of eastern Venezuela. The principal gas reservoir is the Merecure of Eocene-Oligocene age. It is a hard sandstone that has similar characteristics to the Wilcox trend in South Texas. The Oficina group of fields and the Lake Maracaibo fields both have large oil and gas reserves.

During 1959 gas production amounted to more than three billion cubic feet per day, of which almost half was employed for fuel and shrinkage, industrial uses, domestic and oil company use, and reinjection. The remainder was flared. This is a production rate of about one trillion cubic feet a year.

Gas reserves are about 33 trillion cubic feet. This compares with United States reserves of 264 trillion cubic feet.

Maracaibo is supplied with gas, and there are two pipe lines serving Caracas, Valencia, and Puerto La Cruz respectively. The 200-mile, 26-inch line with a capacity of 200 million cubic feet daily from the Anaco fields to Caracas has been completed. This is the first link in a one thousand-mile network intended to furnish gas to domestic and industrial users in western and central Venezuela.

Shell has a 200-mile, 20-inch pipe line from the La Paz Field to its Cardon refinery. This line has a capacity of 100 million cubic feet a day. A government-owned twenty-five-mile line runs from Guacara to the petrochemical center at Moron. Another line is planned from Anaco to Ciudad Bolivar and Puerto Ordaz, the location of the government steelworks.

A growing volume of natural gas liquids is being recovered. Some twelve natural gas plants processed about 400 million cubic feet of gas daily during 1958, obtaining three and one-half million barrels of natural gasoline and seventy million barrels of liquefied petroleum gas.

With a population of about six million, Venezuela cannot expect to utilize fully all its gas reserves. If the export of natural gas in liquefied form by sea proves practicable, these reserves can be more readily used.

Argentina

Argentina has become an active center of oil and gas exploration and development as the result of a new oil policy effected in 1958. This policy invited the assistance of private companies through drilling and development contracts.

In 1958 gas production was reported to be 50 billion cubic feet. During 1960 the figure increased greatly as a result of the completion of the 1,100-mile gas pipe line from Campo Duran to Buenos Aires in March of 1960. This line is a twenty-four- and twenty-two-inch line with a capacity of 243 million cubic feet daily. It extends south and east from the Bolivian border. The gas line is paralleled by a twelve-inch products pipe line which is nine hundred miles long and terminates at San Lorenzo. The products line carries products from propane through condensate recovered at the 300,000 MCF a day capacity Campo Duran processing plant. The undertaking was engineered and constructed for Yacimientos Petroliferos Fiscales (Y.P.F.), the government controlled oil and gas industry of Argentina, by International Pipeline Contractors, S. A. Fish International Corporation performed all engineering and supervised the construction.

Gas pipe-line projects in the planning stage are: an eight-hundred-mile gas line east from Salta in northern Argentina to Resistencia and

Rosario, a gas line from Salta west to Antofagasta in northern Chile. Under a contract with Gas del Estado, the state gas authority, the construction of a 1000-mile 30-inch gas line northeast from Comodoro Rivadavia to Buenos Aires with a delivery capacity of 350 million cubic feet a day has been begun by the E.N.I., the Italian petroleum organization.

Comodoro Rivadavia is estimated to have developed gas reserves of two trillion cubic feet at the beginning of 1960. Development plans call for the drilling of 4,500 wells in Comodoro.

The State Gas Agency in Argentina plans to spend $458,000,000 through 1964 to expand gas lines, distribution facilities, and related equipment.

The availability of natural gas has attracted foreign capital for the petrochemical industry. In 1962 the PASA project, a petrochemical complex at San Lorenzo, was under construction. The PASA facilities are owned by Fish International, Continental Oil Company, Cities Service Oil Company, U. S. Rubber, and Witco Chemical Company. Kopper's plans a $17,000,000 styrene and polyethylene plant at La Plata.

The increased drilling activity will increase the proved gas reserves and their availability.

Other South American Countries

Bolivia has a sizable gas reserve at the Madrejones Concession on the Argentine border. Fish Engineering Company has drilled and completed several gas-condensate wells at about ten thousand feet.

Brazil has several excellent sedimentary basins. Petrobras, the government-controlled oil and gas company, is in charge of oil and gas operations. The principal oil fields are Dom Joac and Mata. About fifty gas wells have been completed.

In Chile, Empressa Nacional de Petroleo (E.N.A.P.) is in charge of the oil and gas industry. The largest oil fields found to date are Cullen, Sombrero, Victoria Sur, Tres Lagos, Gaviota, Punta Delgada, and Delgada Este, all in the Magellan district. About eighty gas wells have been completed to date.

AFRICA

Africa, the slumbering giant, is awakening. It has large marine sedimentary basins which are just beginning to be explored. The recent oil and gas finds in Algeria and Libya are only the beginning of the discovery and development of its resources.

Algeria

In 1956, a major gas field was found by Société Nationale de Recherches et d'Exploitation des Pétroles en Algérie (S.N. REPAL) at Hassi R'Mel, 130 miles south of Algiers, about seven thousand feet from formations of Triassic age. Eight wells have been drilled to date, and an area of 600,000 acres is indicated to be proved for gas. The reserves are estimated at 15 to 35 trillion cubic feet, which would make this field second only to the Panhandle-Hugoton gas field in the United States in reserve size.

Hassi R'Mel produces a wet gas that is about 83 per cent methane. Each well is expected to produce 35 million cubic feet a day through four and one-half inch tubing. Bottom hole pressure is 4,350 pounds per square inch.

The discovery of Hassi R'Mel will have a tremendous economic impact on not only North Africa, but Europe itself. Work already is underway to supply Algeria and Western Europe with this cheap power. A twenty-four-inch line is being laid to Arzew, 350 miles away. The pipe-line system Société de Transport du Gaz Naturel d'Hassi er R'Mel à Arzew (SOTH RA) will be owned 65 per cent by S. N. REPAL and Compagnie Française des Pétroles (Algérie), CFP (A), the two oil companies jointly operating the Hassi R'Mel gas field, and 35 per cent by Electricité Gas d'Algérie. A major customer will be the steel industry to be established at Bone, Algeria, by 1962. In collaboration with Conch (Comstock Methane and Shell), S. N. REPAL has formed a company known as C.A.M.E.L. to erect a gas liquefication and storage plant at Arzew which will supply liquid methane for transportation in specially built ships to British and French markets.

A pipe-line crossing of the Mediterranean Sea has been studied, and three possible crossing routes proposed. One is a Straits of Gibraltar crossing. This is the simplest crossing. The pipe line would go to Morocco, and the water crossing to Spain would involve only an eighteen-mile distance and a depth of 1,400 feet. It is estimated that a line to Essen, Germany, via this route would cost $430,000,000 for a twenty-eight-inch line carrying 630 million cubic feet daily, and $725,000,000 for a forty-one-inch line carrying one and one-fourth billion feet a day. This is the Société D'Etude du Transport et de la Valorisation des Gaz Naturels du Sahara (SEGANS) proposal. SEGANS is owned by S. N. REPAL (35 per cent), CFP(A), (35 per cent), and the Bureau des Recherches de Pétrole (30 per cent). Another proposal is a crossing from Mostaganem, Algeria, to Cartagena, Spain. This involves water depths of five thousand feet and an underwater crossing of 125 miles, and is the Société d'Etude du Transport du Gaz d'Hassi er R'Mel par Canalisation Transméditerranéenne (SETREL) proposal. (SEGANS 50 per cent, Gaz de France 50 per cent.) The total distance to Essen is lessened and the cost is estimated at $311,000,000 for a twenty-eight-inch line to $531,000,000 for a forty-one-inch line. The third proposal is for a crossing from Cape Bon in Tunisia to Sicily and Italy. This involves a depth of one thousand feet, and an underwater crossing of seventy-seven miles to Sicily, and then into Italy. Italian interests have organized GOTA to study this project. It has some attraction because of the immediate markets for gas in Italy and Sicily. All these routes are being studied. It is possible that an international group will be formed to finance this project.

It is interesting to note the prices of Hassi R'Mel gas to be sold in Algeria. Ordinary customers will pay 27.5 cents per MCF. New industries will get special low rates of 20 cents per MCF. This compares to prices for Lacq gas in France from 63 cents to 75 cents per MCF.

There are important gas reserves at Zait La, Tirechoumine, Berge, Oued Djaret, Dichel Mousdoine, Ouan Taradert, Oued Zenani, and Tiguentourine-La Reculee. There are substantial gas reserves in the large oil fields of Hassi Messaoud, Zarzaitine, Edjele, and Tiguentourine-La Reculee. Algeria must have at least 50 trillion cubic feet of proved gas reserves.

Libya

Libya's first discovery of oil at Atshan in 1957 was a well that tested 500 barrels of oil a day from Devonian sandstone at two thousand feet. Since then there has been an extensive exploratory drilling program, and large oil reserves have been discovered at Zelten, Dahra, Mobruk, Tahara, Seit S'Rin, and Amal. Although no large gas fields have been reported to date, it is very probable that large gas reserves will be found. There is a considerable gas reserve contained in the oil that has been found.

Other African Countries

In Tunisia there is the Cape Bon gas field, located in the extreme northeast corner of Tunisia, which was discovered in 1949 and supplies the city of Tunis with about 200 million cubic feet annually.

Nigeria, with the oil discoveries by Shell/British Petroleum, shows evidence of a good petroliferous province. Although no major gas discoveries have been reported, there are possibilities.

Gas discoveries have been reported by Société Africaine des Pétroles near Dakar in Senegal in 1959.

The Spanish Sahara has possibilities and is the center of much exploratory activity.

THE FAR EAST

Pakistan

Pakistan has one of the world's large gas fields in the Sui Field. The gas reserves of Sui are about five trillion cubic feet, and the country's reserves probably approach eight trillion cubic feet.

A 16-inch pipe line connects Karachi with the Sui Field. Sui is 350 miles north of Karachi and 400 miles southwest of Lahore. A 211-mile, 16-inch line extends from Sui northwards to Multan. Planned is a 20-inch line to Multan, Lyallpur, Sargodha, Rawalpindi, Islamabad, and Wah.

During 1959 the Sui Field produced about sixteen billion cubic feet of gas. Another important gas field is the Dhuban Field, which produced about five billion cubic feet.

Pakistan Petroleum, Limited (Burmah Oil), and Pakistan Oilfields, Limited, account for most of the gas reserves in Pakistan. In 1959 Pakistan Petroleum discovered a new gas reserve at Chhatak in the Sylhet district. Reserves there have been reported at 20 billion cubic feet. This discovery is twenty-five miles north of its Haripur gas discovery (1955) where reserves are estimated at 150 billion cubic feet. An 8-inch, 145-mile pipe line is planned from the Sylhet district to Dacca, and a smaller line will be laid north to a cement plant.

A carbon black plant using gas is planned for Sui. Two fertilizer plants to operate on natural gas and produce 250,000 tons each yearly were constructed during 1960, one in Muttar in West Pakistan and the other at Jenchuganj near the Sylhet gas field in East Pakistan.

380

Other Far Eastern Countries

Australia has several sedimentary basins, and many oil and gas exploration efforts are being carried out.

A deep gas discovery was reported at Kapuni near Hawera in New Zealand by the Shell/British Petroleum-Todd group in 1959.

Communist China reports an exploration effort in progress for oil and gas.

The following articles and books concerning the search for and use of gas throughout the world were helpful to the authors in writing this chapter:

"Argentine Pacts in Mill," *Oil and Gas Journal*, Vol. LVI, No. 49 (December 8, 1958).

"Bright Prospects for Lacq Gas," *Petroleum Press Service*, Vol. XXV, No. 6 (June, 1958).

"Changed Outlook for Argentina," *Petroleum Press Service*, Vol. XXVII, No. 10 (October, 1960).

"The Development of Lacq Gas," *Petroleum Press Service*, Vol. XXVII, No. 7 (July, 1960).

"ENI as a Basic Factor in the Italian Miracle," *New York Times*, January 10, 1961, p. C–55.

Fox, W., "The Recent Development of Natural Gas Production in Western Europe," *Erdöl-Zeitschrift*, Vol. LXXIV, No. 11 (November, 1958).

Fraser, Duncan, "The Lower Volga Oil and Gas Industry," *Petroleum Times*, Vol. LXII, No. 1580 (February 28, 1958), 170.

"French Are Rushing Plans to Move Sahara Gas to Europe," *Petroleum Week*, Vol. XII, No. 3 (January 20, 1961).

"French Plans for Sahara Gas Are Stirring," *Petroleum Week*, Vol. IX, No. 7 (August 14, 1959).

Garcia-Rojas, Antonio, "The Mexican Gas Industry," an address before the General Management Section, American Gas Association, Pittsburgh, Pennsylvania, March 1, 1960.

———, "Mexico Should Look for New Energy Sources," *Petroleo Interamericano*, Vol. XX, No. 11 (November, 1962), 70.

"Gas in Europe," *Petroleum Press Service*, Vol. XXV, No. 10 (October, 1958).

Grill, R., "Oil-geological Conditions in Austria," *World Petroleum Report,* Vol. XXX, No. 6 (June, 1959).

Hagemann, Richard F., "French Move to Meet Soaring Demand," *Oil and Gas Journal,* Vol. LVIII, No. 44 (October 31, 1960).

Hassmann, Heinrich, *Oil in the Soviet Union,* Princeton, N. J., 1953.

"Lacq Gas," *American Gas Journal,* Vol. CLXXXVII, No. 5 (May, 1960), 3.

"La Distribution du Gas de Lacq et ses Problems," *Journal des Carburants,* No. 243 (June 5, 1958).

"Lifelines from the Jungle," *Flow Line,* Vol. XX, No. 1 (January, 1961).

"Mexico's Bold Petrochemical Program," *Petroleum Press Service,* Vol. XXVII, No. 9 (September, 1960).

"Netherlands, a Major Gas Find," *Petroleum Press Service,* Vol. XXVIII, No. 1 (January, 1961), 23.

"Netherlands Confirms Large Gas Reserves," *Oil and Gas Journal,* Vol. LVIII, No. 48 (November 28, 1960), 58.

Newman, L. L., "Inside Russia, Gaswise," *Gas,* Vol. XXXVI, No. 11 (November, 1960).

"The New Synthetic Rubber Factory at Ravenna," *Petroleum Times,* Vol. LXII, No. 1586 (May 23, 1958), 424.

OEEC Gas Committee, *Gas in Europe 1960, Production, Availability, Consumption,* Paris, 1960.

OEEC, *Report on the Position of Natural Gas in the European Economy,* Paris, 1957.

"Oil and Natural Gas in Italy," *Petroleum Times,* Vol. LXI, No. 1570 (October 11, 1957), 895.

"Possibilities for West Pakistan's Gas," *Petroleum Press Service,* Vol. XXVII, No. 9 (September, 1960).

Powell, J. Richard, *The Mexican Petroleum Industry, 1938–50,* Berkeley, Calif., 1956.

"Prices Vary for Sahara Oil," *Petroleum Week,* Vol. XI, No. 12 (September 23, 1960).

Revolle, Edouard, "World's Second Largest Gas Field Seeks a Market," *Oil and Gas Journal,* Vol. LVIII, No. 44 (October 31, 1960).

Roma, Banco di, and Alfredo Giarrantana, *Hydrocarbons in Italy,* Rome, 1956.

"Saharan Natural Gas Will Explode into European Markets," *International Oilman,* Vol. XIV, No. 9 (North Africa Report, 1960), 244c.

Smith, Gene, "Natural Gas Powers Industrial Surge in France," *New York Times,* May 12, 1958.

"Soviets Claim Huge Reserves in Desert Area," *Oil and Gas Journal,* Vol. LVIII, No. 41 (October 13, 1960).

"Special Report, Argentina," *Petroleo Interaméricano,* Vol. XVIII, No. 2 (February, 1960).

Weeks, Lewis G., "Foreign Reserves, Occurrence, Production," a paper presented at the Institute on Economics of the Gas Industry, International Oil and Gas Education Center, Dallas, Texas, March 1, 1962.

World Petroleum Report, Vol. V (1960).

15

THE FUTURE OF
THE NATURAL GAS INDUSTRY

by John C. Jacobs

THE PREVIOUS chapters of this book describe in detail the part played by natural gas in the "energy revolution"[1] and the present condition of the industry. In this chapter the future of the natural gas industry will be considered in relation to future demand, future supply, competition among fuels, and government regulation.[2]

In studying the future of the natural gas industry, it will be necessary to scan the intriguing field of future energy supply and demand studies. The studies are numerous and are prepared from many points of view. Some cover all energy sources; some only natural gas. Some forecast the next ten years; some the next 150 years. Some predict for the entire world; others predict only for the United States of America.[3]

---

[1] For more about the "energy revolution" see Robert L. Heilbroner, "The Energy Revolution," *American Petroleum Institute Quarterly* (Centennial Issue), (Spring–Summer, 1959), 26; James A. Clark, "The Energy Revolution," in *History of Petroleum Engineering*, 1; and E. B. Swanson, "The Natural Gas Invasion," in *Mineral Economics*, 32.

[2] It should be stressed that, aside from the future problems under discussion here, the natural gas industry's present position, as described in Chapter 4, above, is secure in view of its presently adequate reserves, its assured long-term markets, its plants being financed and constructed, and its inability to expand without meeting governmentally imposed standards regarding adequacy of reserves, markets, economic feasibility, and financial ability. This statement is made, even though the industry's "twenty-year" reserve life may equal only full availability for fourteen years assuming no more gas discoveries, in view of the large, continuing program of exploration for gas being carried on in the United States.

[3] The studies of United States and world energy requirements and probable sources of supply are listed in the bibliography at the end of the chapter. Some of these studies consider the period through 1975, some through 1980, and some through 2000. One group of these studies is concerned with particular regions of the United States.

One can only surmise—but ponder for a moment the optimistic charts regarding future whale oil demand which must have been exhibited at the 1859 annual meeting of the

All carry the deceptive face of arithmetic exactitude. These numerical results contain the potentially significant errors[4] resulting from judgments about the trend of births, economic conditions, and the political situation twenty and more years from now. Regardless of the magnitude of inherent error, the twenty-year figure should be more exact than the one-hundred-year figure.

Energy studies are used for many purposes, primarily business decisions and government planning.[5] Business decisions involve the more reliable, short-term data. The government may intervene in the market place as an umpire to correct inequities apparent in the immediate, or short-term, outlook or as a prophet to change the form of an industry in order to prevent evils apparent only in long-term data. A great deal of long-term public control of business is done in the name of conservation.[6] Any conservation decision necessarily involves

American Whaling Association (held in Mystic, Connecticut?) when "Colonel" Drake was supervising the drilling of the first oil well in western Pennsylvania.

[4] Perry D. Teitelbaum, *Nuclear Energy and the U. S. Fuel Economy, 1955–1980* (Reports on the Productive Uses of Nuclear Energy, National Planning Association, 1958), 3, says "Projections extending over a 25-year period are at best educated guesses." Table 22 shows that a difference of 0.5 per cent in growth rate will result in a difference of approximately 20 per cent in the energy demand projected forty years into the future.

[5] C. C. Anderson and T. W. Hunter, "Methods for Evaluating Sources and Requirements for Solid and Liquid Fuels in the United States," a paper presented at the World Power Conference, Madrid, Spain, June 5–9, 1960, and published in *Transactions, q.v.,* 117–27. In their paper, Mr. Anderson and Mr. Hunter say:

> Although the United States has large reserves of energy and high productive capacity in its energy industries, particularly with respect to the conventional fuels (coal, oil, and natural gas), there are many compelling reasons for both periodic and continuing evaluations of energy demand, whether for one or another of the respective energy sources of their derivative products or for energy as a whole. Among these reasons are such factors as changing patterns of energy consumption, competition among the respective fuel industries, limitations to expandability of hydroelectric installations, variations in production costs and consumer prices, changing standards of living, changing volumes and methods of transportation, periodic imbalances in supply, changes in efficiencies of production and utilization conservation, prudent programming of production development and capital investment, long-range policy determinations, security planning, and innumerable other important factors in our highly integrated and extensive economic system.

Regarding the methods used in making energy requirement and supply studies, see E. S. Mason, *et al.*, "Energy Requirements and Economic Growth," a paper presented at the International Conference in the Peaceful Uses of Atomic Energy, 1956, and published in *Proceedings, q.v.,* I, 50; and Sam H. Schurr and Bruce C. Netschert, *Energy in the American Economy, 1850–1975.*

[6] Orris C. Herfindahl, "What Is Conservation?" in *Three Studies in Mineral Econom-*

not only the pursuit of the millenium,[7] but also an increase in today's cost of living in exchange for a promised benefit tomorrow. Any judgment as to the desirability of a proposed conservation measure should involve a weighing of these two factors.

FUTURE DEMAND

Predictions of future energy demand are based upon the projection of detailed statistical data regarding energy consumption trends and the assumption that these trends will continue in the future.[8] Demand studies may be built up from a consideration of the future outlook in each of the consuming sectors—residential-commercial, industrial, and motive uses—or built down from estimates of population growth and increased industrialization, or based on a combination of the two methods. Built down studies may be based on a total energy input calculated as the product of Gross National Product (GNP) in constant dollars times energy input per dollar of GNP, which decreases as GNP increases, or as the quotient of population times effective energy used per capita, which increases with increased industrialization, di-

---

ics, 1; Courtney C. Brown, *et al., Energy and Man;* Henry Jarrett (ed.), *Perspectives on Conservation;* Richard L. Meier, *Science and Economic Development: New Patterns of Living;* Harrison Brown, *The Challenge of Man's Future.*

Regarding conservation as a basis for the public control of oil and gas production, see the authorities cited in footnote 11 of Chapter 12, above. See also Charlton H. Lyons, "Why Conservation?" a paper presented before the 38th Annual Meeting of the American Petroleum Institute, Chicago, Illinois, November 11, 1958; and Michel T. Halbouty, "Conservation—Total or Partial," a paper presented before the American Petroleum Institute, Division of Production, Southwest District, Dallas, Texas, March 2–4, 1960.

[7] Norman Cohn, *The Pursuit of the Millenium.*

[8] One of the basic assumptions is that industrialization of the world will increase with a resultant increase in per capita income, but consider the following passage from Palmer C. Putnam's *Energy for the Future,* 64:

> *Forces Opposing the Democratic Transition.* It is easy to describe the obstacles to change in the underdeveloped countries. Their populations lack mechanical equipment, the skills to produce it, and the capital to finance it. They do not eat very well. They have high birth rates and high death rates. There is much biological waste. Mothers die young from overbreeding, having produced babies few of whom survive to augment the labor force. The education to correct these conditions is lacking. And the terms of trade make it more difficult to finance the smashing of the vicious circles than in 1913, when a quantum of raw material commanded two-thirds more of a quantum of manufactured product than it does today.

Despite all the increases in industrial output in the world from 1955 to 1960, the per capita income in Latin America has fallen because of the high birth rates.

TABLE 22

PROJECTIONS OF TOTAL ENERGY CONSUMPTION

Projector	Base		Projections, 10^{15} Btu's						Annual Growth Rate
	Year	Value, 10^{15} Btu's	1965	1967	1970	1975	1980	2000	Per cent
Ayres and Scarlott	1947	35.1	——	——	61.6	——	——	——	2.5
Putnam	1949	31.4	——	——	——	——	——	150	3.1
President's Materials Policy Commission	1950	34.6	——	——	——	67	——	——	2.7
McKinney Panel	1954	37.4	——	——	——	——	87.5	——	3.3
National Planning Association	1955	40.3	——	——	——	——	80.0	——	2.8
Sporn	1955	40.3	——	——	——	72	——	——	2.9
Parson	1955	40.3	——	——	——	——	——	112	2.3
Coqueron, Hamman, and Winger	1957	42.1	——	63.5	——	——	——	——	4.2
Davis and Schweitzer	1958	41.9	——	——	57	——	——	——	2.6
Melnick	1958	41.9	55.1	——	——	——	——	——	3.9
Schurr and Netschert	1955	39.7	——	——	——	74.5	——	——	3.2

(Source: Elliott, "Fuels in the Future" [1961], 14.)

vided by the efficiency of utilization, which increases with improving technology.[9]

Table 22 summarizes all recent studies of total United States energy consumption. The recent Texas Eastern study shows a 1980 consumption of 81.4×10^{15} Btu, which represents a growth rate of 3.3 per cent per year from a 1960 base of 42.3×10^{15} Btu.

Table 23 summarizes several estimates of future natural gas demand. In addition the 1960 "Resources for the Future" study shows a 1975 consumption of 19.881 trillion cubic feet, which represents an annual growth rate of 3.7 per cent, and the 1960 Texas Eastern study shows a 1980 consumption of 23.1 trillion cubic feet, which represents an annual growth rate of 3.4 per cent.

A recent representative study predicts the *residential-commercial sector*, energy used to heat, cool, and operate machines in homes, stores, and office buildings, which constituted 28 per cent of the United States energy requirement in 1959, will grow from now until 1980 at a rate of 2.5 per cent a year. It further predicts that the *industrial sector*, energy used for producing goods excluding fuel for power generation, which constituted 42 per cent of the national end-use energy consumption in 1959, will grow at a future rate of 3.8 per cent each year; and that the *motive sector*, fuel requirements for all types of transportation, which represented 30 per cent of total 1959 requirements, will grow at a future rate of 2.2 per cent a year.

In the residential-commercial sector, gas competes with coal, petroleum, and electricity. In the future, the use of coal is expected to drop and that of petroleum to remain constant, with the consequence that the gain will be shared by gas and electricity. Note that growth in this sector is for low load factor service which requires the use of peak shaving by the gas distributor.[10]

In the industrial sector, gas competes with coal, petroleum, and

[9] Schurr and Netschert, *Energy in the American Economy, 1850–1975;* Texas Eastern Transmission Corporation, "Energy and Fuels in the United States . . . 1947–1980," *The Inch,* Vol. XI, Nos. 1, 2, and 3 (Winter, Spring and Summer, 1961), 2, a study later published in Houston, Texas, 1961; Putnam, *Energy in the Future;* Martin A. Elliott, "The Long Range Supply of Gas," a paper presented at the 1960 Meeting of the Society of Gas Lighting, New York, New York, January 14, 1960.

[10] Regarding the steps the gas industry has taken to make low load factor gas available to the consumer, see chapters 6, 10 and 11, above.

TABLE 23

Projections of the Demand for Gas

| Projector | Base | | Projection, Trillion Cu. Ft. | | | | | Annual Growth Rate |
	Year	Value, Trillion Cu. Ft.	1965	1967	1970	1975	1980	2000	Per cent
President's Materials Policy Commission	1950	6.3	—	—	—	15.0	—	—	3.0
McKinney Panel	1954	8.7	—	—	—	—	21.0	—	3.5
National Planning Association	1955	10.1	—	—	—	—	18.0	—	2.3
Parson	1955	10.1	—	—	—	—	—	36.6	2.9
Coqueron, Hamman, and Winger	1957	11.5	—	17.2	—	—	—	—	4.1
Melnick	1958	11.5	14.6	—	—	—	—	—	4.4
Davis and Schweitzer	1958	11.5	—	—	16.8	—	—	—	3.2

(Source: Elliott, "The Long Range Supply of Gas" [1960], 4.)

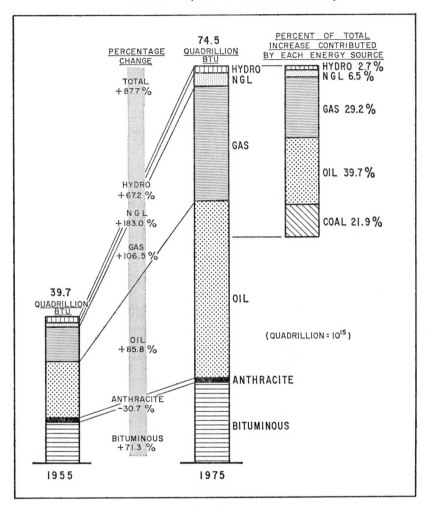

Fig. 35.—The Energy Source Mix, 1955 and Estimated 1975.

electricity. It is predicted that future increases in industrial energy consumption will be shared by all fuels, with a reversal of the past trend of decreased coal consumption. This sector is characterized by easy interchangeability in fuel use on the basis of price.

Gas is not used in the motive sector, and coal has virtually been displaced by dieselization of the railroads, with the consequence that the

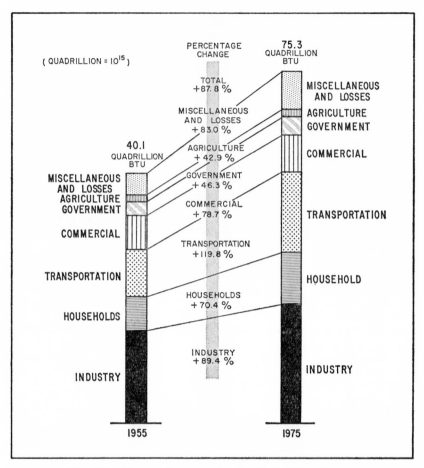

FIG. 36.—Energy Consumption by Consuming Sector,
1955 and Estimated 1975.

future growth will be enjoyed by petroleum. Figures 35 and 36 summarize another recent and complete energy study.[11]

All the cited studies indicate a large future increase in total energy demand and in the demand for natural gas in particular. This statement raises the question of whether necessary supplies will be available.

[11] Schurr and Netschert, *Energy in the American Economy, 1850–1975.* Concerning the competition among fuels and its influence on future demand for natural gas, see the bibliography at the end of this chapter.

FUTURE SUPPLY

Table 24 summarizes reserve estimates for the fossil fuels of the United States of America.[12] Note how considerable the coal and oil shale reserves are compared with petroleum and natural gas. Estimates of total future natural gas reserves are obtained by multiplying a ratio representing the cubic feet of gas discovered per barrel of oil discovered times estimated future oil discoveries. Future oil discoveries are, in turn, estimated on the basis of an analysis of all the sedimentary rock area of the world in which oil-productive area is delineated and a factor applied representing discovery experience in areas already drilled.[13] Table 25 summarizes natural gas reserve estimates.[14] An estimate of 1200 to 1500 trillion cubic feet was generally accepted in 1961 as the ultimate recoverable natural gas reserve for the United States.[15] Ultimate natural gas reserves for the world have been estimated at 5000 to 6000 trillion cubic feet.[16]

---

[12] In regard to the reserves of all fossil fuels, see Schurr and Netschert, *Energy in the American Economy, 1850–1975;* Putnam, *Energy in the Future,* and Bruce C. Netschert, *The Future Supply of Oil and Gas* (A Resources for the Future, Incorporated, study). For further references concerning coal reserves, oil and gas reserves, natural gas reserves, and oil shale reserves, see the bibliography at the end of this chapter.

[13] Lewis G. Weeks, "Fuel Reserves of the Future," *Bulletin* of the American Association of Petroleum Geologists, Vol. XLII, No. 2 (February, 1958), 431–41.

[14] To Table 25 should be added:

(1) The 1960 estimate appearing in Schurr and Netschert, *Energy in the American Economy, 1850–1975,* of 1,200 trillion cubic feet;

(2) The 1958 estimate by Daniel Parson in "Long Term Gas Supply Outlook Good," *American Gas Association Monthly,* Vol. XL, No. 6 (June, 1958), or 1,400 trillion cubic feet.

(3) The 1958 estimate by R. L. Miller in "A New Look at Ultimate Natural Gas Reserves," *World Oil,* Vol. CXLVII, No. 5 (October, 1958), 222–24, of 1,100 to 1,550 trillion cubic feet.

[15] Schurr and Netschert, in their study completed in 1960, adopted 1,200 trillion cubic feet as a figure for the total future supply of natural gas, after a survey of all the data. Martin A. Elliott presented an estimate of 1,500 trillion cubic feet in "Fuels in the Future," a special lecture delivered at the 33rd Annual National A.S.M.E. Oil and Gas Power Conference, New Orleans, Louisiana, April 9–13, 1961. Lyon F. Terry suggests 1,200 trillion cubic feet as of January 1, 1957, in his article, "Future Life of the Natural Gas Industry," in *Economics of the Gas Industry,* I, 284.

[16] See Weeks, "Fuel Reserves of the Future," *Bulletin* of the American Association of Petroleum Geologists, Vol. XLII, No. 2 (February, 1958), 431–41; Wallace E. Pratt, "The Impact of the Peaceful Uses of Atomic Energy on the Petroleum Industry," in *The Peaceful Uses of Atomic Energy,* II, 86–106; and Lewis G. Weeks, "World Gas Reserves, Production, Occurrence," in *Economics of the Gas Industry,* I, 71.

TABLE 24
FOSSIL FUEL RESOURCES

Fuel	Range of Most Recent Resource Estimates	Estimate Selected For Present Analysis	
		Quantity	Heating Value, Btu's§
Coal			
Recoverable at or Near Present Prices	237 x 10⁹ short tons	237 x 10⁹ short tons	5.1 x 10¹⁸
1¼ to 1½ Times Present Prices	285 x 10⁹ short tons	237 x 10⁹ short tons	6.2 x 10¹⁸
1½ to 4 Times Present Prices	426 x 10⁹ short tons	426 x 10⁹ short tons	9.2 x 10¹⁸
TOTAL	948 x 10⁹ short tons	948 x 10⁹ short tons	20.5 x 10¹⁸
*Petroleum**	150–300 x 10⁹ barrels	250 x 10⁹ barrels	1.45 x 10¹⁸
*Natural Gas**	1,350–1,700 x 10¹² cu. ft.	1,500 x 10¹² cu. ft.	1.50 x 10¹⁸
*Natural Gas Liquids**			0.16 x 10¹⁸**
Oil Shale (Green River Formation)	959–1,500 x 10⁹ barrels†	1,200 x 10⁹ barrels‡	6.96 x 10¹⁸
		TOTAL	30.6 x 10¹⁸

(Source: Elliott, "The Role of Fossil Fuels in Meeting Future Energy Demands.")

Ultimate reserves recoverable, in present terminology, is equal to cumulated production plus proved reserves and estimated future discoveries.

†In place, with no allowance for losses in mining or processing.

‡75 per cent of this is recoverable in mining.

§Assumed heating values:

Coal (average)	21.6 x 10⁶	Btu's/short ton
Petroleum	5.8 x 10⁶	Btu's/barrel
Natural Gas	1,000	Btu's/Standard Cu. Ft.
Natural Gas Liquids	4.2 x 10⁶	Btu's/barrel
Shale Oil	5.8 x 10⁶	Btu's/barrel

**Approximate value for this analysis $= \dfrac{\text{cumulative natural gas liquids discovered through 1958, 44 x 10}^{15}\text{ Btu's}}{\text{cumulative natural gas discoveries through 1958, 414 x 10}^{15}\text{ Btu's}} \times$ Ultimate discoveries, 1.5 x 10¹⁸ Btu's

TABLE 25

ESTIMATES OF TOTAL RECOVERABLE RESERVES OF NATURAL GAS
IN THE UNITED STATES
(In Trillion Cu. Ft.)

Source and Date	Estimated Total Future Supply	To Be Discovered As of Time of Estimate	As of Jan. 1, 1960*	Ratio of Total Future Supply to 1959 Production
(1)	(2)	(3)	(4)	(5)
Terry, 1950	>510	>330	>247	>41
Hinson, 1954	586	375	323	47
Interior Dept., 1956	875	663	612	71
Pratt, 1956	725	513	462	58
Pogue and Hill, 1956	570	358	307	46
Hubbert, 1956	730	506	467	59
Terry and Winger, 1957	>1,200	>984	>937	>97

(Source: Schurr and Netschert, *Energy in the American Economy, 1850–1975*, 393.)
* Column 2 minus proved reserves as of January 1, 1960.

The principal reason for the increase, with time, of the Table 25 estimates is an increase in assumed ratio of future gas to oil discoveries. In 1961 a ratio of 5000 to 7000 cubic feet per barrel was considered reasonable as compared with the ratio of 4000 cubic feet per barrel acceptable in 1950. This trend of increase in ratio represents our experience that, as the average depth to which wells are drilled increases, relatively more gas is discovered than oil.[17] An ultimate natural gas reserve of 1200 to 1500 trillion cubic feet represents approximately a one-hundred-year supply at current production rates of 13.1 trillion cubic feet a year. This would appear to represent adequacy for any short-term outlook of up to twenty years. And, from the long-term outlook of one hundred years or more, the United States reserve may be augmented by imports from other countries and by synthetic gases produced from coal and oil shale. It has been estimated that by 1980 one trillion cubic feet a year of gas will be available for

[17] See the discussion in Schurr and Netschert, *Energy in the American Economy, 1850–1975*, 401–15. Netschert, "Economic Aspects of Natural Gas Supply," in *Economics of the Gas Industry*, I, 27; and Lyon F. Terry and John G. Winger, *Future Growth of the Natural Gas Industry*, 22–24.

import by pipe line from Canada.[18] Similar figures on the import potential of Mexico are not available. The demonstrated feasibility of
shipping liquefied methane by tanker opens the possibility of making a
share of the 3800 to 4800 trillion cubic feet of foreign gas available
for consumption in the United States.[19] Additional future requirements for energy can be met from nuclear and solar sources.[20]

Progress is continually being made in developing methods for producing synthetic gases at lower costs. Gas may be produced from oil
shale or coal for sixty-five cents per million Btu's. After transportation to market, such gas would cost about two and one-half times as
much as natural gas in 1955.[21] Nevertheless, the possibility of producing synthetic gas serves as a ceiling on the price of natural gas.

The foregoing indicates adequacy of natural gas supply from a
total reserve standpoint,[22] but these reserves must be put in the proved

[18] John Davis, *Canadian Energy Prospects*, 182.

[19] See Chapter 11, above. See also Schurr and Netschert, *Energy in the American Economy, 1850–1975*, 416.

[20] For nuclear and solar energy possibilities, see the studies listed in the bibliography which follows this chapter.

[21] Schurr and Netschert, *Energy in the American Economy, 1850–1975*, 419–27. See also the bibliography which appears at the end of this chapter.

[22] At this point the reader should note several things:

(1) The word *reserve* has several meanings. In oil and gas circles reserves connote only those future sources of supply which are considered to be productive and available for future use. On the other hand, in coal circles "reserve" usually means the
total estimated amount of coal which can be found and mined in the United States,
regardless of cost. The difference in meanings becomes apparent when we consider
that our oil reserves have a life of twelve years; our gas reserves, twenty years; and our
coal reserves, one thousand years. On a coal reserves basis we obtain a life for oil and
gas (plus shale oil) of hundreds of years. As pointed out on pages 295–301 of Schurr
and Netschert, *Energy in the American Economy, 1850–1975*, it is more correct to
speak of *reserves, resources,* and *resource base,* which are compared in the following
table:

TERMS	ASPECTS		
	Occurrence	Economic	Technologic
Reserves	Known	Present Cost Level	Currently Feasible
Resources	Known Plus Unknown	Any Cost Level Specified	Currently Feasible and Feasibility Indicated in the Future
Resource Base	Known Plus Unknown	Irrelevant	Feasible Plus Infeasible

396

category through exploration and discovery and made available to the market.[23]

From the standpoint of physics, *availability* connotes the natural decrease in the producing ability of some gas wells as reserves are

(2) Any useful concept of fossil fuel reserves, or resources, must recognize the dynamic, as opposed to the static, nature of exploring for and producing such fuel. The dynamic concept emphasizes such things as the importance of availability as well as reserves, and the importance of the myriad factors, especially economic and technical, which help to determine, and might radically change, the future rates at which a given fuel may be searched for, discovered, and produced. The dynamic approach differs from the usual static approach as calculus differs from arithmetic.

(3) The question of whether our future supplies of a given fuel will be adequate or inadequate is most difficult to answer. In fact, the more of the factors influencing future supply one considers, the less certain one is that an answer is possible. Yet an answer to the question of the future adequacy of fuel supply is the *sine qua non* to the planning of a public control program for such fuel industry which involves "saving" the fuel in one way or another. Other bases for a public control program might involve the aim of freeing access to the market, or such considerations as national defense which are outside the realm of marketplace economics. For example, the Natural Gas Act was passed to protect the consumer, not to save natural gas. Often very little consideration is given to the question of adequacy of supply by the advocates of particular public control programs.

(4) Are we running out of gas or oil? It is not helpful in answering this question to make the obvious statement that, since fossil fuels are of finite (though unknown) future quantity (i.e., not inexhaustible), these fuels will be used up sometime in the future. The discussion in this chapter would indicate that we are not running out of gas, certainly not in the reasonably foreseeable future period of twenty years. The great possible variation in the myriad of factors which affect supply beyond the foreseeable future would seem to make prediction impossible. It should be remembered that all past reserve estimates of oil and gas of the United States have been too low. And we do not precipitously run out of a fuel. In our complex economy there is a gradual substitution or augmentation of one fuel by others. The interchangeability of coal, oil, gas, and electricity in many markets is discussed in this chapter. The possible augmentation of natural gas by synthetic gases is discussed by Elliott in "Fuels in the Future."

See, generally, in regard to the foregoing four points, Morgan J. Davis, "The Dynamics of Domestic Petroleum Resources," in *Proceedings* of the American Petroleum Institute (Section I, General, 1958), XXXVIII, 22.

[23] B. W. Beebe, in his article "Natural Gas Whooses from Infant to Giant in 25 Years," *Oil and Gas Journal*, Vol. LIX, No. 17 (April 24, 1961), 100, says:

Various authorities have estimated total gas reserves of the United States at from 750 to 1,700 trillion cubic feet. Several methods have been used, all of them intriguing. They are exercises in mathematical skill; extrapolation and ingenuity based on several assumptions, all or any of which could be in error, and are fundamentally meaningless in terms of availability of natural gas. These so-called reserves are mere possibilities. They do not tell us where the gas is to be found, the depths at which it may occur, whether or not it can be profitably produced, or whether it will ever be found.

Mr. Beebe is special editor of the multi-volume symposium, *Natural Gases of North America,* compiled and published by the American Association of Petroleum Geologists. The cited issue of the *Oil and Gas Journal* contains several articles on exploration for natural gas.

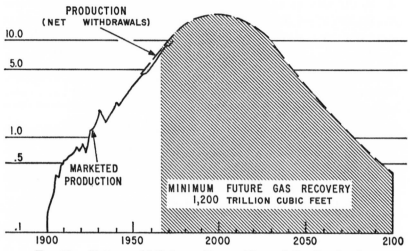

FIG. 37.—Pattern of Minimum Future Natural Gas Production
in the United States.

depleted and pressure in the underground reservoir decreases. For example, a given reserve may be dedicated to a market requirement equal to 5 per cent a year of the reserve. As such, a twenty-year life index has been established. In those cases where there is no water drive, a representative calculation will show that after fourteen years, gas cannot be made available at the rate of 5 per cent a year because of a loss of deliverability from the well. In the gas industry compensation is made for this loss of deliverability by adding new wells completed in recently discovered reservoirs to the gas supply of the gas company. Thus the rate at which gas wells will be drilled in future years becomes important in predicting whether an adequate supply will be available for the large increases in demand that are anticipated.

Figure 37 sets forth a calculation of the future availability of natural gas in the United States. Table 26 summarizes most recent estimates of availability. These estimates generally indicate an adequate availability of natural gas through 1980. After that time, gas supply can be supplemented with imports and synthetic gases, as discussed above. The recent "Resources for the Future" study adopts an availability of 22.5 trillion cubic feet for 1975.

398

TABLE 26

Estimates of Future United States Natural Gas Production

Source and Date (1)	Peak* (2)	Year† (3)	Estimated Production Trillion Cu. Ft. (4)	Future Supply Thru Jan. 1, 1960 Trillion Cu. Ft. (5)	Per cent of 1959 Production† (6)
President's Materials Policy Commission, 1951		1975	15.3	528§	123
Egloff, 1951		1960	11.4	595§	92
		1975	18.0 }		145
Pettyjohn, 1955	X	1960	12.0	240§	97
Ayres, 1955	X	1965	12.0	600**	97
		1975	11.0 }		89
Interior Department, 1956		1975	19.0	875**	153
Pratt, 1956		1965	13.5	725**	109
		1975	15.0 }		121
Pogue and Hill, 1956		1965	14.2	364§	115
		1965	15.2 }		123
	X	1970	16.0	570**	129
		1975	15.5 }		125
American Gas Association, 1956		1975	22.5	850**	181
Tippy, 1956	X	1970	13.0	475**	105
		1975	12.5 }		101
	X	1975	15.0	725**	121
	X	1980	17.0	875**	137
Hubbert, 1956	X	1970	14.0	725**	113
		1975	13.5 }		109
Ayres, 1956	X	1965–70	13.0	600**	105
Terry and Winger, 1957		1966	16.3 }		131
	X	1980–90	20.0	1,200**	161

(Source: Schurr and Netschert, *Energy in the American Economy, 1850–1975*, 397.)

*An X in column 2 indicates that the production for the year shown in column 3 is projected as the historical peak of production by the author of the estimate.

†Year to which each estimate refers.

‡Estimates as per cent of 1959 production of 12.4 trillion cubic feet.

§Implied minimum future supply.

**Explicit total future supply.

The studies indicating an ample availability[24] through 1980 emphasize that oil and gas reserve estimates have always been subject to upward revision; that the ratio of gas to oil discoveries is rising; that the United States added about 1.9 cubic feet of gas to its reserves for each cubic foot produced between 1945 and 1959 when an addition of 1.7 cubic feet would maintain the reserve life at twenty years under a 3.5 per cent a year increase in demand; that the oil industry has maintained a twelve-year reserve life for many years; that gas production in the Appalachian region, which theoretically should have declined sharply from the 1910 maximum of 522 billion cubic feet, has remained close to 80 per cent of this maximum for the last twenty years and shows no signs of declining;[25] that there should be a parallel between the gas industry and the oil industry, where for every increase in annual production rate there has been a corresponding increase in discovery rate;[26] that the rate of increase in marketed production is falling off and has not exceeded the 1938–1958 median since 1951; that reserve life has leveled off at twenty years since the drop of 1946–52 and decreased at an annual rate of only 1 per cent a year between 1952 and 1957; and that a greater part of the exploratory effort is now directed towards gas, as opposed to oil.

On the other hand, since 1958, other commentators[27] have ques-

[24] Schurr and Netschert, *Energy in the American Economy, 1850–1975;* Parson, "Long Term Gas Supply Outlook Good," *American Gas Association Monthly*, Vol. XL, No. 6 (June, 1958), 2; Boni, Watkins, Jason and Company, "Louisiana: Key to Future U. S. Gas Supply?" *Gas Age*, Vol. CXXIII, No. 1 (January 8, 1959), 17; American Gas Association Rate Committee, *Gas Rate Fundamentals*, 61–73; Netschert, "Economic Aspects of Natural Gas Supply," in *Economics of the Gas Industry*, I, 27.

[25] Terry and Winger, *Future Growth of the Natural Gas Industry*, 24.

[26] Richard J. Gonzalez, "Petroleum for Our Future Progress," *Journal of Petroleum Technology*, Vol. IX, No. 3 (March, 1957), 14. See especially figures 8 and 9.

[27] The commentators are: H. K. Hudson, *et al.*, "Phillips Says Domestic Gas Reserves' Future Gloomy Unless Exploration Is Increased," *Oil and Gas Journal*, Vol. LVIII, No. 11 (March 14, 1960); H. K. Hudson, *et al.*, "The Future of Domestic Gas Reserves"; H. K. Hudson, *et al.*, "Supplement to Presentation Entitled 'The Future of Domestic Gas Reserves' "; William B. Golush, "A Management Look at Natural Gas," paper number 1445–G presented before the annual meeting of the A.I.M.E., New York, New York, February 14–18, 1960, and published in the *Journal of Petroleum Technology*, Vol. XII, No. 7 (July, 1960), 11–16; David T. Searles, "The Necessity of Increasing Exploration for and Discovery of Natural Gas and the Problems Facing the Industry Relative to this Operation," a paper presented before the annual meeting of the Independent Natural Gas Association of America, Miami Beach, Florida, October 3–4, 1960. See the comment in *Petroleum Press Service*, Vol. XXVII, No. 11 (November, 1960), 426–27. A

tioned whether an adequate gas exploratory and drilling program is being carried out in the United States. These commentators emphasize the drop in natural gas reserve life, the drop in exploratory activities such as seismic parties, and the fact that reserve additions for the 1945–1960 period amounted to 16.6 trillion cubic feet a year whereas an addition of 23 trillion cubic feet a year is needed to maintain reserve life during the 1960–1970 decade.

The foregoing indicates that, for the foreseeable future, gas supply will be adequate to meet demand, given the proper incentive.

COMPETITION AMONG FUELS[28]

Regardless of reserves, availability, cost-of-service, or other factors, the sales of any fuel are determined, in a free economy,[29] by the choice of an unregulated customer who is largely interested in price. All fuels are subject to upward price pressures, and each is sold against a price ceiling established by the competitive fuels. Inflation should have an equal effect on each fuel in the future.

As pointed out above, the future of coal lies in industrial and power generation uses, and the future there is one of expanding demand. Coal reserves are bountiful; and, during the past five years, coal productivity has increased in that employment declined 50 per cent while production declined only 10 per cent. At the same time probably no more than 10 per cent of existing reserves can be mined at present costs. Also the exposure of coal to demands for increased labor rates is shown in the fact that labor represented 50 per cent of minehead value of coal in 1953. Consequently coal prices should increase as fast as the prices of other fuels.

paper by the same title was given by Searls at the annual meeting of the A.I.M.E., Saint Louis, Missouri, February 26–March 2, 1961. Another commentator is Ira H. Cram, "Introduction to the Problem of Developing Adequate Supplies of Natural Gas," in *Economics of the Gas Industry*. These commentators advocate higher field prices for natural gas as a spur to exploration. Olof W. Nelson uses the same arguments in "Gas Supply in F.P.C. Certificate Proceedings" to advocate more stringent standards for industry expansion and changing of the quantity (take or pay for) provisions of field gas purchase contracts. Note also Ralph E. Davis, *Natural Gas: What the Consumer Should Know About the Nation's Gas Supply*.

[28] Parson, "Long Term Gas Supply Outlook Good," *American Gas Association Monthly,* Vol. XL, No. 6 (June, 1958), 21, is closely followed here.

[29] Regarding the free market, see Ludwig von Mises, *The Anti-Capitalistic Mentality,* 34–43. On the controlled market, see Frederick A. Hayek, *The Road to Serfdom,* and Eugen von Bohm-Bawerk, *Karl Marx and the Close of His System.*

Electricity competes with gas for the household-commercial demand. Electric companies have an enviable past record of few rate increases as a result of being able to absorb rising costs through increasing efficiency of power generation. It is generally agreed that the limit of such increases in efficiency has been reached, with the result that prices for electricity in the future should show the same trends as those of competing fuels.[30]

There is no expectation that nuclear or solar power sources will be competitive in price with the fossil fuels in the near future. It has been estimated that the atom may supply 3 per cent of Free World energy demand in 1975.[31] Fossil fuels now supply 95 per cent of United States energy demand.

Petroleum is expected to hold its own in future residential-commercial consumption, to share the gains in industrial usage, and to enjoy all the increase in motive energy consumption. Petroleum competes with gas for the industrial and residential-commercial markets. An excess of world petroleum supply continued to exist in 1961 to such an extent that crude oil import controls are exercised by the United States government to maintain the domestic oil industry. This excess, coupled with the low annual increases in domestic crude oil consumption, is a price-depressing factor in the petroleum market, but it should prove to be only temporary in view of the large percentage increases in oil consumption being experienced in other countries. Foreign oil is subject to the upward price pressures of demands for

[30] Regarding the competition between gas and electricity, some of the recent developments which favor the use of gas as a source of electricity are important. See R. D. Adams, et al., Fuel Cells: Power for the Future; Elliott, "Fuels in the Future," 29–30; C. G. von Fredersdorff, "New Methods of Generating Electricity from Gas Sources," paper CEP–60–12 presented before the Operating Section of the American Gas Association, Pittsburgh, Pennsylvania, March 1–3, 1960; "Gas Turbine Generators Can Be Marketed Now," Oil and Gas Journal, Vol. LIX, No. 21 (June 26, 1961), 125; "Natural-Gas Fuel Cells May Supply Home Power," Oil and Gas Journal, Vol. LIX, No. 15 (April 10, 1961), 74; E. V. Schultz, et al., "Natural Gas Fuel Cells for Power Generation in Dwellings," a paper presented at the American Gas Association Research and Utilization Conference, Cleveland, Ohio, April 5, 1961; E. V. Somers and J. C. R. Kelly, "Thermoelectric Power," Mechanical Engineering, Vol. LXXXII, No. 7 (July, 1960), 40–42; and "Thermo-electricity . . . a New Demand for Natural Gas," Oil and Gas Journal, Vol. LIX, No. 12 (April 10, 1961), 93.

[31] Weeks, "Fuels Reserves of the Future," Bulletin of the American Association of Petroleum Geologists, Vol. XLII, No. 2 (February, 1958), 431–41. See also the nuclear energy authorities cited in the bibliography at the end of this chapter.

increased royalties to the country of production. Increases in foreign oil prices should be reflected in the price of domestic crude oil. It appears that future United States petroleum prices will behave in a manner comparable to future gas prices.

The relationship between oil and gas is unique among fuels.[32] Oil and gas are the object of a joint exploration program carried out by oil companies and are often produced together. Lowered rates of increase in domestic oil consumption and the excess of available foreign crude have caused oil companies to look to gas sales for income.[33] More of the exploratory effort is being directed towards finding gas, and gas must bear a larger share of the cost of the exploration program. Also exploration and drilling become more costly each year as the depth of the average well increases. As pointed out above, worldwide increases in demand are so great that oil should be able to carry its fair share of the exploratory burden. Although deeper drilling has increased the average well cost from $22,000 in 1941 to $58,000 in 1960, the increase is only 26 per cent if the effect of inflation is eliminated, while the average depth of such wells has increased 30 per cent. As has been noted, the deeper wells also discover greater relative amounts of natural gas.

From the standpoint of the price pressures, the natural gas industry leads the precarious life which is characteristic of all industry.[34] Any business may "price itself out of the market," but very few do.[35] Natural gas is a premium fuel in that it supplies heat at the burner with unequaled efficiency and convenience. Natural gas enjoys a price advantage over other fuels even though some of this advantage has

[32] Davis and Schweitzer, "Natural Gas—Partner and Competitor," *Journal of Petroleum Technology,* Vol. XI, No. 5 (May, 1959), 13.

[33] Thus we have the paradox of excess foreign crude oil's acting as a factor tending to increase the field prices of natural gas and simultaneously acting to depress, through the lowering of competitive fuel prices, the price at which gas can be sold to the consumer. In the March, 1962, issue of *The Petroleum Situation,* the Chase Manhattan Bank makes the point that gas is displacing oil from the energy markets, but the additional income from gas is far less than the loss of income from oil sales.

[34] The man at the helm of a gas company must steer a careful course on the ink-dark economic seas between the Scylla of inadequate field prices and the Charybdis of exorbitant market prices.

[35] The number is even fewer in an industry subject to the completeness of public control characteristic of the natural gas industry. Note the discussion in Chapter 12 of the requirements which must be met under the Natural Gas Act before a gas company can expand. See *In the Matter of Kansas Pipe Line and Gas Company, et al.,* 2 FPC 29 (1940).

been lost since 1950 through price increases growing, in part, out of increases in the price of gas purchased in the field.[36] The high proportion of fixed charges in gas transportation dictates that our pipe-line system must operate at high load factors. At the supply end this means that a high enough price must be paid to attract the necessary volumes of gas and to permit carrying out an exploration program adequate to replenish reserves. At the sales end this means that gas must be sold with prices low enough to meet competition in the low load-factor household-commercial market and in the price-sensitive industrial usage market. Further, in order to maintain prices at competitive levels in the low load-factor household-commercial market, it is necessary that off peak gas be sold in the industrial fuel market. The volumes of gas involved are so large that, in spite of the rapid growth of underground storage and the possible future use of liquefied storage above ground, industrial sales must be made.[37] Theoretically a price increase from any source, such as increased field prices, which would cause the loss of off peak industrial sales, could, in turn, cause the loss of household sales because of necessarily higher household

[36] G. M. Mitchell, in "Fuels Competition and Gas Pricing," a paper presented before the A.I.M.E. Gas Technology Symposium, Tyler, Texas, April 20–21, 1961, shows a price advantage for gas, as compared with oil and electricity, in the residential market of the so-called "marginal areas for gas"—New England and the Pacific Northwest.

It is beyond the scope of the discussion here to consider the mechanics of field pricing; nevertheless, the following data regarding the highest initial prices contracted to be paid by a gas pipe-line buyer in South Louisiana are of interest. The following information is taken from the testimony of J. Rhodes Foster in the CATC case, Docket No. G–11024, et al.:

Year	c/MCF @ 15.025 psia	Purchaser
1947	6.07298	Transcontinental
1948	8.522245	Trunk Line
1949	9.997	United Gas Pipeline
1950	9.997	United Gas Pipeline
1951	13.0	Southern Natural
1952	21.0	United Fuel Gas
1953	21.0	American Louisiana
1954	17.0	Transcontinental
1955	21.0	Texas Gas
1956	22.4	Tennessee Gas
1957	22.8	Transcontinental
1958	23.3	Trunk Line

[37] Note that over one-half of all gas consumption represented industrial usage, much of which is unassociated with the peak-shaving problem.

prices.[38] Sales could also be lost because of the higher selling prices necessarily resulting from an inadequacy of supply.

The foregoing paragraphs describe conditions essentially the same as those of the 1950–1960 decade during which the industry expanded rapidly and successfully to meet its public responsibilities. That the industry is not unaware of the price limitations within which it must operate is shown by the minimizing of field prices, the increasing use of storage, and the application of automation and other design improvements to reduce transportation charges.[39] There is nothing from the competition-between-fuels standpoint to prevent further growth of the natural gas industry.

REGULATION

The natural gas industry has been, and probably will continue to be, subject to a complete scheme of government regulation.[40] Perhaps

[38] William R. Connole, "Energy, Its Use and Abuse," a paper presented before the annual meeting of the Independent Natural Gas Association of America, Houston, Texas, September 10, 1957, and printed in *Energy Resources and Technology, q.v.*

[39] Goodrich, "Natural Gas—The Pipeline Industry."

[40] On the future of regulation, see James M. Landis, *Report on Regulatory Agencies to the President-Elect* (Submitted by the Chairman of the Subcommittee on Administrative Practice and Procedure to the Committee on the Judiciary of the U.S. Senate), 86 Cong., 2 sess., December, 1960; Charles R. Ross, "The Landis Report and the Federal Power Commission 1962," a paper presented before the Public Utility Law Section of the American Bar Association, San Francisco, California, August 7, 1962; *Independent Regulatory Commissions* (Report of the Special Subcommittee on Legislative Oversight of the Committee on Interstate and Foreign Commerce, Oren Harris, chairman) 86 Cong., 2 sess., House Report No. 2238, January 3, 1961; John F. Kennedy, *Special Message on Regulatory Agencies* to the Congress of the United States, April 13, 1961; John Osborne, "Natural Gas and the Authoritarian 'Liberals,'" *Fortune*, Vol. XLVII, No. 5 (May, 1952), 124; Smith, "The Unnatural Problems of Natural Gas," *Fortune*, Vol. LX, No. 3 (September, 1959), 120ff; and Otto Ekstein, "Natural Gas and Patterns of Regulation," *Harvard Business Review*, Vol. XXXVI, No. 2 (March–April, 1958). This last article discusses standards for field pricing of natural gas.

Representative of the vigorous attack being made upon regulatory practices and problems are the following papers written by members of the Federal Power Commission: Joseph C. Swidler, "Regulation of the Small Natural Gas Producer," a paper presented before the Texas Independent Producers and Royalty Owners Association, Houston, Texas, September 4–6, 1962; Joseph C. Swidler, "New Directions in Gas Regulation," a paper presented before the Independent Natural Gas Association, Miami, Florida, October 22–24, 1961; Lawrence J. O'Connor, "Progress in Gas Regulation," a paper presented before the Independent Natural Gas Association, Dallas, Texas, November 10–12, 1962; Howard Morgan, "Gas Price Regulation: An Optimistic View," a paper presented before the West Central Texas Oil and Gas Association, Abilene, Texas, October 10, 1961.

the most important problems that faced the industry in 1962 were those concerning the future course of public control of the industry. These regulatory problems are perhaps the most difficult, involving as they do, the challenge of developing a scheme of control which not only offers the consumer low-priced services, but which also recognizes the consumer interest in adequate incentives to the several parts of the industry to insure continuity of service.

Gas industry regulatory authorities are faced with finding solutions to a number of problems. There is the problem of administrative delay. The backlog of dockets and length of time necessary to reach a decision must be reduced. In the area of field prices for gas, there is the problem of establishing prices which are low and stable from the consumer's point of view and yet high enough to provide the necessary drilling and exploration program. Here the competition between intrastate and interstate markets must be considered.[41] The cost-of-service theory has been abandoned as a standard for field pricing because of difficulties of its application and the lack of relation between the results and the realities of gas exploration and development. Area pricing standards are now being used to measure the fairness of field

[41] One result of Federal Power Commission control of field prices for sales in interstate commerce has been a preference on the part of gas producers to sell to intrastate markets even, in some cases, at prices one to two cents per thousand feet below interstate prices. See "Intrastate Sales Gain Momentum," *Oil and Gas Journal,* Vol. LVII, No. 11)September 21, 1959), 101; Roger L. Conkling, "Home Markets Offer Growing Outlet for Texas-Louisiana Gas Reserves," *World Oil,* Vol. CXL, No. 4 (September, 1960), 84–85; and the statewide studies cited in the bibliography immediately following this chapter.

For example, Pan American Petroleum Corporation, the nation's second largest producer, reorganized its gas sales department in September, 1959, to develop and expand intrastate markets in the fifteen states where it has production. Involved in this program is a subsidiary, Pan American Gas Company, which operates a gas pipe-line system in the Gulf Coast area. This line carries and sells 190,000,000 cubic feet of gas daily to industrial users in the Texas City neighborhood.

Earlier in 1959, Pan American and others sold the large reserves of Old Ocean Field on the Gulf Coast to Texas Electric Service Company, Fort Worth, Texas. See *Petroleum Week,* Vol. XI, No. 23 (December 9, 1960), 40–41. Up to 150,000,000 cubic feet or more will be piped daily in a 360-mile pipe line to North Texas power plants. The price starts at 21.5c/MCF and escalates to 29.5c/MCF.

The potential of intrastate sales is limited as compared with the volume of new gas reserves developed each year. "If the producer wants to continue selling gas on a large scale, then he will sell much of it interstate." *Oil and Gas Journal,* Vol. LVII, No. 39 (September 21, 1959), 102.

prices. The problems of limiting indeterminate pricing clauses of gas purchase contracts are now actively pursued. A rate of return must be provided which will permit marketing gas industry securities and provide the incentive for expansion. This rate of return should be provided in official statements which are not devious. The problem of the vanishing rate base must be faced. In the exercise of end-use controls, freedom should be given the industry to meet competition in any market necessary to provide gas service to all the public at the lowest reasonable prices, rather than establishing a rigid prohibitory system which would deny markets to gas, regardless of the economics of the situation, because of the horror or running out of gas in the far distant future. Portentous for the future of gas regulation is the fact that the Congress of the United States had under consideration in 1961 a study which could result in the creation of a National Energy Board to plan and co-ordinate all energy use in the United States.[42]

The natural gas industry should continue to expand. A continually increasing demand for natural gas is indicated even in the face of increased competition from other fuels. Natural gas reserves continue to grow; and, barring an adverse turn in governmental regulation of the industry, it should be possible to sell the large dollar amounts of securities necessary to expansion. It is reasonable to expect that the industry will double its size in the next twenty years.[43]

[42] See Statement of Secretary of the Interior, Stewart L. Udall, before the Senate Interior and Insular Affairs Committee, June 12, 1961, in Support of a National Fuels and Energy Study (Department of the Interior, Information Service, June 12, 1961).

And see Connole, "The Role of Regulation in Developing the Transportation and Use of Liquefied Methane," in *Energy Resources and Technology,* 336; William R. Connole, "Take One Giant Step," in *Energy Resources and Technology,* 431; and John H. Lichtblau and Lillard P. Spriggs, *Energy Policy and Competition.*

[43] Terry, "Future Life of the Natural Gas Industry," *Economics of the Gas Industry,* I, 275.

Many studies have recently been made in an effort to determine how future fuel demand may be matched with available reserves and thus supplied. Those studies which were employed by the author in the writing of this chapter are listed below.

The studies of world energy requirements and probable sources of supply which consider the period through the year 2000 are:

Ayres, Eugene, "The Fuel Situation," *Scientific American*, Vol. CXCV, No. 4 (October, 1956), 43. Mr. Ayres is pessimistic about the life span of fossil fuel reserves because of the great indicated demand.

———, and Charles A. Scarlott, *Energy Sources—The Wealth of the World*, New York, 1952.

Cadle, Austin, "United States Petroleum Forecast and Dynamic World Growth in Petroleum Demands," a paper presented at the American Petroleum Institute, Section VI, Interdivisional, 1958, and published in *Proceedings, q.v.*, XXXVIII, 24.

Guyol, Nathaniel B., "The Role of Petroleum in the World Energy Supply," a paper presented at the Fifth World Petroleum Congress, New York, New York, 1959, and published in *Proceedings, q.v.*, IX, 25.

Hubbert, M. King, "Nuclear Energy and Fossil Fuels," in *Drilling and Production Practice—1956*, New York, 1957, 7ff.

Petroleum Press Service, Vol. XXVIII, No. 5 (May, 1961), 190.

Putnam, Palmer C., *Energy in the Future*, New York, 1953.

Searl, Milton F., *Fossil Fuels in the Future*, Washington, D.C., 1960.

United Nations Department of Economic and Social Affairs, "World Energy Requirements in 1975 and 2000," a paper presented at the International Conference on Peaceful Uses of Atomic Energy, 1955, and published in *Proceedings, q.v.*, I, 3.

Studies which consider world energy uses and supplies through 1975 are:

Chapman, A. H., and James Terry Duce, "The Economics of the International Petroleum Industry," *Journal of Petroleum Technology,* Vol. VII, No. 3 (March, 1955), 9–10.

Panel on the Impact of the Peaceful Uses of Atomic Energy (Robert McKinney, chairman), *Peaceful Uses of Atomic Energy,* 2 vols., Washington, D. C., 1956.

Pratt, Wallace E., "The Impact of the Peaceful Uses of Atomic Energy on the Petroleum Industry," in *Peaceful Uses of Atomic Energy,* II, 89–106.

The studies covering the United States of America's requirements and sources of supply for the long-term period through 2000 include, in addition to those listed above, the following:

American Gas Association Rate Committee, *Gas Rate Fundamentals,* New York, 1960, pp. 61–73.

Coqueran, Frederick G., Harold H. Hamman, and John G. Winger, *Future Growth of the World Petroleum Industry,* New York, 1958.

Elliott, Martin A., "Fuels in the Future," a special lecture presented at the 33rd Annual National A.S.M.E. Oil and Gas Power Division Conference, New Orleans, Louisiana, April 2–4, 1961. This paper deals primarily with analytical methods of predicting future gas availability and the possibility of supplementing natural gas supplies with synthetic gases.

———, "The Long Range Supply of Gas," a paper presented at the 1960 Meeting of the Society of Gas Lighting, New York, New York, January 14, 1960.

Energy Resources and Technology, hearings before the Subcommittee on Automation and Energy Resources of the Joint Economic Committee of the U. S. Congress, 86 Cong., 1 sess., October 12–16, 1959. Of particular interest are the statements by Richard J. Gonzalez on page 133, Carl T. Kallina on page 122, Bruce C. Netschert on page 25, Sam H. Schurr on page 5, Philip Sporn on page 49, and Boni, Watkins, Jason and Company on page 344.

Parson, Daniel, "Long Term Gas Supply Outlook Good," *American Gas Association Monthly,* Vol. XL, No. 6 (June, 1958), 21.

Terry, Lyon F., and John G. Winger, *Future Growth of the Natural Gas Industry,* New York, 1957.

Studies dealing with United States energy requirements and probable sources of supply through 1980 are:

Batchelder, H. R., and H. W. Nelson, "Future of Synthetic Liquid and Gaseous Fuels," a paper presented before the Joint Fuels Conference, A.S.M.E.–A.I.M.E., Columbus, Ohio, October 19–20, 1955, and reported in the *Journal of Commerce,* October 21, 1955.

Davis, W. B., and J. L. Schweitzer, "Natural Gas—Partner and Competitor," *Journal of Petroleum Technology,* Vol. XI, No. 5 (May, 1959), 13. This article is particularly concerned with the competition between petroleum and gas.

Dewhurst, J. Frederic, and Associates, *America's Needs and Resources,* New York, 1955.

Guyol, Nathaniel B., "Oil in the Total Energy Market," a paper presented before the 35th Annual Meeting of the American Petroleum Institute, San Francisco, California, 1955.

Melnick, Jack, "A Statistical Analysis of Future Energy Consumption in the U. S. (1959–1965)," *Oil and Gas Journal,* Vol. LVII, No. 18 (May 25, 1959), 146.

Netschert, Bruce C., *The Future Supply of Oil and Gas,* Baltimore, Md., 1958. This is a Resources for the Future, Incorporated, study.

Phelps, Thomas W., "Petroleum's Place in the Future Energy Requirements of the United States," *Journal of Petroleum Technology,* Vol. XI, No. 7 (July, 1959), 22.

President's Materials Policy Commission, *Resources for Freedom,* 5 vols., Washington, D. C., 1952. This report was compiled by the Paley Commission of which George R. Brown, chairman of the board of Texas Eastern Transmission Corporation, was a member. Volume III of the report, *The Outlook for Energy Sources,* is of special interest.

Schurr, Sam. H., and Bruce C. Netschert, *Energy in the American Economy, 1850–1975,* Baltimore, Md., 1960. This 774-page book, published by Resources for the Future, Incorporated, is the most complete and up-to-date United States energy study.

Sporn, Philip, "The Role of Energy and the Role of Nuclear Energy in the United States," a paper presented at the International Conference on the Peaceful Uses of Atomic Energy, 1956, and published in *Proceedings, q.v.,* I, 414–24.

Teitelbaum, Perry D., *Nuclear Energy and the U. S. Fuel Economy, 1955–1980* (One of the National Planning Association's Reports on the Preductive Uses of Nuclear Energy), New York, 1958.

Texas Eastern Transmission Corporation. "Energy and Fuels in the United States . . . 1947–1980," *The Inch,* Vol. XI, Nos. 1–3 (Winter, Spring, and Summer, 1961).

Zapp, A. D., *Future Petroleum Producing Capacity of the United States,* New York, 1962. Mr. Zapp concludes that "the outlook for future domestic supply of natural gas and natural gas liquids is even more favorable than [it is for] crude oil."

Studies exploring the resources and demands of particular regions are:

Boni, Watkins, Jason and Company, Incorporated, "Louisiana: Key to Future U.S. Gas Supply?" *Gas Age,* Vol. CXXIII, No. 1 (January 8, 1959), 17.

García-Rojas, Antonio, "The Mexican Gas Industry," an address before the Annual Conference of the American Gas Association General Management Section, Pittsburgh, Pennsylvania, February 29–March 2, 1960.

Gardner, Frank J., "Natural Gas Is Texas' Industrial Lifeblood," *Oil and Gas Journal,* Vol. LIX, No. 11 (March 13, 1961), 167.

Hill, Kenneth E., and John G. Winger, "Future Growth of the West Coast Petroleum Industry," a paper presented at the Spring Meeting of the A.P.I. Division of Production, Pacific Coast District, Los Angeles, California, May 16, 1957.

O'Donnell, John P., "California Becoming Nation's No. 1 Gas Market," *Oil and Gas Journal,* Vol. LIX, No. 11 (March 13, 1961), 122.

OEEC Energy Advisory Committee, *Towards a New Energy Pattern in Europe,* Paris, 1960.

OEEC Gas Committee, *Gas in Europe, 1960, Production, Availability, Consumption,* Paris, 1960.

Stanford Research Institute, *The California Economy: 1947–1985,* Palo Alto, 1958.

Testimony by Roger L. Conkling at CATC certificate case hearing before the Federal Power Commission in Docket No. G–11024 *et al.,* on March 15, 1960, in Major Industrial Markets and Forecasted Requirements for Texas and Louisiana Reserves. Reported in *Foster Associates Report,* No. 210 (March 24, 1960), 21–24.

Trexel, Carl A., Jr., "Impact of Natural Gas on the Economy of the Pacific Northwest," a paper presented before the American Institute of Chemical Engineers, Seattle, Washington, June 10, 1957.

Concerning the competition among fuels and its influence on future demand for natural gas, see:

Adams, Francis L., "Impact of Electric Power Production on the Coal Industry," a paper presented at the 1958 Annual Meeting of the Northern West Virginia Coal Association, Fairmont, West Virginia, October 12–14, 1958.

American Gas Association Rate Committee, *Gas Rate Fundamentals,* New York, 1960.

Davis, W. B., and J. L. Schweitzer, "Natural Gas—Partner and Competitor," *Journal of Petroleum Technology,* Vol. XI, No. 5 (May, 1959), 13.

Eisemann, Eugene F., "Some Aspects of the Competition Between Fuels in the United States," a paper presented at the annual meeting of the A.I.M.E., Saint Louis, Missouri, May 16–18, 1961.

Jaworek, W. Gibson, and John J. Schantz, Jr., "Bituminous Coal Consumption, Estimating Its Long Term Growth and Annual Variation," a paper presented at the annual meeting of the A.I.M.E., New York, New York, November 21–23, 1960.

———, and ———, "Fuel Interchangeability—Measuring Its Extent in U. S. Energy Markets," a paper presented at the annual meeting of the A.I.M.E., Saint Louis, Missouri, May 16–18, 1961.

Miller, Raymond W., "Review of 1960 Domestic Production," a paper presented at the annual meeting of the A.I.M.E., Saint Louis, Missouri, May 16–18, 1961.

Mitchell, G. M., "Fuels Competition and Gas Pricing," a paper presented before the A.I.M.E. Gas Technology Symposium, Tyler, Texas, April 20–21, 1961.

OEEC Energy Advisory Committee, *Towards a New Energy Pattern in Europe,* Paris, 1960.

Parson, Daniel, "Long Term Gas Supply Outlook Good," *American Gas Association Monthly,* Vol. XL, No. 6 (June, 1958), 21.

Robinson, Myles E., and W. L. Kurtz, "Competitive Markets—The Fossil Fuels," a paper presented at the annual meeting of the A.I.M.E., Saint Louis, Missouri, May 16–18, 1961.

Skinner, C. E., "Battle of the Fuels—Who's Winning?" *Oil and Gas Journal,* Vol. LVII, No. 32 (July 27, 1959), 142.

Regarding coal reserves, see:

Averitt, Paul, Louise R. Berryhill, and Dorothy A. Taylor, *Coal Resources of the United States* (U.S.G.S. *Circular 293),* Washington, D.C., 1953.

Panel on the Impact of the Peaceful Uses of Atomic Energy (Robert McKinney, chairman), *Peaceful Uses of Atomic Energy,* 2 vols., Washington, D.C., 1956.

Concerning oil and gas reserves, see:

Coqueran, Frederick G., Harold H. Hamman, and John G. Winger, *Future Growth of the World Petroleum Industry,* New York, 1958.

Hubbert, M. King, "Nuclear Energy and Fossil Fuels," in *Drilling and Production Practice—1956,* New York, 1957, 7 ff.

Murrell, John H., "Is Oil Nearing a Production Crisis?" *Petroleum Week,* Vol. II, No. 11 (March 16, 1956), 9–10.

Pratt, Wallace E., "The Impact of the Peaceful Uses of Atomic Energy on the Petroleum Industry," in *Peaceful Uses of Atomic Energy* (the report of the Panel on the Impact of the Peaceful Uses of Atomic Energy to the Joint Committee on Atomic Energy), II, 89–106.

Weeks, Lewis G., "Fuel Reserves of the Future," *Bulletin* of the American Association of Petroleum Geologists, XLII, No. 2 (February, 1958), 431–41.

For a discussion of the outlook for natural gas reserves, see:

American Gas Association Rate Committee, *Gas Rate Fundamentals,* New York, 1960.

Miller, R. L., "A New Look at Ultimate Natural Gas Reserves," *World Oil,* Vol. CXLVII, No. 10 (October, 1958), 222–24.

Parson, Daniel, "Long Term Gas Supply Outlook Good," *American Gas Association Monthly,* Vol. XL, No. 6 (June, 1958), 21.

Terry, Lyon F., and John G. Winger, *Future Growth of the Natural Gas Industry,* New York, 1957.

————, and ————, "Sees 1,200 Trillion CF U.S. Recoverable Gas," *American Gas Association Monthly,* Vol. XXXIX, Nos. 7–8, July–August, 1957), 10–12, 38–39.

Regarding oil shale reserves, see:

Donnell, J. R., *Preliminary Report on Oil Shale Resources of Piceance Creek Basin, Northwestern Colorado* (U.S.G.S. *Bulletin 1042–11*), Washington, D.C., 1957.

Concerning the development of methods for producing synthetic gases, see:

Batchelder, H. R., and H. W. Nelson, "Future of Synthetic Liquid and Gaseous Fuels," a paper presented before the Joint Fuels Conference, A.S.M.E.–A.I.M.E., Columbus, Ohio, October 19–20, 1955, and reported in the *Journal of Commerce,* October 21, 1955.

Elliott, Martin A., "Coal Gasification for Production of Synthesis and Pipeline Gas," a paper presented at the annual meeting of the A.I.M.E., Saint Louis, Missouri, February 26–March 2, 1961 (preprint 61 F61).

————, "Fuels in the Future," a special lecture presented at the 33rd Annual National A.S.M.E. Oil and Gas Power Division Conference, New Orleans, Louisiana, April 2–4, 1961.

————, "The Long Range Supply of Gas," a paper presented at the 1960 Meeting of the Society of Gas Lighting, New York, New York, January 14, 1960.

Gasification and Liquefaction of Coal, Symposium at the Annual Meeting of the A.I.M.E., New York, New York, February 20–21, 1952 (1953).

413

Hartley, Fred L., "Oil Shale . . . How Soon?" *Chemical Engineering Progress,* Vol. LV, No. 3 (March, 1959), 59–64.

Henry, Hall M., "What About Gas Supply and Price?" *Gas Age,* Vol. CXV, No. 5 (March 10, 1955), 36–49, 70.

Miller, E. P., and R. J. Cameron, "Shale Oil Nears Competitive Level with Domestic Production," *Journal of Petroleum Technology,* Vol. X, No. 8 (August, 1958), 25–27.

Morgan, Jerome T., *Gasification of Hydro-Carbons,* New York, 1953.

Ongstad, O. C., M. H. Chetrick, and W. H. Oppelt, *Cost Data for Gasification of Lignite in an Externally Heated Retort* (U.S. Department of the Interior, Bureau of Mines, Report of Investigations 5272), Washington, D. C., 1956.

Pyrcioch, E. J., H. A. Dirksen, C. G. von Fredersdorff, and E. S. Pettyjohn, "Pipeline Gas from Coal," paper CEP 54–24 presented at the American Gas Association, Operating Section, Chemical Engineering and Manufactured Gas Production Conference, Pittsburgh, Pennsylvania, May 24–26, 1954.

Rubel, A. C., "Shale Oil as a Future Energy Resource," *The Mines Magazine,* Vol. XLV, No. 10 (October, 1955), 72–76.

———, "Liquid Fuels from Oil Shale—A Critical Review," paper 293–G presented before the Southwest Meeting of the Petroleum Branch of A.I.M.E., Dallas, Texas, October 20, 1949.

Schultz, E. B., and H. D. Linden, "From Oil Shale to Production of Pipeline Gas by Hydrogenalysis," *Industrial and Engineering Chemistry,* Vol. LI, No. 4 (April, 1959), 573–76.

Stanfield, K. E., J. W. Smith, H. N. Smith, and W. A. Robb, *Oil Yields of Sections of Green River Oil Shale in Colorado, 1954–57* (U.S. Department of the Interior, Bureau of Mines, Report of Investigations RI–5614), Washington, D. C., 7960.

U.S. Department of the Interior, Bureau of Mines, *Synthetic Liquid Fuels,* Part II, *Oil from Oil Shale* (Report of Investigations 4866), Washington, D. C., 1952.

U.S. Department of the Interior, Bureau of Mines Bituminous Coal Staff, *The Bureau of Mines Synthetic Liquid Fuels Program, 1944–55* (Report of Investigations 5506), Washington, D.C., 1959.

For information about nuclear energy possibilities, see:

Doan, R. L., "The Challenge of the Future," a paper presented at the annual meeting of the Western Petroleum Refiners Association, San Antonio, Texas, March 17, 1959.

Dwyer, Cornelius J., *Nuclear Energy and World Fuel Prices* (one of the

National Planning Association's Reports on the Productive Uses of Nuclear Energy), Washington, D. C., 1958.

Elliott, Martin A., "Fuels in the Future," a special lecture presented at the 33rd Annual National A.S.M.E. Oil and Gas Power Division Conference, New Orleans, Louisiana, April 2–4, 1961.

Hubbert, M. King, "Nuclear Energy and Fossil Fuels," in *Drilling and Production Practice—1956,* New York, 1957, 7ff.

Panel on the Impact of the Peaceful Uses of Atomic Energy (Robert McKinney, chairman), *Peaceful Uses of Atomic Energy,* 2 vols., Washington, D.C., 1956.

Putnam, Palmer C., *Energy in the Future,* New York, 1953.

Schurr, Sam H., and Bruce C. Netschert, *Energy in the American Economy, 1850–1975,* Baltimore, Md., 1960.

———, and Jacob Marschak, *Economic Aspects of Atomic Power,* Princeton, N. J., 1950.

Sporn, Philip, "The Role of Energy and the Role of Nuclear Energy in the United States," a paper presented at the International Conference on the Peaceful Uses of Atomic Energy, 1956, and published in *Proceedings, q.v.,* I, 414–24.

Teitlebaum, Perry D., *Nuclear Energy and the U. S. Fuel Economy, 1955–1980* (one of the National Planning Association's Reports on the Productive Uses of Nuclear Energy), New York, 1958.

Regarding the possibilities of solar energy, see:

Proceedings of the World Symposium on Applied Solar Energy, Phoenix, Arizona, November 1–5, 1955. New York, 1956.

Putnam, Palmer C., *Energy in the Future,* New York, 1953.

Schurr, Sam H., and Bruce C. Netschert, *Energy in the American Economy, 1850–1975,* Baltimore Maryland, 1960.

The following is a list of studies on which the information contained in tables 22, 23, 25, and 26 was based:

American Gas Association Bureau of Statistics, "Supply of, and Demand for, Natural Gas in 1975," August 3, 1956.

Ayers, Eugene, "Energy Resources for the Future," *Oil and Gas Compact Bulletin,* Vol. XIV, No. 1 (June, 1955), 21.

———, "The Fuel Situation," *Scientific American,* Vol. CXCV, No. 4 (October, 1956), 47.

———, and Charles A. Scarlott, *Energy Sources—The Wealth of the World,* New York, 1952.

Coqueran, Frederick G., Harold H. Hamman, and John G. Winger, *Future Growth of the World Petroleum Industry,* New York, 1958.

Davis, W. B., and J. L. Schweitzer, "Natural Gas—Partner and Competitor," *Journal of Petroleum Technology,* Vol. XI, No. 5 (May, 1959), 13.

Egloff, G., "Oil and Gas as Industrial Raw Materials," in *Resources for Freedom,* IV, 193.

Hinson, H. H., "What's the Present Picture for Natural Gas Reserves?" a report presented before the American Gas Association Financial Forum, October 8, 1954.

Hubbert, M. King, "Nuclear Energy and Fossil Fuels," in *Drilling and Production Practice—1956,* New York, 1957, 7ff.

Melnick, Jack, "A Statistical Analysis of Future Energy Consumption in the U.S., 1959–1965," *Oil and Gas Journal,* Vol. LVII, No. 18 (May 25, 1959), 146.

Panel on the Impact of Peaceful Uses of Atomic Energy (Robert McKinney, chairman), *Peaceful Uses of Atomic Energy,* 2 vols., Washington, D.C., 1956.

Parson, Daniel, "Long Term Gas Supply Outlook Good," *American Gas Association Monthly,* Vol. XL, No. 6 (June, 1958), 21.

Pettyjohn, E. S., "Coal . . . Gas Source of the Future," *Coal Age,* Vol. LX, No. 3 (March, 1955), 57.

Pogue, J. E., and Kenneth T. Hill, *Future Growth and Financial Requirements of the World Petroleum Industry,* New York, 1956. Presented at the annual meeting of the American Institute of Mining, Metallurgical and Petroleum Engineers, Petroleum Branch, February 21, 1956.

Pratt, Wallace E., "The Impact of the Peaceful Uses of Atomic Energy on the Petroleum Industry," in *Peaceful Uses of Atomic Energy* (report of the Panel on the Impact of the Peaceful Uses of Atomic Energy to the Joint Committee on Atomic Energy), II, 89–106.

President's Materials Policy Commission, *Resources for Freedom,* 5 vols., Washington, D. C., 1952.

Putnam, Palmer C., *Energy in the Future,* New York, 1953.

Schurr, Sam H., and Bruce C. Netschert, *Energy in the American Economy, 1850–1975,* Baltimore, Maryland, 1960.

Sporn, Philip, "The Role of Energy and the Role of Nuclear Energy in the United States," a paper presented at the International Conference on the Peaceful Uses of Atomic Energy," 1956, and published in *Proceedings, q.v.,* I, 414–24.

Terry, Lyon F., "The Future Supply of Natural Gas," *Proceedings,* American Gas Association, 1950, pp. 155–59.

Teitlebaum, Perry D., *Nuclear Energy and the U. S. Fuel Economy, 1955–1980* (one of the National Planning Association's Reports on the Productive Uses of Nuclear Energy), New York, 1958.

————, and John G. Winger, "Sees 1,200 Trillion CF of U. S. Recoverable Gas," *American Gas Association Monthly,* Vol. XXXIX, Nos. 7–8 (July–August, 1957), 10–12, 38–39.

Tippy, W. B., "Where Does the Gas Industry Go From Here—" *American Gas Journal,* Vol. XVIII, No. 3 (October, 1956), 66–67.

APPENDIX
REGULATION OF GAS PRODUCTION—1956

by John C. Jacobs

DEVELOPMENTS in state regulation of gas production over the past few years have been principally in the direction of more perfectly achieving "ratable take," that is, an equitable allocation of field deliveries between wells. A major occurrence in this connection has been the recent issuance of Louisiana statewide order Number 29–F under which allowables will be established monthly for each of the gas fields in Louisiana.[2] Table A compares the mechanics for establishing allowables under the new Louisiana order with the procedure described in the Texas statewide order Number 24.[3]

The individual field problems which have arisen under state allowable orders have been occasioned by at least two causes:

(a) difference in the market demand of each of several purchasers from a common reservoir which results in different desired rates of depletion for the reserves dedicated to each such purchaser, and

(b) differences between the state assigned well allowables, which are based usually upon a well and acreage factor, and daily contract quantities calculated under gas purchase contracts on a reserve basis as required by the Federal Power Commission's sales certification standards of an approximate twenty year reserve supply and availability.

---

[1] The article from which the following material was taken appeared in the *Fourth Institute on Mineral Law,* Baton Rouge, La., 1960, pp. 58–61. In the sections reprinted here by permission of Louisiana State Press, Mr. Jacobs describes the problems involved in state control of ratable taking.

[2] State of Louisiana, Department of Conservation statewide order No. 29–F, November 8, 1955, *Oil and Gas Reporter,* Vol. V (1955), 474.

[3] The assistance of Mr. S. L. Windham, Ch. Eng., of Cuero, Texas, in the preparation of Table C is gratefully acknowledged.

The states have recently dealt with at least four types of individual field problems:

(a) The problem of exaggerated forecasts which result in allowables greater than the true market demand for the field. In this situation the purchaser is faced with the question of whether to take gas in accordance with the contractual daily quantities or to take the same percentage of each producer's assigned allowable. In the Texas Henze Field decision[4] and in the Louisiana Spider Field decision[5] orders were issued which will result in the taking of the same percentage of each producer's assigned allowable. These decisions accord with the Kansas Supreme Court's ruling that overforecasting on the part of a producer is legally reprehensible.[6]

(b) A second problem involves the handling of allowables for unconnected wells. Under the Alco-Mag Field order[7] the Texas Railroad Commission will assign allowables to non-connected wells, thereby reducing the amount of drainage which the connected wells may enjoy. Under Louisiana Order No. 29–F allowables will not be assigned to a well until the well is connected to a line.

(c) A third problem has to do with the handling of underproduction resulting from the physical inability of wells to meet their allowables. In the Texas Alco-Mag and Waskom field orders[8] the usual practice of deducting such underproduction from the field allowable has been reversed.

[4] *In re Conservation and Prevention of Waste of Crude Petroleum and Natural Gas in the Henze Field, DeWitt County, Texas,* Railroad Commission of Texas, Oil and Gas Docket No. 1239, No. 2–31,835, August 8, 1955, 4 O.& G.R. 1846.

[5] Order concerning the application of C. A. Hilburn for a Ratable Take from the Anthony Sand of the Spider Field, De Soto Parish, Louisiana, Department of Conservation, State of Louisiana, Order No. 92–13, March 2, 1955, 4 O.& G.R. 1851.

[6] *Republic Natural Gas Co.* v *State Corporation Commission,* 173 Kan. 172, 244 P.2d 1196 (1952). Also, the March 14, 1955, Railroad Commission of Texas Memorandum to All Operators of Gas Wells in Non-Associated Prorated Gas Fields states that the allowable system will not function properly unless producers' forecasts are accurate.

[7] *In re Conservation and Prevention of Waste of Crude Petroleum and Natural Gas in the Alco-Mag Fields, Harris County, Texas,* Railroad Commission of Texas, Oil and Gas Docket No. 128, No. 3–32,602, December 12, 1955, *Oil and Gas Reporter,* Vol. V (1955), 423.

[8] Railroad Commission of Texas, Oil and Gas Docket No. 146, No. 6–32–647, Order of December 23, 1955, 5 O.& G.R. 423.

(d) A fourth problem involves the excessive overproduction or under production resulting in fields served by two or more purchasers whose differing market demands result in a widely different desired rate of production of their dedicated reserves. In answer to this problem at the Waskom field in Texas future allowables will be set monthly on the basis of all pertinent factors, instead of the previous system of monthly allowables based on a mathematical calculation whereby producers' forecasts were adjusted for over- and underproduction.

Suggestions for future changes in the gas allowable system should be judged from at least two points of view, namely, (a) does the suggested change assume a meaning of "ratable take" which is aimed at providing a fair share of the field production for each producer, or does the assumed meaning of "ratable take" result in providing more than a fair share of the field production to those wells having the largest market outlet, and (b) does the suggested rate change include the most reasonable means of achieving ratability.

Perfect ratability may be defined as the opposite of operation under the rule of capture, that is, allowing each producer the opportunity to produce the reserves underlying his properties. Since administrative agencies have usually not adopted reserve basis allocation factors, the practical definition of ratability amounts to allowing each producer a fair opportunity to produce that share of the field reserve which is proportionate to his well's allocation factor. This aim dictates the use of the allowable systems presently in use in the producing states wherein the market demand for the field is adjusted by subtracting past underproduction and by adding past overproduction prior to making an allocation between wells. This system results in an average rate of depletion of the field reserves between the maximum and minimum rates desired by the several purchasers in the field. The suggested revisions of the existing allowable systems usually involve establishing the field allowable at the highest requested level and the elimination (or weakening) of overproduction and underproduction adjustments with a resultant greater opportunity for drainage between wells and an increased rate of depletion of the field reserves. It should be noted that if such revisions were carried to the extent, with the large market outlet wells draining those with smaller market outlets, of substantially increasing the rate of depletion of field reserves (and decreasing the available life of the field) there would be a reduction of the anticipated life of reserves which have served as the basis of certificates issued by the Federal Power Commission, with the consequence of a possible conflict wherein, under the paramount federal jurisdiction, the burden would be upon the proponents of the new allowable system to prove that the increased production rates are in the public interest.

Under the existing allowable systems ratable take is achieved by shutting in overproduced wells and allowing underproduced wells an additional amount of time during which underproduction may be "made up." Under this system all wells share equitably in the field allowable and there are no conflicts between state and federal jurisdiction. In some recent orders underproduction is declared available to be taken by any purchaser who desires to make a connection at the underproduced well. Such a means of achieving ratability raises a possible state-federal conflict in the form of the legal question: "Does a state agency have the power to authorize another producer to so take gas which has been dedicated to interstate commerce?"

TABLE A

COMPARISON OF LOUISIANA STATE-WIDE ORDER #29–F WITH TEXAS STATE-WIDE ORDER #24

LOUISIANA #29–F	TEXAS #24
Application	
Applicable to all non-associated gas reservoirs in State except those wherein Special Field Orders have been assigned by reason of a gas cycling project. Does not cover associated gas nor oil reservoirs.	Applicable to all non-associated gas fields wherein Special Field Rules are in effect as a result of Commission hearing.
Nominations (Basis for Allowable)	
Filed quarterly by gatherer, user, transporter or purchaser of gas. On same form is reported actual production from field in corresponding period of preceding year.	Filed monthly by purchaser. Nominations filed by transporter, etc., are not used.

Calculation of Field Allowables

Not mathematical. Commissioner will weigh purchasers' forecasts with previous years production and available market information and will grant what it considers a reasonable allowable.

Straightforward mathematical calculation. Allowable is based on producers' forecasts with adjustment for field status and production three months previously.

Calculation of Well Allowables

(1) Prorated as provided by Statewide Rule, or Special Field Rules. If Special Field Rules are not applicable, proration will be on the basis of 100% Acreage.
(2) Allowable constant for three months.
(3) No well will be granted an allowable until all physical connections are made to permit utilization of allowable.

(1) Prorated as provided by Special Field Rules only.
(2) Allowable varies monthly.
(3) Wells granted allowable regardless of whether market available.

Production Restriction

Production restricted to 150% of current allowable.

Production restricted to 200% of normal allowable (average allowable for most recent 6 months).

Calculation of Well Allowable Status

Calculated by producer and reported monthly to Commissioner.

Calculated by Commission monthly and publishel semi-annually.

Overproduced Wells

Any well overproduced as of July 1 of any year will be shut in until such overproduction is made up: *however,* if a well is becoming overproduced to a considerable degree it may be possible to obtain an emergency allowable which would serve to cancel all or a portion of accumulated overproduction.

Any well overproduced as of two successive balancing dates (March 1 and September 1), and which remained overproduced throughout the six month period between the two dates, is shut in until the overproduction is made up.

422

SOURCES OF FIGURES

THE FIGURES in this book were published through the courtesy of the following authors, publishers, and companies who generously consented to their use.

Figures 2, 5, 6, and 7, *Natural Gas Production and Transmission,* by J. D. Parent, published by the Institute of Gas Technology, 1952.

Figures 3 and 9, "Principles of Orifice Measurement," in *American Gas Fundamentals,* a series published by the *American Gas Journal.*

Figure 10, the *Petroleum Engineer,* and Southern Counties Gas Company, Los Angeles, California.

Figures 14, 15, 16, 20, 21, 22, 23, and 24, *1961 Gas Facts,* published by the American Gas Association.

Figures 17, 18, 35, and 36, *Energy in the American Economy, 1850–1975,* by Sam H. Schurr and Bruce C. Netschert, published by the Johns Hopkins Press for Resources for the Future, 1960.

Figure 19, *1956 Gas Facts,* published by the American Gas Association.

Figure 29, "The Economic Significance of Liquefied Natural Gas—The Distribution Company's Viewpoint," by Michael Anuskiewitz, Jr.

Figure 30, Texas Eastern Transmission Corporation, Houston, Texas.

Figure 32, *The Natural Gas Industry: Monopoly and Competition in Field Markets,* by Edward J. Neuner, published by the University of Oklahoma Press, 1960.

Figure 34, Ebasco Services, Incorporated, New York, New York.

Figure 37, *Future Growth of the Natural Gas Industry,* by Lyon F. Terry and John G. Winger, published by the Chase Manhattan Bank, 1957.

BIBLIOGRAPHY

I. GOVERNMENT PUBLICATIONS

Averitt, Paul, Louise R. Berryhill, and Dorothy A. Taylor. *Coal Resources of the United States.* A progress report. U.S.G.S. *Circular 293,* October 1, 1953.

Clark, Colin. *The Real Productivity of Soviet Russia.* 87 Cong., 1 sess. (1961). Printed for Committee on the Judiciary, U.S. Senate.

Energy Resources and Technology. Hearings before the Subcommittee on Automation and Energy Resources of the Joint Economic Committee of the U.S. Congress, 86 Cong., 1 sess., October 12–16, 1959.

Federal Power Commission. *Annual Report* of 1955. Washington, D.C., 1955.

———. *Direct Sales by Producers of Natural Gas to Interstate Natural Gas Pipeline Companies, 1960.* Washington, D.C., 1961.

———. *General Rules and Regulations, Including Rules of Practice and Procedure.* Washington, D.C., 1948.

———. "General Rules and Regulations Under the Natural Gas Act." Sec. 154.91: Applicability, Independent Producers.

———, *Natural Gas Investigation,* Docket G–580. 2 vols. *(Smith-Wimberly Report* and *Olds-Draper Report).* Washington, D.C., 1948.

———. *Statistics of Natural Gas Companies.* Washington, D.C., 1960.

———. "Uniform System of Accounting for Natural Gas Companies." Sec. 201.3–16: Regarding Transmission Systems and Distribution Systems.

Federal Trade Commission. *Reports on Natural Gas and Natural Gas Pipelines . . . .* Washington, D.C., 1940.

Independent Regulatory Commissions. Report of the Special Subcommittee on Legislative Oversight of the Committee on Interstate and Foreign Commerce. Oren Harris, chairman. 86 Cong., 2 sess., House Report No. 2238, January 3, 1961.

Kennedy, John F. *Special Message on Regulatory Agencies* to the Congress of the United States, April 13, 1961.

Landis, James M. *Report on Regulatory Agencies to the President-Elect.* Submitted by the Chairman of the Subcommittee on Administrative Practice and Procedure to the Committee on the Judiciary of the U.S. Senate. 86 Cong., 2 sess., December, 1960.

Panel on the Impact of the Peaceful Uses of Atomic Energy. Robert McKinney, chairman. *Peaceful Uses of Atomic Energy.* 2 vols. Washington, D.C., 1956.

President's Materials Policy Commission. *Resources for Freedom.* 5 vols. Washington, D.C., 1952.

Statement of Secretary of the Interior, Stewart L. Udall, before the Senate Interior and Insular Affairs Committee, June 21, 1961, in Support of a National Fuels and Energy Study.

U.S. Department of Commerce. *Census of Manufacturers.* Washington, D. C., 1960.

U.S. Department of the Interior, Bureau of Mines. *Mineral Facts and Problems.* Revised edition. Washington, D.C., 1960.

————, Bureau of Mines. *1958 Minerals Yearbook* (II: Fuels). Washington, D. C., 1959.

————, Bureau of Mines. *1959 Minerals Yearbook* (II: Fuels). Washington, D.C., 1960.

U.S. House of Representatives, *Hearings on H.R. 4560 Before the Committee on Interstate and Foreign Commerce, Amendments to the Natural Gas Act, 1955.* 2 parts.

U.S. Senate. *Amendments to the Natural Gas Act, Hearings Before the Committee on Interstate and Foreign Commerce.* Washington, D.C., 1955.

II. NEWSPAPERS

Colwell, William B. "Electric Heat," *Wall Street Journal,* Vol. XXII, No. 118 (December 16, 1958), 1, 6.

Commercial and Financial Chronicle, Vol. CLXXXV, No. 5650 (June 27, 1957). Section 2 is devoted to the 41st Annual Convention of the Investment Dealer's Association of Canada at Jasper Park Lodge, Jasper, Alberta, June 11–14, 1957.

Fowler, Elizabeth M. "Powerful Consumer—An Appraisal of the Need for Studies of Buying Habits at the Grass Roots," *New York Times,* February 13, 1959. Business section.

Heffernan, Paul. "Personality: Builder of Pipelines in Wall Street," *New York Times,* Sunday, June 9, 1957, p. 3. Financial section.

Lewis, Richard A. "Resurgent Rayon," *Wall Street Journal,* April 19, 1962.

Moody, Joseph E., "Coal and Competition," *Wall Street Journal,* Vol. XXVII, No. 20 (January 30, 1961), 6.

"Natural Gas Sweeps Toronto," *New York Times,* January 8, 1958, p. 57.

New York Herald Tribune, July 1, 1956.

New York Times, Saturday, July 13, 1957.

New York Times, January 15, 1961.

New York Times, January 24, 1961, pp. 31, 58.

Oil Daily, Tuesday, May 23, 1961, p. 4.

"Onward to Yesterday," *Wall Street Journal,* Vol. XXVII, No. 4 (January 6, 1961), 8.

"Pipeline Builder, a King of Sports," *New York Times,* October 9, 1957, p. 51.

Raskin, A. H., "Big Factory Cities Losing Top Place as U.S. Jobs Rise," *New York Times,* Sunday, July 26, 1959, pp. 1, 35.

"Storage of Gas in Pools Gaining," *New York Times,* October 30, 1960.

"Texas Eastern Studying Coal Pipeline in West," *Houston Post,* No. 28,343 (November 9, 1962), p. 2, sec. 3.

Wall Street Journal. Southwest edition. May 2, 1940, p. 20.

Yorath, D. C., "Canada's Leading Authorities Evaluate Its Economic Prospects," *Commercial and Financial Chronicle,* Vol. CXCIII, No. 6024 (January 26, 1961), 39.

III. BOOKS

Adams, D. R., *et al. Fuel Cells: Power for the Future.* Cambridge, Mass., 1960.

Adelman, M. A. *The Supply and Price of Natural Gas.* Oxford, 1962.

American Bar Association, Section of Mineral Law. *Conservation of Oil and Gas: A Legal History, 1948.* Chicago, 1949.

————. *Conservation of Oil and Gas: A Legal History, 1958.* Chicago, 1960.

————. *Legal History of Conservation of Oil and Gas.* Chicago, 1939.

American Gas Association Rate Committee. *Gas Rate Fundamentals.* New York, 1960.

American Petroleum Institute. *History of Petroleum Engineering.* Dallas, Texas, 1961.

Astle, Melvin J. *The Chemistry of Petrochemicals.* New York, 1956.

Ayres, Eugene, and Charles A. Scarlott. *Energy Sources—The Wealth of the World.* New York, 1952.

Barnes, Irston C. *The Economics of Public Utility Regulation.* New York, 1942.

Beaton, Kendall. *Enterprise in Oil.* New York, 1957.

Blanchly, Frederick F., and Miriam E. Oatman. *Natural Gas and the Public Interest*. Washington, D.C., 1947.

Bohm-Bawerk, Eugen von. *Karl Marx and the Close of His System*. New York, 1898.

Bonbright, James C. *Principles of Public Utility Rates*. New York, 1961.

Boyd, Frank A., and Charles W. Studt, comp. *The Acquisition of Underground Gas Storage Rights*. New York, 1958.

Brame, J. S. S., and J. J. King. *Fuel—Solid, Liquid and Gaseous*. Fifth edition rewritten by J. J. King. London and New York, 1955.

Breeding, Clark W., and Gordon A. Burton. *Income Taxation of Oil and Gas Production*. New York, 1954.

Bright, James R., ed. *Technological Planning on the Corporate Level*. Boston, 1962.

Britt, Steward. *The Spenders*. New York, 1960.

Brooks, Benjamin T., and A. E. Dunstan, eds. *The Science of Petroleum*. 5 vols. New York, 1953.

Brown, Courtney C., *et al. Energy and Man*. New York, 1960.

Brown, Harrison. *The Challenge of Man's Future*. New York, 1954.

——, *et al. The Next Hundred Years*. New York, 1957.

Buckley, Stuart E., ed. *Petroleum Conservation*. Dallas, 1951.

Childs, John F. *Long-term Financing*. New York, 1961.

Christenson, C. L. *Economic Redevelopment in Bituminous Coal*. Cambridge, Mass., 1962.

Clark, Norman J. *Elements of Petroleum Reservoirs*. Dallas, Texas, 1960.

Clemens, Eli Winston. *Economics and Public Utilities*. New York, 1950.

Cohn, Norman. *The Pursuit of the Millenium*. New York, 1957.

Coleman, Charles M. *P. G. & E. of California: The Centennial Story of Pacific Gas and Electric Company, 1852–1952*. New York, 1958.

Davidson, Ralph Kirby. *Price Discrimination in Selling Gas and Electricity*, Baltimore, Md., 1955.

Davis, John, *Canadian Energy Prospects*. Ottawa, 1957.

Davis, Ralph E. *Natural Gas: What the Consumer Should Know About the Nation's Gas Supply*. Houston, Tex., 1954.

——. *The Story of Natural Gas*. Houston, Tex., 1962.

Denny, Lyon C., *et al.*, eds. *Handbook of Butane-propane Gases*. Fourth edition. Los Angeles, Calif., 1962.

De Chazeau, Melvin G., and Alfred E. Kahn. *Integration and Competition in the Petroleum Industry*. New Haven, 1959.

Economics of the Gas Industry, I. Dallas, 1962.

Engler, C., and H. v. Höfer. *Das Erdöl seine Physik, Chemie, Geologie, Technologie und sein Wirtschaffsbetriel*. 6 vols. Leipzig, 1916.

Essential Factors in the Future Development of the Oil Industry. Published by the Institute of Petroleum. London, 1956.

Falck, Edward, and Francis X. Welch. *Federal Regulation of Natural Gas in the United States.* Washington, D.C., 1958.

Fuchs, Victor Herbert. *Changes in the Location of Manufacturing in the United States Since 1929.* New Haven, 1962.

Glaeser, Martin G. *Public Utilities in American Capitalism.* New York, 1957.

Hanson, Eric J. *Dynamic Decade.* Toronto, 1958.

Hardwicke, Robert E. *Antitrust Laws, et al. v. Unit Operations of Oil or Gas Pools.* New York, 1948.

Hayek, Frederick A. *The Road to Serfdom.* New York, 1944.

Haynes, Williams. *American Chemical Industry—A History.* 5 vols. New York, 1954.

Henshaw, Richard C., Jr. *Natural Gas Statistics.* Austin, Tex., 1955.

———. *A Selected and Annotated Bibliography of Natural Gas.* Austin, Tex., 1954.

History of Petroleum Engineering. New York, 1961.

Hoffman, Leo J. *Voluntary Pooling and Unitization, Oil and Gas.* New York, 1954.

Hooley, Richard W. *Financing the Natural Gas Industry: The Role of Life Insurance Investment Policies.* New York, 1961.

Hubbert, M. King. *Resources of Texas.* Houston, Tex., 1958.

Huntington, R. L. *Natural Gas and Natural Gasoline.* New York, 1950.

Interstate Oil Compact Commission Engineering Committee. *Oil and Gas Production: An Introductory Guide to Production Techniques and Conservation Methods.* Norman, 1951.

Iulo, William. *Natural Gas in the Pacific Northwest—Some of Its Economic Aspects.* Pullman, Wash., 1953.

Jarrett, Henry, ed. *Perspectives on Conservation.* New York, 1958.

Katona, George. *The Power Consumer.* New York, 1960.

Katz, Donald, D. Cornell, R. Kabyashi, F. H. Poettman, C. F. Weinaug, A. Vary, and Jack B. Ellenbaas. *Handbook of Natural Gas Engineering.* New York, 1959.

Kobe, Kenneth A., and John J. McKetta, Jr. *Advances in Petroleum Chemistry and Refining.* 5 vols. New York, 1962.

Kornfeld, Joseph A. *Natural Gas Economics.* Dallas, 1948.

Lepine, William H. *Come in, Gasman.* New York, 1962.

Lichtblau, John H., and Dillard P. Spriggs. *Energy Policy and Competition.* New York, 1961.

Lief, Alfred. *Metering for America.* New York, 1961.

428

McKeage, Everett C. *Public Utility Regulatory Law*. New York, 1956.

McKie, James W. *The Regulation of Natural Gas*. Washington, D.C., 1957.

Meier, Richard L. *Science and Economic Development: New Patterns of Living*. New York, 1956.

Mineral Economics. New York, 1932.

Mises, Ludwig von. *The Anti-Capitalist Mentality*. New York, 1956.

Muckleroy, J. A. *Bibliography on Hydrocarbons, 1946–1960*. Tulsa, Okla., 1962.

Myers, Raymond M. *The Law of Pooling and Unitization, Voluntary— Compulsory*. New York, 1957.

Netschert, Bruce C. *The Future Supply of Oil and Gas*. A Resources for the Future, Incorporated, study. Baltimore, Md., 1958.

Neuner, Edward J. *The Natural Gas Industry: Monopoly and Competition in Field Markets*. Norman, 1960.

Petrie, D. *Petroleum*. New York, 1961.

Purdy, G. A. *Petroleum*. Vancouver, 1958.

Putnam, Palmer C. *Energy in the Future*. New York, 1953.

Redford, Emmette S., ed. *Public Administration and Policy Formation,* Austin, Tex., 1956.

Robie, Edward H., ed. *Economics of the Mineral Industries*. New York, 1959.

Rockwell Manufacturing Company. *The Orifice Meter for Measurement of Flow of Gases and Liquids*. Pittsburgh, 1953.

Rohm and Haas Company. *Chemicals for the Industry*. New York, 1956.

Roma, Banco di, and Alfredo Giarrantana. *Hydrocarbons in Italy*. Rome, 1956.

Rostow, Eugene V. *A National Policy for the Oil Industry*. New Haven, 1948.

Schurr, Sam H., and Bruce C. Netschert. *Energy in the American Economy, 1850–1975*. Baltimore, Md., 1960.

Springborn, Harold W. *The Natural Gas Industry*. New York, 1959.

Steiner, H., ed. *Introduction to Petroleum Chemicals*. London and New York, 1961.

Stephenson, Eugene A., ed. *Natural Gas*. Lawrence, Kan., 1956.

Stockton, John R., Richard C. Henshaw, Jr., and Richard W. Graves. *Economics of the Natural Gas Industry in Texas*. Austin, Tex., 1952.

Stotz, Louis, and Alexander Jamison. *History of the Gas Industry*. New York, 1938.

Stovel, John A. *Canada in the World Economy*. Cambridge, Mass., 1960.

Swanson, E. B. *A Century of Oil and Gas in Books: A Descriptive Bibliography*. New York, 1960.

429

Terry, Lynn F., and John G. Winger. *Future Growth of the Natural Gas Industry.* New York, 1957.

Three Studies in Mineral Economics. New York, 1961.

Troxel, Emery, *Economics in Public Utilities.* New York, 1947,

Welch, Francis X. *Preparing for the Utility Rate Case.* New York, 1954.

———. *Conduct of the Utility Rate Case.* New York, 1955.

Wheeler, J. L., and R. A. Whited. *Oil—From Prospect to Pipeline.* Houston, Tex., 1958.

Yaseen, Leonard C. *Plant Location.* Third edition, revised. New York, 1961.

Young, G. J., ed. *Fuel Cells.* New York, 1960.

Zimmermann, Erich W. *Conservation in the Production of Petroleum: A Study in Industrial Control.* New Haven, 1957.

———. *World Resources and Industries.* Second edition. New York, 1951.

IV. ARTICLES AND PERIODICALS

Abrams, Earnest R. "Another Peak Year Seen for Gas Home Heating," *Barron's,* Vol. XXXVIII, No. 11 (March, 1958), 27.

Adams, Ernestine, "The Bristling Battle of Mattei," sec. E–2–5, *Petroleum Engineer,* Vol. XXXIII, No. 2 (February, 1961).

"Alberta-California Line to Start Soon," *Oil and Gas Journal,* Vol. LXIII, No. 34 (August 22, 1960), 57.

"The Amazing Vigor of Transcontinental Gas," *Forbes,* Vol. LXXXVI, No. 2 (July 15, 1960), 15.

American Gas Association Monthly, Vol. XLI, No. 5 (May, 1959), 32–36.

American Gas Journal, Vol. CLXXXVI, No. 12 (December, 1959), 28.

American Gas Journal, Vol. CLXXXVII, No. 2 (February, 1960), 26.

American Gas Journal, Vol. CLXXXVII, No. 11 (October, 1960), 42.

American Petroleum Institute. *Oil Facts,* Vol. II, No. 5 (October–November, 1960).

"America's Expanding Pipeline System," *U.S. Steel News,* Vol. XXI, No. 1 (July, 1956), 3.

"Are 'Conventional Methods' Necessary in Natural Gas Rate Regulation?" *Cornell Law Quarterly,* Vol. XLI, No. 3 (Spring, 1956), 438.

Atkinson, Edward L. "Federal Regulation of Natural Gas—the Independent Producer's Status," *Southwestern Law Journal,* Vol. XIII, No. 4 (Fall, 1959), 425.

Atwood, Albert W. "The Eternal Flame—Natural Gas," *National Geographic,* Vol. C, No. 4 (October, 1951), 540.

"The Automatic Pipeline," *Oil and Gas Journal,* Vol. LV, No. 27 (July 8, 1957), 89.

Ball, Douglas. "Storage of Gas in Water Sands," *The Mines Magazine,* Vol. XLVIII, No. 11 (November, 1959).

————. "The Why of Underground Gas Storage," *The Mines Magazine,* Vol. XLVI, No. 6 (June, 1958), 55–58.

Beebe, B. W. "Natural Gas Whooses from Infant to Giant in 25 Years," *Oil and Gas Journal,* Vol. LIX, No. 17 (April 25, 1961), 98.

Bickel, H. J., and F. B. Burdine. "A Unique Approach to Estimating Future Energy Requirements," *Journal of Petroleum Technology,* Vol. XIV, No. 10 (October, 1962), 1097.

"Bids for Big System Going Out Soon," *Oil and Gas Journal,* Vol. LVIII, No. 35 (August 29, 1960), 47.

"Big Boost for Canadian Gas," *Petroleum Press Service,* Vol. XXVII, No. 6 (May, 1960), 171–73.

Brinegar, Claude S. "National Fuels Policy—The Controversy and the Data," *Journal of Petroleum Technology,* Vol. XIV, No. 9 (September, 1962), 942–43.

"The Buoyant Gas Industry," *Fortune,* Vol. LXVI, No. 4 (October, 1962), 98–99.

Burke, Gilbert, and Sanford S. Parker. "The Dynamic Force of the Energy Industries," *Fortune,* Vol. LXVI, No. 4 (October, 1962), 93.

"California: Growing Market for Gas," *Oil and Gas Journal,* Vol. LVII, No. 10 (March 2, 1959), 68.

Cameron, Lee. "Effect of Gas Proration on Recent Special Orders," *Journal of Petroleum Technology,* Vol. XII, No. 3 (March, 1960), 22.

Campbell, L. W. A. "When Do You Build a Gas-transmission System?" *Oil and Gas Journal,* Vol. LVII, No. 3 (January 19, 1959), 81.

"Canada's Top Oil-Gas Expert Is Named Energy Boss," *Oil and Gas Journal,* Vol. LVII, No. 38 (September 14, 1959), 72.

"Canada-to-California Line Hits Snag," *Oil and Gas Journal,* Vol. LVIII, No. 17 (April 25, 1960), 108.

"Charting Weather Years Ahead," *Business Week,* No. 1519 (October 11, 1958), 45.

Chinitz, Benjamin, and Raymond Vernon. "Changing Forces in Industrial Location," *Harvard Business Review,* Vol. XXXVIII, No. 1 (January–February, 1960).

Clark, Jim. "The Gassing Game," *Gas,* Vol. XXXVIII, No. 3 (May, 1962).

Collins, James H. "Gas Really Has a Hard Sell," *Public Utilities Fortnightly,* Vol. LXIII, No. 6 (March 12, 1959), 379–89.

"Compression of Natural Gas," *American Gas Journal,* Vol. CLXXVII, No. 7 (December, 1952), 19.

Conkling, Roger L. "Home Markets Offer Growing Outlet for Texas-Louisiana Gas Reserves," *World Oil,* Vol. CXL, No. 4 (September, 1960), 84–85.

Connole, William R. "Rate of Return—The Utilities' Most Tilted Windmill," *Public Utilities Fortnightly,* Vol. LXIV, No. 8 (October 8, 1959), 584–600.

————. "Russian Gas Industry," *Oil and Gas Journal,* Vol. LIX, Nos. 32, 34, and 35 (August 7, 21, and 28, 1961).

"Corrosion and Pipe Protection," *American Gas Journal,* Vol. CLXXVI, No. 4 (April, 1952), 25.

"Cost Ruling Tightens Gas Controls," *Oil and Gas Journal,* Vol. LIX, No. 5 (January 30, 1961), 96.

Creveling, J. D. "A Brief History of the Natural Gas Industry," *Natural Gas,* Vol. XVI, No. 5 (May, 1935), 5–8.

Cunningham, Bruce. "Gas Does Everything Better in Dallas' New Statler Hilton," *American Gas Journal,* Vol. CLXXXIII, No. 2 (February, 1956), 14ff.

Davis, W. B., and J. H. Schweitzer. "Natural Gas—Partner and Competitor," *Journal of Petroleum Technology,* Vol. XI, No. 5 (May, 1959), 13.

"Delayed Payoff," *Forbes,* Vol. LXXXVI, No. 5 (September 1, 1960), 25.

"Diary of an Industry," *American Gas Journal,* Vol. CLXXXVI, No. 11 (October, 1959), 21.

Douglas, Paul H. "The Case for the Consumer of Natural Gas," *Georgetown Law Journal,* Vol. XLIV, No. 4 (June, 1956), 566.

"East Coast LNG-storage Project Cleared," *Oil and Gas Journal,* Vol. LX, No. 45 (November 5, 1962), 61.

Ebdon, J. Fred. "Energy Packages—Natural Gas Fired," *Gas,* Vol. XXXVIII, No. 4 (April, 1962), 59.

————. "Pacific Gas and Electric Builds a Line," *Gas,* Vol. XXXVII, No. 8 (August, 1961).

Eckles, Robert B. "The FPC and Industry Contracts," *Public Utilities Fortnightly,* Vol. LXVI, No. 7 (September 29, 1960), 466.

"The Economics of Gas Transportation by Sea," *Petroleum Press Service,* Vol. XXVII, No. 3 (March, 1960).

Ekstein, Otto. "Natural Gas and Patterns of Regulation," *Harvard Business Review,* Vol. XXXVI, No. 2 (March–April, 1958).

"Eldon Hunt: A Busy Canadian Pipeliner," *Oil and Gas Journal,* Vol. LVIII, No. 2 (January 11, 1960), 144–45.

"El Paso Gas Pushes New Frontier," *Business Week,* No. 1430 (January 26, 1957), 76ff.

"Farmout Deal Scored," *Oil and Gas Journal,* Vol. LII, No. 47 (March 29, 1954), 62.

"Features of the U.S. Petrochemical Scene," *Petroleum Press Service,* Vol. XXVII, No. 7 (July, 1960), 254.

"Finishing Trans-Canada Will Be Tough," *Oil and Gas Journal,* Vol. LV, No. 49 (December 9, 1957), 65.

Fischer, Joseph L., and Hans H. Lordsberg. "Natural Resources Projections and Their Contributions to Technological Planning," in *Technological Planning on the Corporate Level, q.v.,* 119–45.

Flanagan, Donald A., and Paul B. Crawford. "How Feasible Is Underground Storage of Liquefied Methane?" *American Gas Journal,* Vol. CLXXXVII, No. 11 (October, 1960), 34.

Forbes, Vol. LXXXIII, No. 1 (January 1, 1959), 112.

Forbes, Vol. LXXXV, No. 1 (January 1, 1960), 70.

Ford, Eric. "Constructing Long Distance Pipe Lines," *Public Works and Muck Shifter* (March, 1958), 199.

Fothergill, C. A., "Storing Hydrocarbons Underground, New Techniques Reviewed," *Petroleum,* Vol. XXV, No. 5 (May, 1962), 162.

"FPC Approves Piping of Canadian Gas to West Coast in $400 Million Deal," *Business Week,* No. 1615 (August 13, 1960).

"FPC Appproves Rock Springs Project," *Oil and Gas Journal,* Vol. LIX, No. 1 (January 2, 1961), 52.

"FPC Cuts Midwestern Rates," *Oil and Gas Journal,* Vol. LVIII, No. 35 (August 29, 1960), 52.

"FPC Cuts Midwestern Rates," *Oil and Gas Journal,* Vol. LVIII, No. 35 (August 29, 1960), 52.

Francis, Charles I. "Rate Regulation of the Natural Gas Companies by the Federal Power Commission," *Law and Contemporary Problems,* Vol. XIX, No. 3 (Summer, 1954), 413.

Fruechtenicht, H. L., "Benefits Are Universal in Underground Gas Storage in Michigan," *Gas Age,* Vol. CXXVI, No. 2 (July 21, 1960).

"Funnel for All New Gas Moving Out of Alberta," *Oil and Gas Journal,* Vol. LVIII, No. 2 (January 11, 1960), 46–47.

Gardner, Frank J. "Natural Gas Is Texas' Industrial Lifeblood," *Oil and Gas Journal,* Vol. LIX, No. 11 (March 13, 1960), 167.

Gas, Vol. XXXIII, No. 8 (August, 1957). Trans-Canada issue.

Gas, Vol. XXXV, No. 11 (November, 1959).

"Gas Balloon," *Fortune,* Vol. IV, No. 2 (August, 1931), 50ff.

"Gas Conditioning," *American Gas Journal,* Vol. CLXXV, No. 6 (November, 1951), 31.

"Gas Lights Europe's Hopes," *World Petroleum,* Vol. XXXI, No. 2 (February, 1960), 66, 81.

"Gas Line to California Approved," *Oil and Gas Journal,* Vol. LVII, No. 34 (August 17, 1959), 94–95.

"Gas: On Call Near the Market," *Business Week,* No. 1357 (September 3, 1955), 102.

"Gas Prices Climb in Western Canada," *Petroleum Week,* Vol. V, No. 10 (September 6, 1957), 9.

"Gas Sales Can Be Limited by End Use," *Petroleum Week,* Vol. XII, No. 4 (January 27, 1961), 9.

"Gas Storage Is Good for the Whole Fuels Industry," *Oil and Gas Journal,* Vol. LX, No. 20 (May 14, 1962), 73.

"Gas Turbine Generators Can Be Marketed Now," *Oil and Gas Journal,* Vol. LIX, No. 21 (June 26, 1961), 125.

Gelhoff, Paul O. "Natural Gas Liquefaction as Means to Solve Transportation Problems," *Erdöl und Kohle,* Vol. XIII, No. 9 (September, 1960), 668–71.

Gilbert, Robert A. "Frozen Gas Expands," *Barron's,* Vol. XL, No. 34 (August 22, 1960).

Glenn, Armon. "Gas Appliances—They Are Making Steady Inroads on Competitive Equipment," *Barron's,* Vol. XXXVIII, No. 40 (October 6, 1958), 11, 13.

Gonzalez, Richard J. "Natural Gas—Part I, Its Expanding Role as an Energy Resource," *The Humble Way,* Vol. XII, No. 1 (May–June, 1956), 4–8.

———. "Natural Gas—Part II, The Market and the Price," *The Humble Way,* Vol. XII, No. 2 (July–August, 1956), 19–23.

———. "Petroleum for Our Future Progress," *Journal of Petroleum Technology,* Vol. IX, No. 3 (March, 1957), 14.

Gramm, Warren S. "The Public Utility Scissors," *Land Economics,* Vol. XXXVIII, No. 1 (February, 1962), 21–31.

Griffith, M. P. "What Does It Cost to Produce Peak Shaving and Substitute Gases?" *American Gas Journal,* Vol. CLXXXV, No. 5 (May, 1958).

Hale, Dean. "Modular Gas Turbine Energy Packages," *American Gas Journal,* Vol. CLXXXIX, No. 3 (March, 1962), 39.

———. "First All-Gas Compact School Underway," *American Gas Journal,* Vol. CLXXXIX, No. 5 (May, 1962), 44.

Harper, William T. "L. T. Potter—Ice Man Turned Gas Man," *Gas.* Vol. XXXVI, No. 1 (October, 1960), 85.

Hatch, Lewis F. "These Petrochemicals Use Ammonia," *Petroleum Refiner,* Vol. XXXV, No. 12 (December, 1956), 145ff.

Heilbroner, Robert L. "The Energy Revolution," *American Petroleum Institute Quarterly* (Spring–Summer, 1959), 26. Centennial issue.

Hill, Kenneth E. "Some Considerations in the Pricing of Natural Gas," *Journal of Petroleum Technology,* Vol. X, No. 5 (May, 1958).

Hilt, Luis. "Chronology of the Natural Gas Industry," *American Gas Journal,* Vol. CLXXII, No. 5 (May, 1950), 29–30.

"Houston Complex," *Fortune,* Vol. LVIII, No. 2 (February, 1958), 127.

Hudson, H. K., *et al.* "Phillips Says Domestic Gas Reserves' Future Gloomy Unless Exploration Is Increased," *Oil and Gas Journal,* Vol. LVIII, No. 11 (March 14, 1960), 160.

Huitt, Ralph K. "Natural Gas Regulation Under the Holding Company Act," *Law and Contemporary Problems,* Vol. XIX, No. 3 (Summer, 1954), 455–73.

"In the Wake of the Methane Pioneer," *Petroleum Press Service,* Vol. XXVI, No. 5 (May, 1959), 172–74.

"Intrastate Sales Gain Momentum," *Oil and Gas Journal,* Vol. LVII, No. 11 (September 21, 1959), 101.

Jurenev, Serge. "Marketing of Petroleum and Natural Gas," in *Economics of the Mineral Industries, q.v.*

Kelly, Dee. "Gas Proration and Ratable Taking in Texas," *Texas Bar Journal,* Vol. XIX, No. 11 (December, 1956), 763.

Kinney, Gene T. "Aggressive Selling and Offbeat Ideas Spark Rebirth of Arkla Gas," *Oil and Gas Journal,* Vol. LVIII, No. 16 (April 18, 1960), 80ff.

Klein, Lloyd J. "Accounting Aspects of Utility Rate Regulation," *Law and Contemporary Problems,* Vol. XIX, No. 3 (Summer, 1954), 435.

Kornfeld, Joseph A. "Aquifers for Underground Natural Gas Storage," *American Gas Journal,* Vol. CLXXXVII, Nos. 4, 5, 6, 8, and 10 (April, May, June, August, and October, 1960), 45ff.

Kuhn, W. E., and J. W. Hutcheson. "The Petroleum Industry—Source of Chemical Raw Materials," *Petroleum Engineer,* Vol. XXIX, No. 6 (June, 1957), E–3ff.

La Grone, Paul G. "Accounting for Gas Line Expansion Project," *Public Utilities Fortnightly,* Vol. LXVI, No. 8 (February 2, 1961), 158–73.

———. "Financing the Expansion Program of the Natural Gas Transmission Industry," *Public Utilities Fortnightly,* Vol. LXVII, No. 3 (October 13, 1960), 535–49.

"Legislative History of the Natural Gas Act," *Georgetown Law Journal,* Vol. XLIV, No. 4 (June, 1956), 695.

Lennon, Duncan E. "Income Tax Problems in Connection with Underground Storage," *Gas Age,* Vol. CXXIII, No. 3 (February 5, 1959), 32–36.

"Liquefied Natural Gas," *Petroleum Times* (January 31, 1958–November, 1959).

435

Luty, B. C. V. "Development of Pipe Manufacture," *Oil and Gas Journal,* Vol. XXIX, No. 3 (June 5, 1930), 85.

"Main-line Block Valves Are Remotely Controlled," *Oil and Gas Journal,* Vol. LIX, No. 6 (February 6, 1961), 132.

Martin, Richard, "Now, an All-Gas City," *American Gas Journal,* Vol. CLXXXIX, No. 4 (April, 1962), 60.

Marvin, C. W. "Centrifugal Compressors of New Design," *Petroleum Engineer,* Vol. XXIV, No. 5 (May, 1952), 624.

————. "The Gas-flow Analyzer for Making Natural Gas Pipeline Flow Studies," *Oil and Gas Journal,* Vol. LIII, No. 20 (September 20, 1954), 152.

"Meet the Men Behind the Borden Commission," *Oil and Gas Journal,* Vol. LVI, No. 44 (November 3, 1958), 46.

Melnick, Jack. "Ammonia Supply and Demand . . . In Balance by 1961?" *Oil and Gas Journal,* Vol. LVI, No. 50 (December 15, 1958), 109–12.

Miller, John T., Jr. "Competition in Regulated Industries: Interstate Gas Pipelines," *Georgetown Law Journal,* Vol. XLVII, No. 2 (Winter, 1958), 224.

Miller, R. L. "A New Look at Ultimate Natural Gas Reserves," *World Oil,* Vol. CLXVII, No. 5 (October, 1958), 222–24.

"Monsanto Planning a Big Chemical Complex," *Chemical and Engineering News,* Vol. XXXIX, No. 2 (January 9, 1961), 31–32.

"Monsanto to Build Ethylene Plant As First Unit in Petrochemical Complex," *Business Week,* No. 1636 (January 7, 1961), 30.

"More Ethylene at Tuscola," *Oil and Gas Journal,* Vol. LIV, No. 70 (September 3, 1956), 108.

"Natural-gas Fuel Cells May Supply Home Power," *Oil and Gas Journal,* Vol. LIX, No. 15 (April 10, 1961), 74.

"Natural Gas—Whoosh!" *Fortune,* Vol. XL, No. 6 (December, 1949), 107ff.

"New Machine Can Make Line Pipe on Right-of-way," *Oil and Gas Journal,* Vol. LVIII, No. 7 (February 15, 1960), 60.

"New Technique Specified for Big Gas Line," *Oil and Gas Journal,* Vol. LVIII, No. 60 (November 14, 1960), 116–17.

"New Wrinkles in Ammonia Manufacture at Tuscola," *Oil and Gas Journal,* Vol. LIV, No. 70 (September 3, 1956), 111.

"News in the Industry" Column, *Petroleum Times,* Vol. LXIII, No. 1625 (November 20, 1959), 723.

Oil and Gas Journal, Vol. LVII, No. 39 (September 21, 1959), 102.

Oil and Gas Journal, Vol. LIX, No. 3 (January 16, 1961), 62.

Oil and Gas Journal, Vol. LIX, No. 5 (January 30, 1961), 84.

Oil and Gas Journal, Vol. LIX, No. 6 (February 6, 1961), 6.

Oil and Gas Journal, Vol. LX, No. 18 (April 30, 1962). Gas processing number.

Oil and Gas Journal and *Oil City Derrick,* "The Diamond Jubilee of the Petroleum Industry," August 27, 1934.

Osborne, John. "Natural Gas and the Authoritarian 'Liberals,' " *Fortune,* Vol. XLVII, No. 5 (May, 1952), 124.

Parson, Daniel. "Long Term Gas Supply Outlook Good," *American Gas Association Monthly,* Vol. XL, No. 6 (June, 1958), 21.

"Petrochemical Outlook," *Petroleum Week,* Vol. VII, No. 12 (September, 1958), 42–70.

Petroleum Engineer, Vol. XXXIII, No. 2 (February, 1961). Special Pipeline Handbook Issue, section on pipe protection, H-60.

Petroleum Press Service, Vol. XXV, No. 12 (December, 1958), 471.

Petroleum Press Service, Vol. XXVII, No. 7 (July, 1960), 246.

Petroleum Press Service, Vol. XXVIII, No. 3 (March, 1961), 98–99.

Petroleum Week, Vol. XI, No. 23 (December 9, 1960), 40–41.

Phelps, Thomas W. "Petroleum's Place in the Future Energy Requirements of the United States," *Journal of Petroleum Technology,* Vol. XI, No. 7 (July, 1959), 22.

"Pipe Laying to Begin on Transwestern," *Oil and Gas Journal,* Vol. LVII, No. 44 (October 26, 1959), 56.

"Pipeline Built in 1929 Is Automated," *Petroleum Week,* Vol. XII, No. 2 (January 13, 1961), 49.

"Presidential Profile," *Gas,* Vol. XXXVIII, No. 10 (October, 1962), 75.

Price, H. C. "Gas Pipeline Construction Brought Up to Date," *The Mines Magazine,* Vol. XLIX, No. 11 (November, 1959), 55.

Priest, A. J. G. "Major Public Utility Decisions in Perspective," *Virginia Law Review,* Vol. XLVI, No. 7 (November, 1960), 1327.

"Principles of Orifice Measurement," *American Gas Journal,* Vol. CLXXVII, No. 6 (November, 1952), 23.

"Prospects of Washington Natural Gas Glow on Rapid Gains in Service Area," *Barron's,* Vol. XL, No. 47 (November 21, 1960), 34–35.

Quarles, W. R. "Trans-Canada Rushes 34″ Line," *Pipe Line News,* Vol. XXIX, No. 8 (August, 1957), 27.

Ransom, Raymond A. "Value of Service and Pipeline Rates," *Public Utilities Fortnightly,* Vol. LXIX, No. 3 (February 1, 1962), 162.

Reed, Paul. "Double-jointing Came Long Way '60 . . . And Greater Progress Foreseen for '61," *Oil and Gas Journal,* Vol. LIX. No. 7 (February 13, 1961), 70.

————, and Gene T. Kinney. "The Florida Pipeline—A New Concept in

Gas Transmission," *Oil and Gas Journal,* Vol. LVII, No. 11 (March 9, 1959), 108ff.

"The Regulation of Natural Gas," a symposium, *Law and Contemporary Problems,* Vol. XIX, No. 3 (Summer, 1954), 323–412.

"Regulation of Producers' Prices: Is Anyone Benefiting?" *Texaco Star,* Vol. XLVI, No. 1 (Spring, 1959).

Reidel, John C. "Expanding Facilities at National Petrochemical," *Oil and Gas Journal,* Vol. LIV, No. 70 (September 3, 1956), 105.

Rich, John F. "The Unlimited Horizons of the Natural Gas Industry," *Public Utilities Fortnightly,* Vol. LXIV, No. 8 (October 8, 1959), 42, 44.

Roth, Ernest E. "Underground Storage of Natural Gas," *Petroleum Engineer,* Vol. XXV, No. 5 (May, 1953), D–86.

Schenker, Eric. "Insurance and Pension Fund Investment in Utility Securities," *Public Utilities Fortnightly,* Vol. LXIX, No. 9 (April 26, 1962), 577–85.

"Sharp Growth Seen for Products Lines as Over-all Demand Continues to Climb," *Petroleum Week,* Vol. X, No. 11 (March 18, 1960), 54ff.

Sheehan, Robert. "Life Insurance's Eighty-four Billion Dollar Dilemma," *Fortune,* Vol. LI, No. 2 (February, 1955), 112.

Shibley, Raymond N., and George B. Mickum, III. "The Impact of Phillips Upon the Interstate Pipelines," *Georgetown Law Journal,* Vol. XLIV, No. 4 (June, 1956), 628.

Smith, Richard Austin. "The Unnatural Problems of Natural Gas," *Fortune,* Vol. LX, No. 3 (September, 1959), 120ff.

Somers, E. V., and J. C. R. Kelly. "Thermoelectric Power," *Mechanical Engineering,* Vol. LXXXII, No. 7 (July, 1960), 40–42.

Stanley, J. W. "Pipeline Surveying and Mapping, a Breakdown of Costs," *Pipe Line News,* Vol. XXV, No. 10 (October, 1953), 43–44.

"Statler Hotel in Los Angeles Chooses Gas for Heating, Cooking, and Incineration," *Gas Age,* Vol. CX, No. 12 (December 4, 1952), 26.

Steves, Sterling W. "FPC Gas Tariff—Solution to the Rate Change Dilemma of the Independent Producer?" *Southwestern Law Journal,* Vol. XV, No. 1 (September, 1961), 46.

"Storage of Liquid Methane in Britain," *Gas Age,* Vol. CXXIII, No. 11 (May 28, 1959).

"A Survey of Texas Administrative Law: The Oil and Gas Division of the Texas Railroad Commission," *Texas Law Review,* Vol. XXXIII, No. 5 (May, 1955), 635ff.

Sweeny, W. F. "Importance and Need of Degree-day Forecasting for the Petroleum Industry," *Weatherwise* (December, 1951), 197ff.

"A Symposium on the Federal Regulation of Natural-gas Producers," *Georgetown Law Journal*, Vol. XLIV, No. 4 (June, 1956), 551–693.

Tanner, James C. "Frozen Heat," *Wall Street Journal*, Vol. XXVIII, No. 67 (October 5, 1960).

"Tennessee Gas Transmission Buys Pan Am's Bastian Bay Gas," *Oil and Gas Journal*, Vol. LIX, No. 6 (February 6, 1961), 86.

Texas Eastern Transmission Corporation. "Energy and Fuels in the United States . . . 1947–1980," *The Inch*, Vol. XI, Nos. 1, 2, and 3 (Winter, Spring, and Summer, 1961), 2. This study was published separately in Houston, Texas, in 1961.

"Thermo-electricity . . . A New Demand for Natural Gas," *Oil and Gas Journal*, Vol. LIX, No. 12 (April 10, 1961), 93.

Thomas, Dana L. "Creslan, Darvan, and Kodel," *Barron's*, Vol. XXXVIII, No. 41 (October 13, 1958), 3, 16, 18.

Thompson, Ernest O. "The Texas Market Demand Statute on Oil and Gas and Its Application," *Texas Law Review*, Vol. XXIX, No. 2 (December, 1960), 139.

Thorley, B. "Carbon Black," in *Introduction to Petroleum Chemicals* (edited by H. Steiner), *q.v.*

Todd, Raymond W. "Progress in Gas Storage," *Gas*, Vol. XXXVIII, No. 5 (May, 1962), 73.

Tongberg, C. O. "Chemicals from Fuels," *Oil and Gas Compact Bulletin*, Vol. XIV, No. 1 (June, 1955), 30.

"Transmission of Natural Gas," *American Gas Journal*, Vol. CLXXV, No. 1 (July, 1951), 29.

"Tremendous New Market for Natural Gas," *Oil and Gas Journal*, Vol. LIX, No. 18 (May 1, 1961), 64.

Tuer, Arnold B., and Charles H. Swartz. "Economics of Field Compressor Stations," *Oil Week*, Vol. X, No. 24 (July 31, 1959), 28.

Vvedensky, G. A. "The Soviet Gas Industry," *Bulletin* of the Institute for the Study of the U.S.S.R., Vol. IX, No. 10 (September, 1962), 24.

Von Allmen, E. "Economics Are Basic for Plant Location," *Chemical Engineering Progress*, Vol. LVI, No. 11 (November, 1960), 37.

Weeks, Lewis G. "Fuel Reserves of the Future," *Bulletin* of the American Association of Petroleum Geologists, Vol. XLII, No. 2 (February, 1958), 431–41.

"What's New in Synthetic Fibers—New Processing Methods and New Raw Materials May Give a Boost to the Burgeoning Synthetic Fibers Industry," *Chemical and Engineering News*, Vol. XXXV, No. 30 (July 29, 1957), 12ff.

Willatt, Morris. "Big Market for Gas," *Barron's,* Vol. XL, No. 33 (August 15, 1960), 5, 6, 18.

Woolcock, J. W. "Some Problems of Raw Material Supply for the Plastics Industry," *Petroleum Times,* Vol. LXIII, No. 1624 (November 6, 1959), 693.

"You Can't Trust Communist Production Figures," *Oil and Gas Journal,* Vol. LX, No. 36 (September 3, 1962), 88.

V. SPECIAL PUBLICATIONS AND MISCELLANEOUS MATERIALS

American Gas Association. "The Natural Gas Story." Edited by Francis X. Welch.

———. *1960 Gas Facts.* New York, 1961.

———. *1961 Gas Facts.* New York, 1962.

———. *Sub-Committee on Underground Storage Legal Forms, Documents and Statutes,* New York, 1961.

———. *Summary of Clauses Used in Present Underground Storage Lease Forms.* New York, 1961.

Anderson, C. C., and T. W. Hunter, "Methods for Evaluating Sources and Requirements for Solid and Liquid Fuels in the United States." Paper presented at the World Power Conference, Madrid, Spain, June 5–9, 1960. Published in *Transactions, q.v.,* 117–27.

Anuskiewitz, Michael, Jr. "The Economic Significance of Liquefied Natural Gas—The Distribution Company's Viewpoint." Address before the American Gas Association General Management Section Conference, Pittsburgh, Pennsylvania, February 29–March 2, 1960.

Baker, Rex G. "The Plight of the Natural Gas Producer," National Oil Scouts' and Landmen's Association Convention *Annual* (for 1956), 34–36.

Ballabio, Giulio. "The Petrochemical Industry in Italy." Paper presented at the Fourth World Petroleum Congress, Rome, Italy, June, 1955. Published in *Proceedings* (Section IV), *q.v.,* 253–59.

Bolzinger, A., and H. Descazeaux. "Developpement et Technique des Grands Transports de Gaz par Pipelines en France." Paper presented at the World Power Conference, Madrid, Spain, June 5–9, 1960. Published in *Transactions, q.v.*

Brandt, Clifford A., and Fred E. Egan. "Gas and Electric Service in Multiple Housing," *Criteria for Determining Costs of Gas and Electric Service in Military and Public Housing Projects.* Report prepared by H. Zinder and Associates, Incorporated, Washington, D.C., 1957.

Cadle, Austin, "U.S. Petroleum Forecast and Dynamic World Growth in Petroleum Demands," *Proceedings,* American Petroleum Institute (Section VI, Interdivisional), Vol. XXXVIII (1958), 24.

Clark, L. J. "Sea Transport of Liquid Methane." Paper presented at the World Power Conference, Madrid, Spain, June 5–9, 1960. Published in *Transactions, q.v.*

Collins, Warren J. "Problems Peculiar to State and Municipal Regulation of Gas Distributing Companies." Paper given at the Eleventh Annual Institute on Oil and Gas Law and Taxation, Dallas, Texas, February 10–12, 1960. Published in *Proceedings, q.v.*

Conn, Miller W. "Petrochemicals—Northeast Rising Star of the Petroleum Industry." Paper presented at the 33rd Annual Convention of the National Oil Scouts' and Landmen's Association, Corpus Christi, Texas, May 10–12, 1956.

Connole, William R. "Energy, Its Use and Abuse." Paper presented before the annual meeting of the Independent Natural Gas Association of America, Houston, Texas, September 10, 1957. Reprinted in *Energy Resources and Technology, q.v.*

———. "The Role of Regulation in Developing the Transportation and Use of Liquefied Methane." Paper presented at the Briefing Conference on Natural Gas and Oil Problems, Federal Bar Association and Bureau of National Affairs, Incorporated, Washington, D. C., March 5, 1959. Summarized in *Oil and Gas Journal,* Vol. LVII, No. 11 (March 9, 1959), 82. Printed in *Energy Resources and Technology, q.v.,* 336.

Consolidated Natural Gas Company. *Annual Report* (for 1958). New York, 1959.

Craze, Rupert C., and James W. Glanville. "Well Spacing," *Fifth Annual Institute on Mineral Law.* Baton Rouge, La., 1957.

Davis, John. *Natural Gas and Canada-United States Relations.* Pamphlet published by the National Planning Association and Private Planning Association of Canada, 1959.

Davis, Morgan J. "The Dynamics of Domestic Petroleum Resources," *Proceedings,* American Petroleum Institute (Section I, General), Vol. XXXVIII (1958), 22.

Davis, N. Knowles. "Influence of Underground Storage Upon a Natural Gas Pipeline System." Paper presented at the 37th Annual Conference, Utility Commission Engineers, San Francisco, California, July, 1959.

D'Leny, W. "Oil's Future as a Source of Chemicals," in *Essential Factors in the Future Development of the Oil Industry, q.v.*

Doggett, Wendell J. "Marketing of Natural Gas Through Means Conventional and Unconventional." Paper published at the Institute on the Economics of the Gas Industry, International Oil and Gas Education Center, Dallas, Texas, 1962.

DeGolyer and MacNaughton. *Twentieth Century Petroleum Statistics.* Annual editions.

Dwyer, Cornelius J. *Nuclear Energy and World Fuel Prices.* One of the National Planning Association's Reports on the Productive Uses of Nuclear Energy. Washington, D.C., 1958.

Elliott, Martin A. "Fuels in the Future." Special lecture presented at the 33rd Annual National A.S.M.E. Oil and Gas Power Division Conference, New Orleans, Louisiana, April 9–13, 1961.

————."The Long Range Supply of Gas." Paper presented at the 1960 Meeting of the Society of Gas Lighting, New York, New York, January 14, 1960.

————. "The Role of Fossil Fuels in Meeting Future Energy Demands." Paper presented at the 24th Annual American Power Conference, Chicago, Illinois, March 27–29, 1962.

Falomo, Gastone. "Economics of Long-distance Fuel Transportation and Electric Transmission." Paper presented at the World Power Conference, Madrid, Spain, June 5–9, 1960. Published in *Transactions, q.v.*

Fletcher, Thomas. "The Gas Producer and the Federal Power Commission: Cases, Statutes and Rulings." Paper presented at the Seventh Annual Institute on Oil and Gas Law and Taxation as It Affects the Oil and Gas Industry, Dallas, Texas, February 1–3, 1956. Published in *Proceedings, q.v.*, 95.

Foster, W. N., and K. W. Finch. "Relative Costs of Transmitting Energy as Electricity or as Natural Gas." Paper presented at the World Power Conference, Madrid, Spain, June 5–9, 1960. Published in *Transactions, q.v.*

Frame, U., and M. Williams. "The B 31.8 Code as It Affects the Purchasing and Stores Function." Address before the American Gas Association General Management Section Conference, Pittsburgh, Pennsylvania, February 29–March 2, 1960.

Francis, Charles I. "Federal Regulation of Interstate Shipment and Sale of Gas." Paper presented at the Fourth Annual Institute on Oil and Gas Law and Taxation as It Affects the Oil and Gas Industry, Dallas, Texas, January 21–23, 1953. Published in *Proceedings, q.v.*, 103.

Frazier, Charles H. "Distribution Company Gas Purchasing Problems, or from Slide-Rule to Crystal Ball." Paper presented to the Briefing Conference on Natural Gas and Oil Problems, Federal Bar Association and Bureau of National Affairs, Incorporated, Washington, D.C., March 6, 1959.

Fredersdorff, C. G. von. "New Methods of Generating Electricity from Gas Sources." Paper CEP–60–12 presented before the Operating Section of the American Gas Association, Pittsburgh, Pennsylvania, March 1–3, 1960.

Fritz, Wilbert G. *The Future of Industrial Raw Materials in North America*. Pamphlet published by the National Planning Association and Private Planning Association of Canada, 1960.

Garcia-Rojas, Antonio. "The Mexican Gas Industry." Address before the American Gas Association General Management Section Conference, Pittsburgh, Pennsylvania, February 29–March 2, 1960.

Golush, William B. "A Management Look at Natural Gas." Paper 1445–G presented before the annual meeting of the A.I.M.E., New York, New York, February 14–18, 1960. Published in the *Journal of Petroleum Technology*, Vol. XII, No. 7 (July, 1960), 11–16.

Goodrich, Baxter D. "Natural Gas—The Pipeline Industry." Paper 60–WA–43, contributed by the Petroleum Division for presentation at the Winter Annual Meeting of the American Society of Mechanical Engineers, New York, New York, November 27–December 2, 1960.

Gordon, Richard Lewis. "Coal Pricing and the Energy Problems in the European Community." Doctoral dissertation, Massachusetts Institute of Technology, 1960.

Gregg, D. H. "Negotiating and Drafting Gas Purchase Contracts on Behalf of Seller." Paper presented at the Thirteenth Annual Institute on Oil and Gas Law and Taxation, Dallas, Texas, February 14–16, 1962. Published in *Proceedings, q.v.*, 87.

Grimm, R. D. "Factors Affecting Gas Supply Control." Paper presented before the Interstate Oil Compact Commission, December 4, 1961.

Halbouty, Michel T. "Conservation—Total or Partial." Paper presented before the American Petroleum Institute, Division of Production, Southwest District, Dallas, Texas, March 2–4, 1960.

Hardwicke, Robert E. "Market Demand as a Factor in the Conservation of Oil." Paper presented at the First Annual Institute on Oil and Gas Law and Taxation as It Affects the Oil and Gas Industry, Dallas, Texas, March 23–26, 1949. Published in *Proceedings, q.v.*

Hargrove, James W. "Money for the Man in the Middle." Address before the American Association of Petroleum Landmen, Houston, Texas, 1961.

Hill, Kenneth E. *Natural Gas*. Published by Eastman Dillon, Union Securities Company. New York, 1961.

Howell, Ben R. "Gas Purchase Contracts." Paper presented at the Fourth Annual Institute on Oil and Gas Law and Taxation as It Affects the Oil and Gas Industry, Dallas, Texas, January 21–23, 1953. Published in *Proceedings*, q.v., 151.

———. "Natural Gas Purchase Contracts." Paper presented at the Fifth Annual Rocky Mountain Mineral Law Institute, Boulder, Colorado, July 31-August 1, 1959. Published in *Preceedings, q.v.*, 221.

Hubbard, M. E. "Pipelines in Relation to Other Forms of Transport." Paper presented at the World Power Conference, Madrid, Spain, June 5–9, 1960. Published in *Transactions, q.v.*

Hudson, H. K., *et al.* "The Future of Domestic Gas Reserves." Bartlesville, Oklahoma, 1960.

———. "Supplement to Presentation Entitled 'The Future of Domestic Gas Reserves.'" Bartlesville, Oklahoma, 1961.

Hunsaker, Jerome C., Jr. "The Institutional Investor Looks at the Gas Business." Address before the American Gas Association General Management Section Conference, Pittsburgh, Pennsylvania, February 29–March 2, 1960.

Institute of Gas Technology. *Natural Gas.* Home study course. Edited by Joseph D. Parent. Chicago, 1952.

Jacobs, John C., Jr. "Government Regulation of Gas Production—1956," *Fourth Annual Institute on Mineral Law.* Baton Rouge, La., 1956.

———. "Problems Incident to the Marketing of Gas." Paper presented at the Fifth Annual Institute on Oil and Gas Law and Taxation as It Affects the Oil and Gas Industry, Dallas, Texas, January 27–29, 1954. Published in *Proceedings, q.v.,* 275.

———. "What Every Landman Should Know About Gas Purchase Contracts," *National Institute for Petroleum Landmen,* Vol. III (1962), 155.

Joseph, Samuel. "Background and Analysis of Trial Examiner's Decision in Phillips Case." Paper Presented at the Eleventh Annual Institute on Oil and Gas Law and Taxation as It Affects the Oil and Gas Industry, Dallas, Texas, February 10–12, 1960. Published in *Proceedings, q.v.,* 1.

Keeton, W. Page. "Federal Regulation of Independent Gas Producers—Developments Since the Phillips Decision." Paper presented at the Fifth Annual Rocky Mountain Law Institute, Boulder, Colorado, July 31–August 1, 1959. Published in *Proceedings, q.v.,* 193.

Klemma, Randall T. "Area Development: Its Advantages to a Gas Company." Address before the American Gas Association General Management Section Conference, Pittsburgh, Pennsylvania, February 29–March 2, 1960.

Land, James N., Sr. "Future Trends of Interest Rates and Their Significance for the Gas Industry." Address before the American Gas Association General Management Section Conference, Pittsburgh, Pennsylvania, February 29–March 2, 1960.

Lebens, Edward P. "Preferred Stock as a Medium for Gas Utility Company Financing." Address Before the American Gas Association General Management Section Conference, Pittsburgh, Pennsylvania, February 29–March 2, 1960.

Ley, Henry A. "Geology of Natural Gas." Paper delivered before the A.A.P.G., Tulsa, Oklahoma, 1935.

Lyons, Charlton H. "Why Conservation." Paper presented before the 38th Annual Meeting of the American Petroleum Institute, Chicago, Illinois, November 11, 1958.

McGinnis, Robert. "The Texas Common Purchaser Statute as Related to Natural Gas." Paper presented before the Mineral Law Section of the State Bar of Texas, July 4, 1958. Published in the *Texas Bar Journal*, Vol. XXI, No. 8 (September, 1958), 521.

McGowen, Norris Cochran. "Natural Gas, the Gulf South's Symbol of Progress." Address before the Newcomen Society in North America, New Orleans, Louisiana, December 13, 1951.

Mason, E. S., *et al.* "Energy Requirements and Economic Growth." Paper presented at the International Conference on the Peaceful Uses of Atomic Energy, 1956. Published in *Proceedings, q.v.*, I, 50.

May, Robert E. "Preparation for Gas Rate Hearing Before the Federal Power Commission." Paper delivered before the Eleventh Annual Institute on Oil and Gas Law and Taxation, Dallas, Texas, February 10–12, 1960. Published in *Proceedings, q.v.* 123.

Mitchell, G. M. "Fuels Competition and Gas Pricing." Paper presented before the A.I.M.E. Gas Technology Symposium, Tyler, Texas, April 20–21, 1961.

Moody, John. *Public Utilities Manual* (for 1959). New York, 1959.

Morgan, Howard. "Gas Price Regulation: An Optimistic View." Paper presented before the West Central Texas Oil and Gas Association, Abilene, Texas, October 10, 1961.

Murphy, John A., and C. G. Filstead. "Ocean Transport of Liquid Methane." Paper presented at the Fifth World Petroleum Congress, New York, New York, June, 1959. Published in *Proceedings, q.v.*, VIII, 23.

Murrell, John H. "Plenty for All." Paper presented at the annual meeting of the American Gas Association, Chicago, Illinois, October 5–7, 1959. Published in *Proceedings*.

Nagler, K. B. "Transportation and Storage of Gaseous Fuels." Paper presented at the World Power Conference, Madrid, Spain, June 5–9, 1960. Published in *Transactions, q.v.*

National Association of Railroad and Utilities Commissioners. *Report of the Committee on Depreciation*. New York, 1943.

National Petroleum Council Committee and Working Sub-committee on Impact of Oil Exports from the Soviet Bloc. George T. Piercy, chairman of the Working Sub-committee. *Impact of Oil Exports from the Soviet Bloc.* 2 vols. Washington, D. C., 1962.

445

Nelson, Olof W. "Gas Supply in F.P.C. Certificate *Proceedings*." Paper presented before the National Association of Utility and Rate Commissioners, Charleston, West Virginia, October 6, 1961.

Newcomb, Marshall. "Federal and State Regulation of Gas Utilities." Paper presented at the First Annual Institute on Oil and Gas Law and Taxation as It Affects the Oil and Gas Industry, Dallas, Texas, March 23–26, 1949. Published in *Proceedings, q.v.*

1962 Symposium on Petroleum Economics and Valuation. Published by the Society of Petroleum Engineers of the American Institute of Mining and Metallurgical Engineers. Dallas, Tex., 1962.

O'Connor, Lawrence J. "Progress in Gas Regulation." Paper presented before the Independent Natural Gas Association, Dallas, Texas, November 10–12, 1962.

OEEC Technical Assistance Mission. *Long Distance Gas Transport in the United States.* Paris, 1956.

Panhandle Eastern Pipe Line Company. *Annual Report* (for 1958). Kansas City, 1959.

Pirone, P. P. "The Effect of Natural Gas on Trees." Address before the American Gas Association General Management Section Conference, Pittsburgh, Pennsylvania, February 29–March 2, 1960.

Proceedings of the American Petroleum Institute, Section VI, Interdivisional, 1958. New York, 1958.

Proceedings of the First Annual Institute on Oil and Gas Law and Taxation as It Affects the Oil and Gas Industry, Dallas, Texas, January 21–23, New York, 1949.

Proceedings of the Third Annual Institute on Oil and Gas Law and Taxation as It Affects the Oil and Gas Industry, Dallas, Texas, January 17–19, 1952. New York, 1952.

Proceedings of the Fourth Annual Institute on Oil and Gas Law and Taxation as It Affects the Oil and Gas Industry, Dallas, Texas, Jenuary 21–23, 1953. New York, 1953.

Proceedings of the Fifth Annual Institute on Oil and Gas Law and Taxation as It Affects the Oil and Gas Industry, Dallas, Texas, January 27–29, 1954. New York, 1954.

Proceedings of the Sixth Annual Institute on Oil and Gas Law and Taxation as It Affects the Oil and Gas Industry, Dallas, Texas, January 19-21, 1955, New York, 1955.

Proceedings of the Seventh Annual Institute on Oil and Gas Law and Taxation as It Affects the Oil and Gas Industry, Dallas, Texas, February 1-3, 1956. New York, 1956.

Proceedings of the Eighth Annual Institute on Oil and Gas Law and Taxa-

446

tion as It Affects the Oil and Gas Industry, Dallas, Texas, January 30–February 1, 1957. New York, 1957.

Proceedings of the Tenth Annual Institute on Oil and Gas Law and Taxation as It Affects the Oil and Gas Industry, Dallas, Texas, February 11–13, 1959. New York, 1959.

Proceedings of the Eleventh Annual Institute on Oil and Gas Law and Taxation, Dallas, Texas, February 10–12, 1960. New York, 1960.

Proceedings of the Twelfth Annual Institute on Oil and Gas Law and Taxation, Dallas, Texas, February 8–10, 1961. New York, 1961.

Proceedings of the Thirteenth Annual Institute on Oil and Gas Law and Taxation, Dallas, Texas, February 14–16, 1962.

Proceedings of the International Conference on Peaceful Uses of Atomic Energy, 1955. New York, 1955.

Proceedings of the International Conference on Peaceful Uses of Atomic Energy, 1956. New York, 1956.

Proceedings of the 36th Annual Convention, Natural Gasoline Association of America, Houston, Texas, April 20–23, 1957. Houston, 1957.

Proceedings of the Second Annual Rocky Mountain Mineral Law Institute, Boulder, Colorado, August 2–4, 1956. New York, 1956.

Proceedings of the Fifth Annual Rocky Mountain Mineral Law Institute, Boulder, Colorado, July 31–August 1, 1959. New York, 1960.

Proceedings (Section IV) of the Fourth World Petroleum Congress, Rome, Italy, June, 1955. Rome, 1955.

Proceedings of the Fifth World Petroleum Congress, New York, New York, 1959. New York, 1959.

Prospectus of Trans-Canada Pipelines, Limited, February 13, 1957.

Richardson, William S. "Producer Contracts for Sale of Natural Gas in Interstate Commerce." Paper presented at the Eleventh Annual Institute on Oil and Gas Law and Taxation, Dallas, Texas, February 10–12, 1960. Published in *Proceedings, q.v.*, 201.

Ross, Charles R. "The Landis Report and the Federal Power Commission, 1962." Paper presented before the Public Utility Law Section of the American Bar Association, San Francisco, California, August 7, 1962.

Russell, Donald K. "The Economic Outlook for the Domestic Producer." Paper presented at the 39th Annual Meeting of the American Petroleum Institute, Chicago, Illinois, November, 1959.

Schultz, E. V., *et al.* "Natural Gas Fuel Cells for Power Generation in Dwellings." Paper presented at the American Gas Association Research and Utilization Conference, Cleveland, Ohio, April 5, 1961.

Schurr, Sam H. "Energy Resources Pattern." Address before the American

Gas Association General Management Section Conference, Pittsburgh, Pennsylvania, February 29–March 2, 1960.

Searles, David T. "Decision of Federal Power Commission in Phillips Petroleum Company Case." Paper presented at the Twelfth Annual Institute on Oil and Gas Law and Taxation, Dallas, Texas, February 8–10, 1961. Published in *Proceedings, q.v.*, 1.

———. "The Necessity of Increasing Exploration for and Discovery of Natural Gas and the Problems Facing the Industry Relative to this Operation." Paper presented before the annual meeting of the Independent Natural Gas Association of America, Miami Beach, Florida, October 3–4, 1960.

Shannon, Charles V. "Revent Developments Affecting Production, Transportation and Sale of Gas." Paper presented at the Eighth Annual Institute on Oil and Gas Law and Taxation as It Affects the Oil and Gas Industry, Dallas, Texas, January 30–February 1, 1957. Published in *Proceedings, q.v.*, 219.

Simms, John F. "Recent Development in the Law of Conservation and the Influence of the Interstate Oil Compact." Paper presented at the Seventh Annual Institute on Oil and Gas Law and Taxation as It Affects the Oil and Gas Industry, Dallas, Texas, February 1–3, 1956. Published in *Proceedings, q.v.*

Simpson, R. A., and L. R. Borden. *A Survey of the Natural Gas Industry in Canada, 1957–1959.* Mineral Resources Division Mineral Information Bulletin MR39. Ottawa, 1960.

Skinner, Walter E. *Oil and Petroleum Year Book* (for 1958). London, September, 1959.

Stone, Oliver L. "Federal Power Commission Developments of Significance to Independent Producers of Natural Gas." Paper presented at the Thirteenth Annual Institute on Oil and Gas Law and Taxation, Dallas, Texas, February 14–16, 1962. Published in *Proceedings*, q.v., 1.

———. "The FPC and the Producer of Natural Gas," *Eighth Annual Institute on Mineral Law.* Baton Rouge, La., 1961.

Swanson, E. B. *The Natural Gas Invasion—An Example of the Sudden Expansion of Transport in Mineral Economics.* A.I.M.E. Series. New York, 1932.

Swidler, Joseph C. "The Natural Gas Act and Free Enterprise." Paper presented before the 41st Annual Meeting of the American Petroleum Institute, Chicago, Illinois, November 15, 1961.

———. "New Directions in Gas Regulation." Paper presented before the Independent Natural Gas Association, Miami, Florida, October 22–24, 1961.

————. "Regulation of the Small Natural Gas Producer." Paper presented before the Texas Independent Producers and Royalty Owners Association, Houston, Texas, September 4–6, 1962.

Teitlebaum, Perry D. *Nuclear Energy and the U.S. Fuel Economy, 1955–1980.* Reports on the Productive Uses of Nuclear Energy, National Planning Association. Washington, D. C., 1958.

Tennessee Gas Transmission Company. *Annual Reports* (for 1954–60).

————. *Annual Report* (for 1960). Houston, Tex., 1961.

Texas Eastern Transmission. *Annual Reports* (for 1954–60).

Texas-Illinois Natural Gas Pipeline Company. *Annual Reports* (for 1957–60).

Thompson, Ernest O. "An Administrator's Views on Conservation in the Production of Oil and Gas," *Sixth Annual Institute on Mineral Law.* Baton Rouge, La., 1958.

Toombs, R. B. "Methods Used in Canada to Achieve Economic Transportation of Fuels by Pipeline." Paper presented at the World Power Conference, Madrid, Spain, June 5–9, 1960. Published in *Transactions, q.v.*

Transactions of the World Power Conference, Madrid, Spain, June 5–9, 1960. 8 vols. Madrid, 1960.

Trans-Canada Pipe Lines, Limited. *Annual Report* (for 1959). Calgary, 1960.

United Gas Corporation. *Annual Report* (for 1958). Shreveport, La., 1959.

————. *Annual Report* (for 1959). Shreveport, La., 1960.

Walker, R. D., and A. B. Jones. "Economic Trends of the Transportation of Fuel by Pipeline." Paper presented at the Canadian Sectional Meeting of the World Power Conference, Montreal, Canada, September 7–11, 1958.

Walton, J. R. "Area Industrial Development." Paper presented before the American Gas Association Sales Conference on Industrial and Commercial Gas, Milwaukee, Wisconsin, April 8, 1958.

Weeks, Joseph D. *Mineral Resources of the United States* (for 1885). Washington, D.C., 1886.

————. *Mineral Resources of the United States* (for 1888). Washington, D.C., 1890.

Wolf, Justin R. "Current Decisions and Problems in the Regulation of Independent Natural Gas Producers." Paper presented at the Second Annual Rocky Mountain Mineral Law Institute, Boulder, Colorado, August 2–4, 1956. Published in *Proceedings, q.v.,* 199.

————. "The Independent Producer and the Federal Power Commission." Paper presented at the Sixth Annual Institute on Oil and Gas Law and Taxation as It Affects the Oil and Gas Industry, Dallas, Texas, January 19–21, 1955. Published in *Proceedings, q.v.*

Woodfin, Gene M. "Recent Developments in Federal Power Commission Control of Independent Producers." Paper presented at the Tenth Annual Institute on Oil and Gas Law and Taxation as It Affects the Oil and Gas Industry, Dallas, Texas, February 11–13, 1959. Published in *Proceedings*, *q.v.*, 25.

Young, A. Russell. "A Review of Economics of Liquefied Natural Gas for Peak Shaving." Paper presented at the American Gas Association General Management Section Conference, Pittsburgh, Pennsylvania, February 29–March 2, 1960.

Zinder, H., and Associates. *Summary of Rate Schedules of Natural Gas Pipeline Companies as Filed with Federal Power Commission.* Eighteenth edition. Washington, D.C., March, 1962.

INDEX OF NAMES

451

GENERAL INDEX

Abandonment pressure: 51
Absorption process: 235
Absorption units: 235
Administrative Procedure Act: 261
Africa: 377–80
Alaska: 42
Alberta Province: 155, 337ff., 345, 348–49; Alberta-California Project, 144–46; importance of gas from, 341–49; *see also* Canada
Algeria: 378–79
Allocation of transmission expenses: 287–89
Allowables: 263–67
Anadarko Basin: 33
Anticline: 13
Appalachian Oil Province: 7, 19–20; discussion of, 38–40
Aquifers: 141n., 244
Aquitaine Basin: 369
Arbitration clause: *see* gas purchase contract
Area industrial development: 201, 203–204
Area prices: promulgated by the FPC, 301, 313; levels of, 314 (table); used to assess fairness of field prices, 406–407
Argentina: 367–77
Artificial gas fields: *see* underground storage
Associated natural gas: 14; estimating reserves of, 50
Australia: 381
Austria: 374
Availability: 396–401
Availability rule: *see* public control

Bahrein: 374
Barlow's formula: 79
Big Inch pipe line: 155
Bolivia: 377
Bottled gas: 229
Boyle's law: 48–49
Brazil: 377
British thermal unit (Btu): definition of, 172n.
Butane: 15; liquefaction of, 255

Cable tool: 52
California: 34–35; Buttonwillow gas field in, 34; efforts to meet rising demand for gas in, 343; consumption in, 344 (table); imports from Canada into, 343, 345, 346 (table), 347–49
Canada: industrial promotion in, 203; discussion of the gas industry in, 337–62; Alberta Province in, 337–39; British Columbia Province in, 337, 339, 341–42, 349–50; Saskatchewan Province in, 339, 356; local markets in, 340, 353–58; exploration activities in, 340; exports to California from, 343–49; sources of supply in, 345–47
Capital structure of natural gas companies: 27–28 (table), 123–25
Carbon black: 209–10
Carthage gas field: 26
Casing: 52
Certificates of public convenience and necessity: terms of, 266–67, 281–83; in relation to termination of service, 299; *see*

461